Advances in
Clinical Child Psychology

Volume 7

ADVANCES IN CLINICAL CHILD PSYCHOLOGY

A Continuation Order Plan is available for this series. A continuation order will bring delivery of each new volume immediately upon publication. Volumes are billed only upon actual shipment. For further information please contact the publisher.

⌐Advances in
Clinical Child
Psychology

Volume 7

Edited by

Benjamin B. Lahey
*University of Georgia
Athens, Georgia*

and

Alan E. Kazdin
*Western Psychiatric Institute and Clinic
University of Pittsburgh School of Medicine
Pittsburgh, Pennsylvania*

Plenum Press · New York and London

The Library of Congress cataloged the first volume of this title as follows:

Advances in clinical child psychology. v. 1–

   New York, Plenum Press, c1977–

   v. ill. 24 cm.
   Key title: Advances in clinical child psychology. ISSN 0149-4732

   1. Clinical psychology — Collected works. 2. Child psychology — Collected
works. 3. Child psychotherapy — Collected works.
RJ503.3.A37   618.9′28′9   77-643411

Library of Congress Catalog Card Number 77-643411

ISBN 0-306-41659-X

© 1984 Plenum Press, New York
A Division of Plenum Publishing Corporation
233 Spring Street, New York, N.Y. 10013

This series is dedicated to
the children of the world, especially
MEGAN, EDWARD, ERIN, NICOLE, and MICHELLE

Contributors

David Bellinger

Children's Hospital Medical Center, Boston, Massachusetts

Helen K. Cleminshaw

Department of Home Economics and Family Ecology, University of Akron, Akron, Ohio

Leonard D. Eron

Department of Psychology, University of Illinois, Chicago, Illinois

Edwin L. Gerwell

Harvard Medical School, Children's Hospital Medical Center, Boston, Massachusetts

John Guidubaldi

Department of Early Childhood Education, Kent State University, Kent, Ohio

Keith Hawton

University Department of Psychiatry, Warneford Hospital, Oxford, England

Anne E. Hogan

Mailman Center for Child Development, University of Miami, Miami, Florida

Christine A. Hovanitz

Harvard Medical School, Children's Hospital Medical Center, Boston, Massachusetts

L. Rowell Huesmann

Department of Psychology, University of Illinois, Chicago, Illinois

Louise A. Lampi

Department of Psychology, Wayne State University, Detroit, Michigan

Herbert L. Needleman

Department of Psychiatry, School of Medicine, University of Pittsburgh, Pittsburgh, Pennsylvania

Madeline Osborn   *University Department of Psychiatry,
                           Warneford Hospital, Oxford, England*

Joseph D. Perry   *Department of Pediatrics, Tod Babies and
                           Children's Hospital, Youngstown, Ohio;
                           and Department of Psychiatry, Northeastern
                           Ohio Universities College of Medicine,
                           Rootstown, Ohio*

Herbert C. Quay   *Program in Applied Social Sciences, Univer-
                           sity of Miami, Coral Gables, Florida*

Annette U. Rickel   *Department of Psychology, Wayne State
                           University, Detroit, Michigan*

Dennis C. Russo   *Harvard Medical School, Children's Hospi-
                           tal Medical Center, Boston, Massachusetts*

Barbara Hanna Wasik   *School of Education, University of North
                           Carolina, Chapel Hill, North Carolina*

Bernard Weiss   *Division of Toxicology and Environmental
                           Health Sciences Center, University of
                           Rochester School of Medicine and Dentistry,
                           Rochester, New York*

Preface

Advances in Clinical Child Psychology is a serial publication designed to bring together original summaries of the most important new developments in the field of clinical psychology and its related disciplines. Each chapter is written by a key figure in an innovative area of research or by an individual who is particularly well qualified to comment on a topic of major contemporary importance. These chapters provide convenient, concise explorations of empirical and clinical advances in the field.

The contents of Volume 7 reflect the broad changes that are occurring within the field. The continuing growth of research emphasis on etiology is seen in two chapters on the causative role played by chemical substances, one chapter on the effects of divorce on children, and one on the influence of televised violence. The difficult issue of suicide by children and adolescents is dealt with, the role of cognition in behavior disorders is explored, and the clinical applications of direct behavioral observation are evaluated. Although the fields of pediatric psychology and prevention have been treated in earlier volumes in the series, progress in these fields has been so rapid that chapters on each topic have been included in the present volume.

We appreciate the roles played by the advisory editors in suggesting excellent topics and thoughtfully editing the chapters. As always, our strongest thanks go to the volume's authors for their outstanding contributions.

BENJAMIN B. LAHEY
ALAN E. KAZDIN

Contents

Cognition in Child and Adolescent
Behavior Disorders

1

Anne E. Hogan and Herbert C. Quay

Television Violence and Aggressive Behavior 2
Leonard D. Eron and L. Rowell Huesmann

Suicide and Attempted Suicide in Children and Adolescents 3
Keith Hawton and Madeline Osborn

The Legacy of Parental Divorce: A
Nationwide Study of Family Status and
Selected Mediating Variables on
Children's Academic and Social
Competencies

4

John Guidubaldi, Joseph D. Perry, and
Helen K. Cleminshaw

Clinical Applications of Direct Behavioral
Observation: A Look at the Past and the
Future

5

Barbara Hanna Wasik

The Developmental Consequences of
Childhood Exposure to Lead: Recent
Studies and Methodological Issues

6

Herbert L. Needleman and David Bellinger

Food Additive Safety Evaluation: The
Link to Behavioral Disorders in Children

7

Bernard Weiss

Behavioral Methods in Pediatric Chronic Illness   8

Christine A. Hovanitz, Edwin L. Gerwell, and Dennis C. Russo

Prevention of Childhood Dysfunction   *9*
Annette U. Rickel and Louise A. Lampi

1   Cognition in Child and Adolescent Behavior Disorders

Anne E. Hogan and Herbert C. Quay

1. Introduction

Sattler (1974, p. 344), in his textbook on the assessment of children's intelligence, states: "Research has shown that intellectual functioning is not usually a major factor of importance in the etiology of childhood behavioral or neurotic disorders." He goes on to suggest, however, that emotional disorders could affect intellectual functioning in many different ways.

Ultimately, the question of interest is whether there is evidence for a causal link between specific cognitive deficits and particular childhood disturbances in either direction, such that the cognitive deficit plays some causative role in the disorder or that the disorder plays a causative role in the cognitive deficit. An affirmative answer would have direct implications for both diagnosis/classification and intervention.

As will be seen, however, research has been almost exclusively correlational in nature. Most studies have looked for the appearance of particular cognitive patterns in known deviant groups. Documentation of such associations, while not providing evidence of causal relationships, can nevertheless be of practical value. Given a good match between child and program, particular cognitively oriented interventions could be beneficial for deviant children regardless of the existence of a causal link between the cognitive deficit and the behavioral problem. For example, if conduct-disordered children show poor verbal self-regulation skills, improvement of those skills might reduce disruptive behavior, although no causal relationship could be shown between the two areas of functioning.

Most studies of cognitive abilities have reflected one of two the-

ANNE E. HOGAN • Mailman Center for Child Development, University of Miami, Miami, Florida 33103.   HERBERT C. QUAY • Program in Applied Sciences, University of Miami, Coral Gables, Florida 33124.

oretical frameworks: the psychometric or the cognitive-developmental. The psychometric approach examines stable individual differences in cognitive functioning; IQ tests are the measures used. In focusing on intellectual functioning (or patterns within) as a trait, this perspective does not provide descriptions of developmental, age-related changes in cognition. (Although the item pools of IQ tests could serve as a beginning for this type of description the tests are not typically used this way.) The well-established reliability and validity of IQ tests, however, make them an invaluable tool in studying mental development. The cognitive-developmental approach (the term is used here in a broad sense) examines skills, concepts, and their integration at different ages, often looking for changes across developmental periods; the task is to characterize the child's thought at various ages. Elkind (1981) has recently called for an integration of these two perspectives, arguing that both the notion of stable individual differences in intelligence and the characterization of thought at different developmental periods are critical to a complete picture of intelligence. Readers interested in this issue are referred to the Elkind paper. As a beginning step toward a synthesis of these perspectives in examining the cognitive development of children with behavior problems, this chapter will review literature from both psychometric and developmental approaches.

Unfortunately, the ways in which samples of deviant children have been selected and described have been unsystematic. Two groups have most commonly been used: those labeled as delinquent or as emotionally disturbed (ED). Subjects have usually not been more precisely classified according to any taxonomic system, either clinical-psychiatric or empirical. It is well known that these gross classifications, one legal and the other often educational, actually subsume a number of more precisely defined disorders (see Quay, 1979). For example, the child labeled ED may be aggressive, withdrawn, or even psychotic. Thus, the interpretation of many research reports is difficult. It may not be clear to whom observed differences apply, or to what extent results appear as a function of the type of child who happened to predominate in the sample. However, a few more recent studies have utilized more precise approaches to classification, such as the DSM-III (American Psychiatric Association, 1980) or factor analytically derived syndromes.

The remainder of this review contains three major sections. The first two review the literature on psychometric and cognitive-developmental functioning of disturbed children, respectively; the final section provides a summary and some conclusions. Two subgroups of deviant children have been excluded. Extensive reviews of cognitive factors associated with attention deficit disorder (hyperactivity) may be found in Douglas and Peters (1979). Cognitive functioning in autism has recently been reviewed by Prior (1979) and DeMyer, Hingtgen, and Jackson (1981).

2. Psychometric Performance of Disturbed Children

A number of studies have examined various clinical groups to determine whether aspects of their performance on standardized tests of intelligence differed significantly from expectations. Several aspects of psychometric performance can be observed: subnormal intelligence, an unusual pattern of Verbal-Performance IQ discrepancies, differences in the obtained factor structure of tests, and atypical profiles of subtest scores. For some comparisons, clinical and nonclinical groups must be matched on nonintellectual variables (e.g., race, SES) that relate to the relevant aspect of IQ test performance. At the same time, when clinical groups score in the normal range with respect to the standardization sample, such a finding can be accepted more or less at face value.

2.1. Has Any Clinical Group Shown IQs Significantly Lower than Normal?

2.1.1. Normal Performance

The standardization sample data from the WISC-R have shown that some variables are associated with group differences in performance. According to Sattler (1982), while there are no sex differences in mean IQ, the mean for black children is approximately 16 points lower than that for white children (86 vs. 102). Parental occupational status is also related to IQ; across the range of occupations from lowest to highest, white children's mean IQs vary by 17 points (from 92 to 109) and black children's mean IQs vary by 9 points (from 82 to 91). These differences underscore the need to control race and SES when making clinical-nonclinical comparisons.

2.1.2. Clinical Group Performance

In an early study, Rutter (1964) reported IQ test data for a large sample of ED children. Although it was found that the observed distribution of scores was significantly different from normal (a greater-than-predicted frequency in the 80–89 range; a lower-than-predicted frequency in the 90–99 range; slightly greater-than predicted frequencies in both tails of the distribution), the finding could be attributed to referral patterns favoring lower functioning children. Rutter concluded that low intelligence was not an important factor in child psychiatric disorder.

Several more recent studies have reported mean Full-Scale (FSIQ) scores for heterogeneous samples of ED children. Fuller and Goh (1981) reported a mean FSIQ of 89.5; Hale and Landino (1981), a mean FSIQ of 93.8; and Beitchman, Patterson, Gelfand, and Minty (1982), a mean FSIQ of 95.0. These last authors noted, however, that even a relatively small IQ deficit *could* place a child at risk for psychiatric disorder, to the extent that even slightly lower IQs could impair school performance, leading to frustration and adjustment problems.

Studies of mean IQs for differentiated subgroups of ED children have reported similar findings. Rutter (1964) reported no differences among groups labeled conduct behavior disorder, neurotic behavior disorder, mixed, and neurotic illness. Beitchman *et al.* (1982) also reported nonsignificant differences among conduct-problem, neurotic, and mixed-problem groups.

Studies of depressed children have also reported IQ scores in the normal range. Brumback, Staton, and Wilson (1980) and Staton, Wilson, and Brumback (1981), in studies of drug effects on IQ performance, found pretest FSIQs in the normal range (for the individuals in Brumback *et al.*, FSIQs were 100 and 102; for the two groups in Staton *et al.*, mean FSIQs were 93.3 and 102.3).

Finegan, Zucker, Bradley, and Doering (1982) investigated the hypothesis that boys with a gender identity disorder would have above-average intelligence. When IQs of feminine boys were compared with their brothers, no difference was found. The mean for the feminine boys was 108.8; the mean for their brothers was 105.4.

There has been much more research on juvenile delinquents. Prentice and Kelly (1963) reviewed approximately 20 studies done between 1943 and 1960 and concluded that delinquents were not generally of low IQ. Caplan (1965) reached a similar conclusion in his review. More recent reports have also found mean IQs in the normal range. Andrew (1977) reported a mean FSIQ on the WISC of 98.2 for a nonincarcerated sample; Hays, Solway, and Schreiner (1978) a mean FSIQ of 87.1 for a sample of status offenders; and Ollendick (1979) a mean FSIQ on the WISC-R of 84.5 for an incarcerated sample. Hubble and Groff (1981a) found a mean FSIQ of 92.5 for a sample of white males who were from low or low-middle SES families. Offord, Poushinsky, and Sullivan (1978) reported no IQ differences between delinquents and their nondelinquent siblings. Riddle and Roberts (1977) reported that on the Test Age of the Porteus Maze Test (similar to a Mental Age estimate) delinquents scored similarly to normals. These reports suggest that Prentice and Kelly's (1963) conclusion is still appropriate and that subnormal (more than one SD below the mean) intelligence is not a major feature of unselected delinquents.

The failure to find a consistent pattern of intellectual differences between delinquents and normals may be a result of the heterogeneity of unselected delinquent groups. By first using some classification system to form more homogeneous subgroups and then examining intellectual differences among these subgroups and between the subgroups and matched nondelinquents, more reliable differences may emerge. Several studies have used subgroups in studying psychometric performance; however, criteria for forming the subgroups have varied from study to study. Typically, distinctions have been made between violent and nonviolent or between psychopathic and nonpsychopathic groups.

It does not appear, however, that any delinquent subgroup delineated on the basis of behavior is more likely to have subnormal intelligence. Quay and Levinson (reported in Quay, 1979, p.29) subdivided two separate samples of incarcerated delinquents into four behaviorally homogeneous subgroups, the conduct-disordered, anxious-withdrawn, immature, and socialized aggressive, and found that mean Beta IQs ranged from about 92 to 98.

Two studies have found that IQ is related to severity of delinquent behavior, however. Gibson and West (1970), in a rare prospective study in Great Britain, found a relationship between IQ and early delinquency (found guilty of a crime by age 14). Early delinquents constituted only 7.3% of their sample but were found to have two significant deficits: they were significantly more socially handicapped than the nondelinquents (social handicap being defined by a set of components including income, occupational status, and housing), and when matched with nondelinquents on social handicap, they were of lower intelligence. It is important to note that the intelligence testing was done when all the children were ages 8 and 9, prior to the delinquent behavior. Since later delinquents (found guilty for the first time after age 14) did not differ from nondelinquents on intelligence measures, lower IQ may predispose children to earlier illegal involvement.

Hays, Solway, and Schreiner (1978) compared juvenile murderers to status offenders in a sample of 15 and 16 year olds. The mean FSIQ for the murderers was 80, whereas the mean for the status offenders was 87.1, a significant difference; however, there was no information on equivalence of SES or race for the two groups.

Although our focus is on children, it is worth noting that researchers have also looked at the relationship between violent crime and IQ among adult criminal populations. Heilbrun (1979) found that while IQ level had no effect on violent crimes for nonpsychopaths, there was a striking effect for a psychopathic group. Among the high-IQ psychopaths, the frequencies of violent and nonviolent crimes were about equal (10 vs. 9), whereas among the low-IQ psychopaths, violent crimes were eight times as frequent as nonviolent crimes (17 vs. 2). Heilbrun argued that his findings supported the notion that IQ may be a moderating variable for violent crime among psychopaths.

Holland, Beckett, and Levi (1981) found a small but significant difference in IQ between violent and nonviolent groups, in an ethnically mixed sample. No information was available on SES of the sample. The violent group had a mean IQ of 100.4 and the nonviolent group had a mean IQ of 104. However, the very small mean difference and the correlation between IQ and offense severity ($r = -.21$) were not considered by the authors to be of sufficient magnitude to be clinically useful. The correlational results were not significantly different when the three ethnic groups were analyzed separately.

2.1.3. Summary

Neither undifferentiated nor differentiated groups of ED children or delinquents have been found to be of subnormal intelligence. A few authors (e.g., Beitchman *et al.*, 1982) have cautioned, however, that deficits of even ten points may constitute a risk factor for behavior problems. One trend is in need of further investigation. Relatively low IQ occurring in psychopathic individuals *may* be a risk factor for the commission of violent, impulsive crimes or for the development of delinquent behavior.

2.2. Has Any Clinical Group Shown a Pattern of Discrepancy between Verbal (V) and Performance (P) IQs That Significantly Differs from the Normal Pattern?

2.2.1. Normal Performance

In interpreting obtained differences in clinical samples, it is necessary to know the prevalence of discrepancies of varying sizes and whether any pattern of discrepancy is more likely among normals. Seashore (1951), using the WISC standardization sample, found that 52% of the sample had VIQ–PIQ differences of 8 points or less. The other 48% were evenly split, with 24% having VIQ greater than PIQ by more than 8 points and 24% having PIQ greater than VIQ greater than 8 points. Kaufman (1976a) reported the frequency of PIQ–VIQ discrepancies of various magnitudes for the WISC-R standardization sample. To be significant at the .05 level, the difference between VIQ and PIQ had to be 12 points; for the .01 level, 15 points were necessary. In the WISC-R sample, one-third of the subjects had 12-point discrepancies and one-fourth had 15-point discrepancies. The mean discrepancy score for the entire sample was 9.7. As in Seashore's (1951) report, a VIQ > PIQ pattern was as frequent as a PIQ > VIQ pattern. Kauman reported that the pattern and degree of discrepancy were similar across age groups, males and females, and blacks and whites. Differences were observed for groups that varied on parental occupation and on intellectual level. Children of parents whose occupation fell into an unskilled category showed more PIQ > VIQ than VIQ > PIQ discrepancies, while children of professionals showed more VIQ > PIQ than PIQ > VIQ discrepancies. In lower IQ groups, fewer discrepancies were observed, although there were still roughly equivalent occurrences of PIQ > VIQ and VIQ > PIQ.

2.2.2. Clinical Group Performance

Studies which have reported PIQ–VIQ discrepancies in undifferentiated groups of ED children have shown conflicting results. Rutter (1964), Morris, Evans, and Pearson (1978), Fuller and Goh (1981), and Beitchman et al. (1982) found no evidence for unusual patterns of discrepancy. Dean (1978), however, did find PIQ significantly higher than VIQ for an ED sample.

Richman and Lindgren (1981) started with 59 subjects taken from outpatient clinic referrals who all showed a pattern of PIQ > VIQ by at least 15 points. The children were in regular classes, and reasons for referral varied. Mean FSIQ was 97; mean PIQ and VIQ were 109 and 85 respectively. Children ranged in age from 7-11 years. The total group was separated into three cognitive ability groups based on performance on two factors derived from a factor analysis of the sample's subtest scores. Factor 1, a conceptualization/abstract reasoning factor, was based on scores on Similarities and Block Design. Factor 2, a short-term memory/sequencing ability factor, was based on scores on Arithmetic, Picture Arrangement, and some other memory tasks. Children who scored high on Factor 1 and low on Factor 2 made up the abstract reasoning group; low scores on Factor 1 and high scores on Factor 2 made up the sequencing memory group. Children who scored low on both factors made up the general language disability group; these children tended to have slightly lower IQs. The authors then looked for behavior problems which were characteristic of each group. The general language disability group showed the highest conduct problems scores, low behavioral inhibition, and low academic achievement in reading and arithmetic. The authors cautioned that no conclusion could be drawn about whether the cognitive deficit could be causing the behavior problems. They did recommend, however, that differentiating children on their type of mediational deficiency (rather than just PIQ > VIQ) might be a useful strategy.

Unusual patterns of VIQ–PIQ discrepancies have not been reported for depressed children. Ossofsky (1974) reported VIQ–PIQ patterns for 152 children diagnosed as depressed. Twenty-seven had PIQ > VIQ of 15 points or more, 25 had VIQ > PIQ of 15 points or more, and 100 had discrepancies of less than 15 points—a distribution of discrepancies appearing similar to that which Kaufman (1976a) had reported for normals. Brumback et al. (1980) and Staton et al. (1981) also reported concordant VIQ–PIQ scores for their very small samples of depressed children.

Finegan et al. (1982) reported that their sample of feminine boys performed comparably on Verbal Comprehension and Perceptual Organization factors, suggesting lack of a significant VIQ–PIQ discrepancy.

As with general IQ performance, there has been considerable research on PIQ–VIQ discrepancies in delinquents. In their review, Prentice and Kelly (1963) reported consistent patterns of PIQ > VIQ in studies of delinquents; however, they cautioned that the pattern should not be used as diagnostic of delinquency. Research done since their review has supported their conclusions.

Camp (1966) looked at PIQ–VIQ discrepancies in delinquent boys and girls. She compared the results for each group to Seashore's (1951) findings. The pattern for girls was not significantly different from the normal pattern. The distribution for boys, however, was significantly different from the normal pattern. Among delinquent boys, 42% had VIQs within 8 points of their PIQs. Of the remaining 58%, only 12% had VIQ > PIQ, while 46% had PIQ > VIQ.

Ollendick (1979) compared the PIQ–VIQ discrepancy in a group of males to the discrepancies for children whose parents were unskilled laborers (Kaufman, 1976a). Among these children, Kaufman had reported that 8% had VIQ > PIQ by 15 points or more, and 13% had PIQ > VIQ by 15 points or more. Ollendick's delinquent sample had a mean PIQ of 90.2 and a mean VIQ of 81.7. Nearly 21% had discrepancies of 15 points or more, all in the direction of higher Performance scores. Ollendick concluded that delinquents can be characterized by a greater frequency of PIQ > VIQ and the absence of VIQ > PIQ. However, he noted that the discrepancy is found so frequently in normals that it is not diagnostically useful.

Hubble and Groff (1981a) also compared the distribution PIQ–VIQ discrepancies in white male delinquents to Kaufman's (1976a) report of discrepancies in the WISC-R standardization sample. As in Ollendick's (1979) study, although the magnitude of the discrepancies did not differ significantly, the direction of the discrepancies was significantly different for delinquents. Significant Verbal elevations were observed for only

9% of the delinquents, whereas the rate in the normal group was 19%. Significant Performance elevations were observed for 43% of the delinquents, while the rate in the normal group was 24%. The authors concluded that, although their results give further support to the finding of a characteristic pattern of VIQ–PIQ discrepancy for delinquents which merits further study, the pattern is not necessarily representative of individual delinquents, and use of the discrepancy for clinical purposes is not yet warranted.

Hubble and Groff (1980) also examined differences in psychometric performance between two groups of delinquents, one subsequently incarcerated and one subsequently placed on probation. No information was given on the nature of offenses for either group or on parental occupations of the sample. While no differences were found between the groups on VIQ or verbal subtests (VIQ means: 87.2 and 90.0 for incarceration and probation groups, respectively), PIQ differences were observed. PIQ was significantly higher for the group later released (90.5 vs. 97.4). Block Design, Object Assembly, and Coding subtest means were significantly different for the two groups. The authors concluded that differences in nonverbal, rather than verbal, abilities differentiate these groups of delinquents and that the two groups must be studied independently with respect to nonverbal abilities.

Henning and Levy (1967) and Hays and Smith (1980) reported larger PIQ–VIQ discrepancies for white relative to black delinquents. This result may, however, be a function of the fact that in both studies the FSIQs were lower for blacks, a finding consistent with Kaufman's (1976a) report of fewer discrepancies in groups with lower mean IQs.

Taking a slightly different perspective on Performance–Verbal discrepancies, Wolff, Waber, Bauermeister, Cohen, and Ferber (1982) made the case that, as a group, low SES male delinquents suffer from a pervasive language deficit relative to low SES male nondelinquents. Across psychometric linguistic tasks, low SES delinquents consistently performed more poorly than low SES normals, while no differences were observed on nonlinguistic tasks, suggesting that a severe and specific learning disability may characterize many low SES male delinquents. The authors nevertheless argued against any necessary relationship between poor language abilities and delinquency.

Two studies have tried to predict particular aspects of delinquent behavior from the size of the PIQ–VIQ discrepancy. Fernald and Wisser (1967) found a correlation of .17 between PIQ–VIQ score and degree of acting out (based on judges' ratings of court offenses). Haynes and Bensch (1981, 1983) found PIQ > VIQ more often in recidivists than in nonrecidivists (70% vs. 42% for males; 83% vs. 58% for females), but no relationship between the size of the PIQ–VIQ difference and recidivism.

Two studies have examined PIQ–VIQ discrepancies in subgroups of delinquents. Hecht and Jurkovic (1978) and Hubble and Groff (1982) divided groups of delinquents into subtypes of psychopathic, neurotic, and subcultural (see Quay & Parsons, 1971). Hecht and Jurkovic found that only the psychopathic group showed the PIQ > VIQ discrepancy, mean PIQ = 101.2 and mean VIQ = 81.4. However, the relative number of subjects in each subtype who had a higher PIQ than VIQ was not significantly different. Hubble and Groff found that psychopathic and neurotic groups showed the PIQ > VIQ discrepancy at significant levels; mean PIQs were 97.3 and 103.1 and mean VIQs were 91.7 and 97.6 for psychopathic and neurotic subjects respectively. Like Hecht and Jurkovic, Hubble and Groff found no difference in the proportion of delinquents in each subgroup with significant PIQ > VIQ discrepancies. While the results of the two studies differ somewhat, with the neurotic subgroup showing significant discrepancies in only one study and the magnitude of the mean discrepancy for psychopathic delinquents differing (roughly 20 vs. 6.5 points), the results indicate the value of differentiating delinquents according to behavioral subtypes in looking at cognitive performance.

2.2.3. Summary

Discrepancies between VIQ and PIQ occur so commonly in normal children that their presence cannot be considered a sign of pathology. It does appear, however, that when clinical groups have shown an unusual pattern of VIQ–PIQ differences, it has been in the direction of a greater prevalence of PIQ > VIQ. Among clinical groups, this pattern is found most consistently in delinquents. There have been no reports of a clinical sample in which there were more VIQ > PIQ than PIQ > VIQ, suggesting that, while there is no reason to *presume* an imbalance in psychometric functioning in disturbed children, when a discrepancy does occur it is likely in the direction of relatively poorer verbal functioning.

2.3. Has the Performance of Any Clinical Group Resulted in a Factor Structure on IQ Tests That Significantly Differs from the Factor Structure Seen in Normals?

2.3.1. Normal Performance

Tests such as the WISC and WISC-R have been subjected to factor analyses to determine the optimal number of factors that account for the variance of the subtests. Most studies of the factor structure of the WISC-R have typically found three factors: Verbal Comprehension (VC),

Perceptual Organization (PO), and Freedom from Distractability (FFD). The VC factor corresponds closely to the Verbal Scale, with the Information, Similarities, Vocabulary, and Comprehension subtests in common (Arithmetic, a Verbal Scale subtest, is not part of the factor). The PO factor corresponds similarly to the Performance Scale, with the Picture Completion, Picture Arrangement, Block Design, and Object Assembly subtests in common (Coding, a Performance Scale subtest, is not part of the factor). The FFD factor is composed of Arithmetic, Digit Span, and Coding subtests.

One recent study used a confirmatory factor analytic technique in which factor structure models were tested against the data to see which model fit best. Harlow, Tanaka, and Comrey (1982) used the WISC-R standardization sample data to test one-, two- and three-factor models at each age level (two-factor model: VC and PO; three-factor model: VC, PO, and FFD). Results indicated that the two-factor model provided the best fit for the data on 6½- and 7½- year-olds, while the three-factor model provided the best fit for each group from 8½ to 16½. The single-factor model did not provide the best fit at any age level.

Another relevant study (Groff & Hubble, 1982) used exploratory factor analytic techniques with two samples of youths with lower IQs (mean FSIQ for 9- to 11- year-olds = 70.4; mean FSIQ for 14- to 16-year olds = 66.5). For the younger group, all three factors (VC, PO, and FFD) emerged with loadings in the typical pattern. For the older group, however, although the VC and PO factors appeared typical, the third factor had significant loadings for only two of three subtests which usually load on FFD (Arithmetic and Coding did load significantly, Digit Span did not).

Findings with normal children, then, have provided robust evidence for two factors in the WISC-R, the VC and PO factors. The FFD factor has appeared to be more sensitive to developmental characteristics of the sample, by appearing inconsistently in low-IQ youths and not at all for 6- to 7-year-olds.

2.3.2. Clinical Group Performance

Overall, it appears that relatively undifferentiated groups of ED children and delinquents have shown factor structures comparable to those of normal children. Several studies (DeHorn & Klinge, 1978; Finch et al., 1979; Hodges, 1982; Peterson & Hart, 1979; Schooler, Beebe, & Koepke, 1978; Stedman, Lawlis, Cortner, & Achterberg, 1978) have all reported clear VC and PO factors for ED samples ranging in age from 6 to 16 years. Evidence for a FFD has been mixed: Stedman et al., DeHorn and Klinge, and Hodges all reported evidence for a FFD factor; however,

Schooler *et al.*, and Finch *et al.* found no third factor and Peterson and Hart's third factor had a "significant" (>.30) loading only for the Arithmetic subtest.

Hubble and Groff (1981b) compared the factor structure from a group of white male delinquents relative to the standardization sample. The three factors that emerged for the delinquents looked very similar to the VC, PO, and FFD factors for the normal sample.

Overall, four studies have found the three-factor solution, whereas three have found only VC and PO factors. In the four studies that reported the three-factor solutions, mean FSIQs for the samples ranged from 88 to 95, with mean ages from 9.5 to 15.5 years. Peterson and Hart (1979) did not report mean IQs and Schooler *et al.* did not report the distribution of subjects' ages. Finch *et al.* (1979) reported a mean FSIQ of 78.7 in a sample that ranged in age from 6.75 to 16.75 years. The older children in the Finch *et al.* sample may have been similar to the older low-IQ group in Groff and Hubble's (1982) study, for which only two factors were found. Perhaps it was this difference in samples that lead to the different findings, since none of the studies that report three-factor solutions included many children of this IQ range.

2.3.3. Summary

It does not appear that the structure of intelligence as indexed by factor structure of the WISC-R subtests is significantly different for heterogeneous groups of disturbed children relative to normals. Some fluctuations may be observed due to sampling characteristics (e.g., preponderance of children at particular age or IQ level), but not to psychopathology.

2.4. Has Any Clinical Group Shown a Profile of Subtest Performance on the WISC-R That Differs Significantly from the Pattern of Normals?

2.4.1. Normal Performance

Sattler (1982) has described the typical pattern of subtest performance and what must be present in order to infer deviance. Subtests are constructed such that for each age the mean is 10 and the standard deviation is 3.0. One can compare each verbal subtest to the mean verbal scaled score or each performance subtest to the mean performance scaled score, and/or compare individual subtest scaled scores, looking for those that differ significantly. For scores to be significant at the .05 level, an individual subtest should differ from the verbal or performance mean by approximately 3 points; individual subtests should differ from each other by approximately 4 points.

2.4.2. Clinical Group Performance

Although Sattler (1980) has stressed that within-individual rather than between-individual analyses should be done when examining profile patterns, most studies have utilized group methods of comparison. Sometimes the comparison group has been a nonclinical group while sometimes the comparison group has been another clinical group (e.g., ED vs. learning disabled, LD).

Three studies have examined subtest profiles of heterogeneous groups of ED children. Morris *et al.* (1978) found that subtest means were significantly lower than normal for their sample of severely ED children. Profiles of white and black subgroups were found to be more variable (not as flat) than the WISC-R standardization sample, with an elevated Picture Completion score for blacks and a depressed Coding score for whites. Dean (1978) used subtest profiles to discriminate between ED and LD children. He found a PIQ > VIQ discrepancy for the ED but not the LD children. The subtests which formed the optimal set of discriminating variables were Block Design, Vocabulary, Picture Arrangement, and Object Assembly. Sattler (1980) and Coolidge (1983) have questioned whether this approach provided an accurate picture of the groups' performance. Fuller and Goh (1981), using procedures similar to those of Dean's to differentiate ED from LD children, found a comparable set of discriminating variables from the WISC-R. Overall PIQ, Picture Arrangement, Object Assembly, Coding, and Vocabulary were significant contributors to the discriminant function.

Hamm and Evans (1978) used factors identified by Cohen (1959) and Witkin, Dyk, Faterson, Goodenough, and Karp (1962) in studying the WISC-R performance of 61 ED children. After examining scores on the three factors (Verbal–Comprehension, Attention–Concentration, and Analytic–Field-Approach), the authors concluded that no unique pattern emerged that could be diagnostically useful.

Vance, Singer, Kitson, and Brenner (1983) reviewed literature on the use of profiles for identifying ED children. They concluded that, although information on intellectual functioning is useful in working with children, there is no evidence of the diagnostic utility of profiles.

Hale and Landino (1981) attempted to use the WISC-R subtest profiles to differentiate among subgroups of ED children based on Behavior Problem Checklist Scores (Quay & Peterson, 1979). Four groups were studied: conduct problem, withdrawn, mixed, and no problem. All children were white males with a mean FSIQ of 93.8. Two discriminant functions were found to differentiate among the groups. For the first function, the important subtests were Digit Span and Picture Completion. For the second function, the important subtests were Digit Span, Similarities, and Arithmetic. The functions did not, however, do a particularly good job of correctly classifying the children into appropriate groups. Only 66% were classified correctly, with 24% of the ED children misclassified as normal and 35% of the normal children misclassified as ED; no children were misclassified as conduct-disordered. Simulation analyses were done, reassigning subjects randomly to the four groups. The discriminant functions which resulted from the random data had hit rates averaging 62.6% correct classifications. Hale and Landino (1981) concluded that, since the observed 66% correct rate was not significantly different from the 62.6% hit rate for random data, the WISC-R profile was not useful for differentiation among subgroups of ED children.

Finegan *et al.* (1982) looked at performances on the VC, PO, and FFD factors of groups of feminine boys, their male siblings, and a psychiatric control group. For all three groups, performance on the FFD factor was poorer than on the VC and PO factors. With respect to specific subtest performance, Finegan *et al.* examined scores on Vocabulary and Block Design for evidence of better verbal skills relative to spatial skills in the feminine boys. Although the brothers and psychiatric controls showed no difference in their performance on these subtests, the feminine boys' scores were significantly higher on the Vocabulary subtest relative to their scores on Block Design subtest; however, the difference between the means was 1.46. Although the feminine boys were not different from the psychiatric controls on the Vocabulary subtest, they were significantly lower than the controls on the Block Design subtest.

Ollendick (1979) compared subtest scatter in a sample of delinquents to the scatter reported for the laborer-standardization sample (Kaufman, 1976b). He found that mean ranges for the scale scores were not significantly different, nor were the frequencies of individual subtest scores that deviated from each subject's mean different for the two groups.

Two studies have examined subtest performance as a potential predictor of aggressive behavior in delinquents or criminals. Kunce, Ryan, and Eckelman (1976) reported that performance on the Similarities subtest of the WAIS discriminated between violent and nonviolent groups. Using a ratio of the Similarities score to the total of all the subtests, the violent criminals had a mean ratio substantially lower than that of nonviolent criminals. Hays *et al.* (1978) were unable to replicate this finding, however, in a comparison of juvenile murderers and status offenders tested with the WISC. In fact, while the difference was nonsignificant, the murderers had a slightly higher mean Similarities ratio. Hays *et al.* also reported that another study had failed to replicate the Similarities ratio prediction of violent crimes using the WAIS and concluded that the Similarities ratio was not a valid index of violent criminal behavior.

Groff and Hubble (1981) used a categorization system for the WISC-R devised by Bannatyne (1974) to compare the performance of 193 male delinquents to the performance of a group of LD children reported by Smith, Coleman, Dokecki, and Davis (1977). Categories in the system are Spatial, Conceptual, Sequential, and Acquired Knowledge. Smith *et al.* had concluded that LD children show a unique pattern, with Spatial skills elevated relative to all others. Groff and Hubble found a similar pattern (elevated Spatial skills) in the sample of delinquents and concluded that the pattern is not diagnostically useful.

2.4.3. Summary

Although only a handful of studies have been done, there is not yet convincing evidence that WISC-R profiles usefully discriminate either between clinical groups and normal or among clinical subgroups. Only two studies have found significant results; both of these (Dean, 1978; Fuller & Goh, 1978) compared ED groups to LD groups. The use of only these two groups, however, has been criticized by Sattler (1980) as methodologically inadequate to reveal useful information about either group. Sattler stressed the need for inclusion of a normal comparison group and for a closer look at individual subjects' profiles. However, the results of Hale and Landino (1981) and Ollendick (1979) suggest that this is probably not a useful area in which to look for differences in cognitive functioning.

3. Cognitive-Developmental Performance of Clinical Groups

Another perspective on cognitive-intellectual performance has been represented in research with ED children and delinquents. Rather than the use of more global measures, these studies have focused on particular aspects of cognitive development. Tasks are selected to be age-appropriate and are presumed to represent an important process or concept during that developmental period; that is, there are developmental and theoretical contexts for the tasks selected. Specific questions can be asked regarding differences in cognitive functioning at various age levels; and ideally, this approach could pinpoint areas of particular weakness in the cognitive development of clinical groups.

While these would seem an advantage over more global psychometric measures, there have nevertheless been some methodological disadvantages with this approach. First, there is no single, agreed-upon theory of cognitive development. Consequently, research has been done from many different perspectives and integration of the results can be an extremely difficult task. Failure to find differences between clinical and nonclinical groups may reflect weakness in the theory, the translation of the theory into tasks, the selection of samples, or a true finding of no difference. Second, because most of the tasks are theoretically age-specific, the need for mental age-matched controls becomes critical. Additionally, great care in task selection must be taken or group differences may be obscured by ceiling or floor effects. Third, reliability of performance can be an issue if few tasks are chosen. And, fourth, while the use of more narrowly defined tasks may be valuable, great caution must be exercised in interpretation and generalization of findings of group differences. A network of studies that tap similar (but not identical) processes in similar (but not identical) contexts should show a consistent pattern of results before that aspect of cognitive functioning is confidently identified as differentiating between clinical and nonclinical groups. The great advantage of this approach, however, is that if these cognitive processes can be identified the implications for intervention are clearer and more specific than they can be when a difference in more global intellectual functioning is found.

Because the cognitive-developmental approach usually stresses an age-related examination of development, this section of the review will progress across the period from infancy to adolescence. Perhaps the best known comprehensive theory of cognitive development is that of Piaget (1941/1965), and much of the research to be reported has chosen tasks rooted in or influenced by his approach. Piaget has made a global division of childhood into four periods: the sensorimotor period, the preoperational period, the concrete operational period, and the formal operational period.

3.1. Has Any Clinical Group Differed Significantly from Appropriate Controls on Cognitive Tasks Mastered in the Sensorimotor Period?

3.1.1. Normal Development

Normal children progress through the sensorimotor period during the first two years of life. During this time, the child masters basic concepts about the permanence of objects, simple tool use, physical causality, gravity and spatial relations, conventional and symbolic uses for objects, and imitation of the actions of others. Theoretically, developments across these areas contribute to the child's developing ability to represent mentally and symbolize events and entities. Problem-solving proceeds from external, sensorimotor action to internal, mental action.

3.1.2. Clinical Group Performance

Not surprisingly, few clinical groups have been studied during the sensorimotor period. Because they are typically of average or near-average intelligence, relatively few disturbed children are likely to present clear cognitive-behavioral deficits before the age of two. Only autistic children, outside the purview of this paper, have shown a pattern of deficits during this early period.

3.2. Has Any Clinical Group Differed Significantly from Appropriate Controls on Cognitive Tasks Mastered in the Preoperational Period?

3.2.1. Normal Development

The preoperational period, roughly from two to six years of age, has been described by Flavell (1977) as marked by development in two broad domains: (1) an expansion of understanding of identities and functions and (2) through the onset of language, an expansion of communication abilities. Both domains reflect the child's shift toward representational thought and increasing symbolic ability. Identities and functions are reflected in the increasing stability of children's concepts and the understanding of functional relationships among events. The expansion of communication skills refers to the child's ability to control himself and others with his speech, and for others to control him with their speech.

3.2.2. Clinical Group Performance

A few studies have used tasks of a preoperational nature, that is, tasks which require understanding particular concepts or the use of verbal self-regulation; however, preschool-aged behavior-problem children have not been studied. Rather, these reports used subjects who most likely were functioning at or very near concrete operations.

Understanding and use of affective labels is an example of the child's developing identities, and those skills emerge in preoperational children (Harter, 1982). Knowledge of affective labels was tested by Nasby, Hayden, and DePaulo (1980), who hypothesized that aggressive ED children would show an attribution bias to infer hostility. Aggressive and nonaggressive ED boys were assigned to two groups and shown a still photo version of the PONS (Profile of Nonverbal Sensitivity; Resenthal, Hall, DiMatteo, Rogers, & Archer, 1979). In the first sample, subjects selected the best label of emotional expression from a multiple-choice format for pictures that varied on two dimensions: positive-negative and submissive-dominant. The score of interest was the incorrect use of negative-dominant labels. The relationship between this score and aggression was moderate but significant ($r = .47, p < .01$). Subjects in sample two were asked to sort the PONS pictures into groups and then provide labels for the picture sets. Judges classified the children's labels as positive-submissive, positive-dominant, negative-submissive, or negative-dominant. Aggression and number of negative-dominant labels used were significantly related ($r = .51, p < .001$). In neither study was there evidence of greater sensitivity and accuracy for the aggressive children in attributing hostility; rather, the aggressive subjects showed a bias toward incorrectly labeling stimuli as negative-dominant. The authors concluded that the social-cognitive bias interferes with adequate social adjustment; however, a simple causal link would be an unlikely explanation. Instead, complex transactional processes between negative attribution and negative experience would have to be explored.

Dodge and his colleagues (Dodge & Newman, 1981; Dodge & Frame, 1982) have explored this social-cognitive process in peer- and teacher-nominated aggressive children. While these children were not clinically identified as ED, a summary of the work would be useful here. An attribution bias similar to that reported by Nasby *et al.* (1980) was found in these relatively aggressive boys, but only under certain conditions (Dodge & Newman, 1981; Dodge & Frame, 1982) that were more personally directed than the PONS task. In addition, relatively quick responding and relatively poor selective recall were associated with attribution of hostility in the aggressive boys.

Camp (1977) reported differences in verbal self-regulation in aggressive and normal 6½- to 8½-year-old boys. Originally, 37 measures of cognition, language, and inhibition were used. A discriminant function correctly identified 88% of the cases. Of the 14 variables in the discriminant function, the aggressive and normal boys were significantly different on four measures: word play and outer speech, baseline fingertapping, irrelevant speech during the Matching Familiar Figures Test (MFFT; Kagan, Rosman, Day, Albert, & Phillips, 1964), and average reaction time on the MMFT. The groups did not differ on PIQ, vocabulary or on the Wide Range Achievement Test. Camp (1977) suggested that absent or ineffective verbal mediation and fast reaction time led to the aggressive boys' poorer performance. She argued that their performance suggests a production deficiency, because the aggressive boys did not have lower overall intellectual or verbal ability. Rather, they were not so likely as normals to *use* their verbal ability for active self-regulation. This analysis would suggest no need to remediate verbal ability *per se*, but to teach aggressive children to recognize situations in which they should exercise linguistic control over their behavior and to develop verbal strategies that effectively serve this function.

3.2.3. Summary

No studies have examined preoperational thinking in clinical groups of preschool-aged children. The two studies that reported use of preoperational-type tasks with older children found patterns of deficits. Nasby *et al.'s* (1980) findings suggested problems in the development of affective concepts (identities), and Camp's (1977) findings suggested problems in the development of language use for self-monitoring and self-control. More attention should be given to preoperational thought in young aggressive children.

3.3. Has Any Clinical Group Differed Significantly from Appropriate Controls on Cognitive Tasks Mastered during the Concrete Operational Period?

3.3.1. Normal Development

The concrete operational period, approximately 7–11 years of age, is perhaps the best known of Piaget's stages. A shift from the prelogic of the preoperational child toward concrete, logical thinking occurs as the child's problem-solving becomes increasingly freed from perceptual cues, decentered (i.e., no longer centered on a single perspective on the problem), and flexible (i.e., mental reversal of the solution is now possible). This change in thought enables mastery of the class inclusion, conservation, and perspective-taking tasks typically used in Piagetian research with school-age children. Perspective-taking skills can be applied to both social and nonsocial contents, and the social applications can include tracing developments in interpersonal problem-solving and empathy. Within this logical framework, there have also been analyses of the origins of moral reasoning (e.g., Kohlberg, 1969). The concrete operational child is typically considered to be rather rigid with respect to social rules. Piaget has called the moral stage of concrete operations the morality of constraint. Further development in moral reasoning occurs in the formal operational period.

3.3.2. Clinical Group Performance

Concrete operational tasks have been used with both school-age and adolescent subjects of various clinical groups. Social-cognitive skills as reflected in perspective-taking, social attribution, and problem-solving have also been studied in ED children.

Waterman, Sobesky, Silvern, Aoki, and McCauley (1981) looked for differences between heterogeneous ED and normal fifth- and sixth-graders on perspective-taking tasks. With differences attributable to mental age removed, the groups differed significantly on cognitive, but not affective, perspective-taking. However, some of the ED children showed adequate perspective-taking skills (i.e., above the median for the entire sample). One unexpected finding specific to the ED group, however, was that within that group, teacher ratings on an antisocial behavior scale were positively related to affective perspective-taking skills (the two variables were unrelated in the normal group).

Finch and Montgomery (1973) studied information-seeking ability in a group of ED children differentiated on the basis of reflectivity–impulsivity. The information-seeking measure was based on Mosher and Hornsby's (1966) 20-question game format to analyze children's sophistication at gathering information. Van Horn and Bartz (1968) found a developmental trend occurring in normal children between 6 and 8 years of age on the question-asking game. The younger children showed a less sophisticated questioning strategy, in which they asked questions which eliminated only one alternative at a time. Older children used what are called constraint-seeking questions. This type of question makes use of stimulus dimensions to eliminate multiple alternatives at a time. Finch and Montgomery selected the 13 most reflective and the 13 most impulsive children from a group of 44 ED children who ranged in age from 7 to 14½. All were of average or above-average intelligence. With mental age effects removed, the reflective children asked more advanced, constraint-seeking questions than did the impulsive children. This finding is similar to Ault's (1973) that more advanced questions were asked by normal, reflective children than by normal, impulsive children. Finch and Montgomery noted, however, that the reflective ED children were more impulsive than normal reflective children. They considered the ED children to show developmental lags in developing reflectivity.

Higgins and Thies (1981) examined the relationship between sociometric ratings of popularity and means–ends problem-solving in a group of ED children in a residential facility. Children rated as high in popularity and children rated as low in popularity were administered the Means–Ends Problem Solving Test (Shure & Spivack, 1972), in which children are presented six stories involving a "problem"—for example, a child is insulted or wants something in a store. The child is told the beginning and the end of the story and is asked to provide as many middles as he or she can. Children were scored for the number of means they provided for reaching the goal or solving the problem. High-popularity children gave significantly more means or solutions than low-popularity children. The popular ED children performed similarly to previous reports for ED children. It was concluded that the particularly poor problem-solving skills of the low-popularity group would be an important target for intervention.

Rather than scoring just the number of responses, Deluty (1981) studied the quality of responses of relatively aggressive children in a nonclinical sample when asked whay they would do in a set of conflict situations (a task similar to the test used by Higgins & Thies, 1981). On the basis of peer nominations, groups of highly aggressive, highly assertive, and highly submissive subjects were formed. Compared to assertive and submissive children, the aggressive children gave significantly more aggressive responses and had a higher percentage of total responses rated as aggressive. Aggressive children also had a significantly lower percentage of responses rated as assertive compared to the assertive children.

Richard and Dodge (1982) found that relatively aggressive boys were equal to popular boys in generating initial effective solutions; the only difference between the groups was on subsequent solutions. The popular boys were more likely to continue to provide successful solutions, whereas the aggressive boys produced ineffective (but not aggressive) solutions after the first one. This finding is consistent with a report of Shure (1982) that alternative solution thinking has consistently related to adjustment.

Nucci and Herman (1982) studied normal and conduct-disordered fourth-graders on a set of moral judgment tasks designed to differentiate among moral, social-conventional, and personal judgments. The authors were interested whether the conduct-disordered children used the same criteria for moral, social, and personal judgments as did normal children. They reported that a consistent pattern has been found among normals from 3 to 25 years of age, with moral transgressions considered the most serious and personal transgressions the least serious. Results showed that for both groups moral transgressions were considered more serious than conventional or personal transgressions. However, among the moral transgressions the normal and aggressive children differed. Two of the moral transgressions (hitting and failing to share abundant goods) rated as serious by the normals were not rated as moral transgressions by the conduct-problem children. Also, aggressive children were less likely to rate personal transgressions as in the personal domain; instead, they rated these transgressions as conventional. Thus, it appeared that the conduct-problem children had an overinclusive social-conventional domain, with some behaviors from both the moral and personal domains rated as wrong because of violation of social consensus.

Bear and Richards (1981) studied the relationship between moral reasoning and conduct problems in a sample of normal school children. Measures used were Kohlberg's Moral Judgment Interview (Kohlberg, Colby, Gibbs, & Speicher-Dubin, 1978) and the Behavior Problem Checklist (Quay & Peterson, 1979). As predicted, both mean conduct problem scores and the variance of the conduct problem scores declined monotonically as moral reasoning stage increased. Regression analysis indicated that, with effects due to sex, verbal ability, and social class removed, moral maturity still accounted for a significant, albeit small, portion of the conduct-problem variance. Results were interpreted as indicating the value of fostering development of moral reasoning. Although an improvement in moral reasoning alone would not be expected to produce dramatic changes in behavior, the combination of a cognitive with a behavioral approach was suggested to be of value.

Selman and his colleagues (Selman, 1976, 1980; Jacquette in Selman, 1980; Cooney & Selman, 1978; Selman, Lavin, & Brion-Meisels, 1982) have developed a comprehensive framework for the development of social cognition in the context of an ongoing clinical and educational program for ED children. A stage-by-domain profile has evolved which includes social-cognitive concepts about individuals, friendships, peer groups, and authority relationships. An early study (Selman, 1976) reported developmental delays in ED children relative to normals on social-cognitive measures. In a structured interview format, the tasks used were Piagetian logicophysical problems, a Kohlberg-type moral reasoning problem, perspective-taking problems, and four problems about interpersonal relations. Although there was not a significant difference between the ED and normal children on the logical-physical tasks, there were significant differences for all the social-cognitive areas. The ED children performed more poorly on perspective-taking, moral reasoning, and interpersonal relations problems. Jacquette (in Selman, 1980) reported on the interpersonal reasoning of ED children in a structured interview versus a naturalistic context. Results indicated that subjects showed less mature reasoning in the naturalistic context, especially when real-life content, rather than hypothetical issues, was the basis for discussion.

Although the mean age of most delinquent groups studied has been beyond that usually considered to be in the concrete operational period, there have been several reports of the use of concrete operational tasks in attempts to differentiate delinquents from nondelinquents. Care must be taken in evaluation of these results, then, because ceiling effects may be observed, leading to the conclusion of no differences. In some cases, interpretation of observed differences may have to rely on performance-utilization factors rather than competence factors (put another way, production rather than mediation deficiency), because the tasks are developmentally simple relative to the subjects' ages (chronological or mental). Delinquent groups have been compared to normals on role-taking tasks and moral reasoning tasks which are representative of the concrete operational period.

Reports on perspective taking in undifferentiated groups of delinquents have been inconsistent in their results. Hains and Miller (1980) found no difference between delinquents and controls. Two studies, however, have reported evidence of poorer performance for delinquents relative to controls. Chandler (1973), in a study designed to provide intervention to improve role-taking skills, carefully documented pretest differences between delinquents and normal controls. The mean FSIQ for the delinquent group was 91; for the control group, the mean was 112.0 (a significant difference). In each group, egocentricity was significantly related to IQ. For delinquents, the correlation was $-.34$ and for normals the correlation was $-.30$. After a covariance analysis to remove IQ, the delinquents were still more egocentric than controls.

Rotenberg (1974) has suggested that a distinction should be made between affective and cognitive role-taking. Affective role-taking could be considered more similar to sympathy, the ability to experience another's feelings or the desire to relieve his distress. Cognitive role-taking, more similar to empathy, would be the ability to take another's perspective without any involvement in his feelings. He hypothesized that delinquents may have adequate cognitive role-taking skills but may show affective role-taking deficits. Previous results that had failed to show consistent patterns of performance within various groups may have been due to a confounding of these two types of role-taking abilities. Rotenberg studied both types of role-taking in delinquents and controls. No difference was found between the two groups in cognitive role-taking ability. A small but significant difference was found in affective role-taking, with the delinquents less able than controls. Cognitive and affective role-taking abilities were not significantly correlated.

Only one study had used exclusively concrete operational tasks of moral reasoning with delinquents, and this was done with a group of undifferentiated female delinquents. Miller, Zumoff, and Stevens (1974) found no difference between the delinquents and controls on tasks which discriminated between two levels of moral reasoning; both levels occur during the concrete operational period. Since the girls were all 13–16 years of age, it was possible that the lack of difference was due to ceiling effects. (Other tests of moral reasoning with delinquents included tasks requiring formal operations and will be discussed in that section.)

Bernstein (1981) studied self-perception and peer perception in differentiated delinquent and nondelinquent teenagers who were administered a questionnaire measure of neurotic and psychopathic behavior. A structured interview was used to collect data; open-ended questions about characteristics of the subject and his best friend were asked. The responses were coded on dimensions of abstraction and integration. Developmental levels used were similar to those of Selman (1980). Although delinquent status *per se* was not related to cognitive level of social perception, psychopathy was associated with less mature perceptions of self and peers.

Somewhat contradictory results have been reported in the area of perspective-taking and empathy. Jurkovic and Prentice (1977) found psychopathic delinquents significantly less skilled at perspective-taking, while subcultural (socialized) delinquents were equal to controls.

Ellis (1982) subsequently studied empathy, measured apparently so as to include both cognitive and affective components, in institutionalized male delinquents and normal controls. The delinquents were also subdivided into subgroups of psychopathic, neurotic, and subcultural and independently as nonaggressive, aggressive against property, and aggressive against persons. Overall, the delinquents were lower in empathy. Among the subgroups, the neurotics were (surprisingly, at least to us) significantly lower than the psychopaths, who were significantly lower than the subculturals, the latter not differing from the controls. The aggressive groups were lower than the nonaggressive, although there were no differences between the person versus property subgroups. In a multiple regression, delinquent subtype (31%) and aggressive subtype (27%) together accounted for a total of 41% of the variance of scores on the empathy measure.

3.3.3. Summary

Most studies of social problem solving at the concrete operational level have found poorer performance to be characteristic of groups of deviant children. Contrasts have included ED and normal, delinquent and normal, ED children differentiated by impulsivity and by popularity, delinquents differentiated by subtype, and normal children differentiated by aggressiveness and by rating of conduct problems. For all contrasts but one (Miller *et al.*'s, 1974, work with delinquent girls), groups identified as having more serious problems (e.g., more aggressive, more psychopathic, less popular) showed poorer social problem-solving skills. Social-cognitive development in school-aged disordered children appears to be a critical area for further study.

3.4. Has Any Clinical Group Differed Significantly from Appropriate Controls on Cognitive Tasks Mastered during the Formal Operational Period?

3.4.1. Normal Development

The period of formal operations, approximately 12 years and older, may be the cognitive-developmental period of greatest theoretical controversy. The failure of many adults to show formal operational reasoning in many problem-solving situations suggests that, for this period more than the previous ones, the notion of a competence–performance/utilization model (cf. Overton & Newman, 1982) may be most appropriate. The individual's optimum level of ability or competence may or may not be observed in his performance on a particular problem. Specific characteristics of the task, the context, and/or the individual may promote or interfere with performance, such that the optimal level may be only one variable contributing to the behavior observed. Models of cognitive difference between clinical and nonclinical groups must take into account these distinctions to predict performance accurately. In general, however, the formal operational period is considered to reflect the capacity for formal, logical thought, for hypothetico-deductive reasoning, and for the ability to think and reason about possibilities as well as realities. Systematic examination of alternatives at a purely mental level is possible. Application of this expanded reasoning capacity to moral judgments enables the individual to transcend social rules and conventions he knows and to consider alternatives systematically, evaluating them from a variety of perspectives simultaneously.

3.4.2. Clinical Group Performance

Juvenile delinquents have been the primary group studied with respect to formal operational tasks. In particular, it is the moral reasoning of delinquents that has been most often reported. The intuitive appeal of a moral reasoning deficit in delinquents, which leads to their socially deviant behavior, is obvious; however, the results have not been as clear-cut as would be hoped.

Campagna and Harter (1975) examined moral reasoning in sociopathic and normal boys matched on IQ and MA at two MA levels. At both levels of MA, the sociopathic subjects showed less mature moral reasoning. An important qualification in these findings, however, is that the sociopathic subjects had significantly poorer verbal skills. Although the groups were matched on FSIQ and MA, the mean VIQ for the normals was 102.5, whereas the mean VIQ for the sociopathic boys was 90.2.

Hudgins and Prentice (1973) first studied mothers and adolescent boys, with both mother–delinquent and mother–nondelinquent pairs. The mothers showed higher levels of moral judgment than adolescents, and nondelinquents showed higher levels of moral judgments than delinquents. Mothers of delinquents appeared more variable in their judgments, with 40% of the mothers of delinquents and 70% of the mothers of nondelinquents showing pure styles of moral reasoning. As the authors noted, however, although the group means were different, there was overlap between the reasoning of the delinquent and nondelinquent groups; some delinquents showed higher moral judgments than did some nondelinquents, an indication that moral judgment measures would no be perfect discriminators between delinquent and nondelinquent groups. Emler, Heather, and Winton (1978) and Hains and Miller (1980) also reported higher mean moral judgment scores for controls relative to delinquents. Both of these studies used the Defining Issues Test (Rest, 1974) as the measure of moral reasoning.

Jurkovic (1980) has recently reviewed the literature on moral reasoning in delinquents and concluded that results generally showed a significant amount of variability both between and within individual delinquents. Although an overall pattern of lower levels of moral judgment has been shown, there are still several potential causes for this poorer performance. Some delinquents may lack the cognitive competence necessary for logical thought or perspective taking. Others may have the sociocognitive capabilities but do not ever use them, or use them rarely. Jurkovic particularly noted the need for a more complex, interactional perspective on the moral judgment process in delinquents, one that recognizes the heterogeneity among those subsumed by the label and takes into account cognitive, social, personal, and situational factors.

In the one study which examined moral reasoning and formal operational thinking in differentiated groups of delinquents, Jurkovic and Prentice (1977) found differences among delinquent subgroups. Psychopathic, neurotic, and subcultural delinquent and nondelinquent groups were equated on age, SES, and ethnic composition. Verbal skills were higher in the nondelinquent group and comparable among delinquent subgroups. When effects of verbal ability were statistically controlled, differences in moral reasoning were found primarily in the psychopathic subgroup relative to the other subgroups and controls; psychopathic delinquents showed a less mature level of moral development than did the neurotic or subcultural delinquents, who were equal to the normal controls. The same pattern held for one of the formal operational tasks; that is, the psychopathic delinquents performed significantly more poorly than the neurotic and subcultural delinquents, who did not differ from nondelinquents. On the second formal operational task, similar ranks for the groups were obtained, although the differences were not significant.

3.4.3. Summary

Relatively little work has been done on formal operational thought in disordered adolescents. Studies have focused on moral reasoning in delinquents, with evidence suggesting somewhat poorer performance for delinquents in general and for psychopathic delinquents in particular. Jurkovic's (1980) call for a much more comprehensive approach to moral reasoning in delinquents should provide a starting point for further research with delinquents, and such a framework could be generalized to other clinical groups.

4. Conclusions

Overall, global IQ deficits, different factor structures, or atypical subtest profiles have not been commonly found when the cognitive functioning of disturbed groups has been assessed by the standard intelligence tests. One consistent finding, however, has been a pattern of poorer verbal intelligence relative to nonverbal intelligence.

There has also been scattered evidence that clinical groups often perform more poorly than do MA-matched normals on cognitive-developmental tasks of a social-interpersonal nature. Types of tasks have included interpersonal problem solving, perspective taking, person perception, and moral reasoning. However, nearly all these cognitive-developmental measures rely on language skills for both comprehension of the task or problem itself and for the production and explanation of the solution. Although these tasks are not meant to test language skill *per se* (e.g., vocabulary), they typically require verbal reasoning to solve the problems they pose. Thus, the finding of relatively poorer psychometrically assessed verbal intelligence and of poor problem-solving skills assessed by tasks which require language use is consistent. More detailed investigation of language ability and language use in problem-solving is clearly called for in future research.

With respect to particular clinical subgroups, the evidence is sketchy, but some patterns have appeared. More aggressive, un-socialized groups of children and adolescents have consistently shown deficits including large (20 point) PIQ–VIQ discrepancies (Hecht & Jurkovic, 1978); poor perspective-taking, moral reasoning, and empathic ability (Ellis, 1982; Jurkovic & Prentice, 1977; Nucci & Herman, 1981), inappropriate overuse of negative attribution (Nasby *et al.*, 1980), poor verbal mediational skills (Richman & Lindgren, 1981), and inadequate use of verbal mediation to monitor behavior effectively (Camp, 1977). These bits and pieces of evidence do suggest that deficits in language development and language use are involved in aggressive, antisocial behavior.

Whether these cognitive deficits are cause or effect or are both functions of other variables cannot be determined from the correlational approach that has characterized research to date. The deficits could play a causative role in mislabeling environmental stimuli, in limiting available response alternatives, in constraining search strategies for appropriate responses already in the repertoire, and in generating frustration as a function of decreased ability to meet academic and social behavior demands.

Cognitive deficits of the type most consistently found seem less readily explainable as the effects of psychopathology. However, persistent aggressivity, clearly aversive to others, could give rise to reduced social interaction which could result in a lessened opportunity to acquire verbal skills, empathic ability, and moral judgment in the social context.

One can also speculate about the influence of factors operating at the psychophysiological level which have been hypothesized to be related to aggressive, psychopathic disorders in adults. Whether dysfunction in the behavioral inhibition system (Fowles, 1980), septal areas (Gorenstein & Newman, 1980), or frontal lobes (Gorenstein, 1982), which have been hypothesized to give rise to disinhibited types of psychopathology, could also produce the observed cognitive deficits is unclear.

With respect to both future research and the interpretation of results of research to date, an important methodological point must be made. Generally, the evidence has indicated that disturbed children show VIQ < PIQ more often than normals. When conducting cognitive-developmental research, if groups are matched on FSIQ or on MA that is based on a FSIQ, it is possible that the groups may still be discrepant on VIQ, as was the case in the Campagna and Harter (1975) study. If MA-matched controls are essential to comparing clinical versus normal groups on cognitive developmental tasks, VIQ and Verbal MA may be the most relevant, sensitive matching variable. Differences attributable to language skill versus language use would then be more accurately detected.

Future research in this area should be consistent both in the use of a classification system that provides behaviorally homogeneous subgroups and in the use of a cognitive-developmental framework that encompasses many categories of social cognitive skills, with techniques for observing their presence or absence across several settings. Only with more clearly differentiated and exact approaches to the selection of both subjects and developmental tasks can a richer picture of the role of cognitive factors in child psychopathology be forthcoming.

Classificatory frameworks which show promise include those developed out of multivariate statistical research (e.g., Achenbach & Edelbrock, 1979; Conners, 1970; Quay, 1977) as well as the more reliably diagnosed categories of DSM-III (American Psychiatric Association, 1980). Researchers interested in studying the cognitive correlates of the conduct disorder must make especially careful differential diagnoses between this disorder and Attention Deficit Disorder, as the latter group manifests a host of cognitive problems apparently growing out of early-onset deficits in sustained attention (Douglas & Peters, 1979).

Examples of social-cognitive frameworks include those of Selman (1981) and Shure (1982). Both of these theorists have outlined sets of social cognitive skills and developmental sequences for their development. It would be important, however, to make explicit the relationship of these skills to language ability and the extent to which language use is a component of each skill.

5. References

Achenbach, T.M., & Edelbrock, C. J. The Child Behavior Profile: II. Boys aged 12–16 and girls aged 6–11 and 12–16. *Journal of Consulting and Clinical Psychology*, 1979, 47, 223–233.

American Psychiatric Association. *Diagnostic and statistical manual of mental disorders* (3rd ed.). Washington, D.C.: Author, 1980.

Andrew, J. M. Delinquency: Intellectual imbalance? *Criminal Justice and Behavior*, 1977, 4, 99–104.

Ault, R. L. Problem-solving strategies of reflective, impulsive, fast–accurate and slow–inaccurate children. *Child Development*, 1973, 44, 259–266.

Bannatyne, A. Diagnosis: A note on recategorization of the WISC scaled scores. *Journal of Learning Disabilities*, 1974, 7, 272–273.

Bear, G. C., & Richards, H. C. Moral reasoning and conduct problems in the classroom. *Journal of Educational Psychology*, 1981, 73, 644–670.

Beitchman, J. H., Patterson, P., Gelfand, B., & Minty, G. IQ and child psychiatric disorder. *Canadian Journal of Psychiatry*, 1982, 27, 23–28.

Bernstein, R. M. The relationship between dimensions of delinquency and the developments of self and peer perception. *Adolescence*, 1981, 63, 543–556.

Brumback, R. A., Staton, R. D., & Wilson, H. Neuropsychological study of children during and after remission of endogenous depressive episodes. *Perceptual and Motor Skills*, 1980, 50, 1163–1167.

Camp, B. W. WISC performance in acting-out and delinquent children with and without EEG abnormality. *Journal of Consulting Psychology,* 1966, *30,* 350–353.

Camp B. W. Verbal mediation in young aggressive boys. *Journal of Abnormal Psychology,* 1977, *86,* 145–153.

Campagna, A.F., & Harter, S. Moral judgment is sociopathic and normal children. *Journal of Personality and Social Psychology,* 1975, *31,* 199–205.

Caplan, N. S. Intellectual functioning. In H. C. Quay (Ed.), *Juvenile delinquency: Theory and research.* New York: Van Nostrand, 1965.

Chandler, M. J. Egocentrism and antisocial behavior: The assessment and training of social perspective-taking skills. *Developmental Psychology,* 1973, *9,* 326–332.

Cohen, J. The factorial structure of the WISC at ages 7–6, 10–6, and 13–6. *Journal of Consulting Psychology,* 1959, *23,* 285–299.

Connors, C. K. Symptom patterns in hyperkinetic, neurotic and normal children. *Child Development,* 1970, *41,* 667–682.

Coolidge, F. L. WISC-R discrimination of learning-disabled and emotionally disturbed children: An intragroup and intergroup analysis. *Journal of Consulting and Clinical Psychology,* 1983, *51,* 230.

Cooney, E. W., & Selman, R. L. Children's use of social conceptions: Towards a dynamic model of social cognition. In W. Damon (Ed.), *Social cognition. New directions for child development* (No. 1). San Francisco: Josey-Bass, 1978.

Dean, R. S. Distinguishing learning-disabled and emotionally disturbed children on the WISC-R. *Journal of Consulting and Clinical Psychology,* 1978, *46,* 381–382.

DeHorn, A., & Klinge, V. Correlations and factor analysis of the WISC-R and the Peabody Picture Vocabulary Test for an adolescent psychiatric sample. *Journal of Consulting and Clinical Psychology,* 1978, *46,* 1160–1161.

Deluty, R. H. Alternative-thinking ability of aggressive, assertive and submissive children. *Cognitive Therapy and Research,* 1981, *5,* 309–312.

DeMyer, M. K., Hingtgen, J. N., & Jackson, R. K. Infantile autism reviewed: A decade of research. *Schizophrenia Bulletin,* 1981, *7,* 388–450.

Dodge, K. A., & Frame, C. L. Social cognitive biases and deficits in aggressive boys. *Child Development,* 1982, *53,* 620–635.

Dodge, K. A., & Newman, J. P. Biased decision-making processes in aggressive boys. *Journal of Abnormal Psychology,* 1981, *90,* 375–379.

Douglas, V. I., & Peters, K. Toward a clearer definition of the attentional deficit of hyperactive children. In G. H. Hale & M. Lewis (Eds.), *Attention and cognitive development.* New York: Plenum Press, 1979.

Elkind, D. Forms and traits in the conception and measurement of general intelligence. *Intelligence,* 1981, *5,* 101–120.

Ellis, P. L. Empathy: A factor in antisocial behavior. *Journal of Abnormal Child Psychology,* 1982, *10,* 123–134.

Emler, N.P., Heather, N., & Winton, M. Delinquency and the development of moral reasoning. *British Journal of Social and Clinical Psychology,* 1978, *17,* 325–331.

Fernald, P. S., & Wisser, R. E. Using WISC Verbal-Performance discrepancies to predict degree of acting out. *Journal of Clinical Psychology,* 1967, *23,* 92–93.

Finch, A. J., Kendall, P. C., Spirito, A., Entin, A., Montgomery, L. E., & Schwartz, D. J. Short form and factor-analytic studies of the WISC-R with behavior problem children. *Journal of Abnormal Child Psychology,* 1979, *7,* 337–344.

Finch, A. J., Jr., & Montgomery, L. E. Reflection–impulsivity and information-seeking in emotionally disturbed children. *Journal of Abnormal Child Psychology,* 1973, *1,* 358–362.

Finegan, J. K., Zucker, K. J., Bradley, S. J., & Doering, R. W. Patterns of intellectual functioning and spatial ability in boys with gender identity disorder. *Canadian Journal of Psychiatry,* 1982, *27,* 135–139.

Flavell, J. H. *Cognitive development*. Englewood Cliffs, N.J.: Prentice-Hall. 1977.

Fowles, D. C. The three arousal model: Implications of Gray's Two Factor Learning Theory for heart rate, electrodermal activity and psychopathy. *Psychophysiology*, 1980, *17*, 87–104.

Fuller, G. B., & Goh, D. S. Intelligence, achievement and visual-motor performance among learning disabled and emotionally impaired children. *Psychology in the Schools*, 1981, *18*, 261–268.

Gibson, H. B., & West, D. J. Social and intellectual handicaps as precursors of early delinquency. *British Journal of Criminology*, 1970, *10*, 21–32.

Gorenstein, E. E. Frontal lobe function in psychopaths. *Journal of Abnormal Psychology*, 1982, *91*, 368–379.

Gorenstein, E. E., & Newman, J. P. Disinhibitory psychopathology: A new perspective and a model for research. *Psychological Review*, 1980, *87*, 301–315.

Groff, M. G., & Hubble, L. M. Recategorized WISC-R scores of juvenile delinquents. *Journal of Learning Disabilities*, 1981, *14*, 515–516.

Groff, M., & Hubble, L. WISC-R factor structures of younger and older youth with low IQs. *Journal of Consulting and Clinical Psychology*, 1982, *50*, 148–149.

Hains, A. A., & Miller, D. J. Moral and cognitive development in delinquent and non-delinquent children and adolescents. *Journal of Genetic Psychology*, 1980, *137*, 21–35.

Hale, R. L., & Landino, S. A. Utility of WISC-R subtest analysis in discriminating among groups of conduct-problem, withdrawn, mixed and nonproblem boys. *Journal of Consulting and Clinical Psychology*, 1981, *49*, 91–95.

Hamm, H. A., & Evans, J. G. WISC-R subtest patterns of severely emotionally disturbed students. *Psychology in the Schools*, 1978, *15*, 188–190.

Harlow, L. L., Tanaka, J. S., & Comrey, A. L. *Restricted factor analysis models of the WISC-R, ages 6½ to 16½*. Paper presented to Division 5 at the 1982 meeting of the American Psychological Association, Washington, D.C., August 1982.

Harter, S. A cognitive-developmental approach to children's understanding of affect and trait labels. In F. C. Serafica (Ed.), *Social-cognitive development in context*. New York: Guilford Press, 1982.

Haynes, J. P., & Bensch, M. The P > V sign on the WISC-R and recidivism in delinquents. *Journal of Consulting and Clinical Psychology*, 1981, *49*, 480–481.

Haynes, J. P., & Bensch, M. Female delinquent recidivism and the P > V sign on the WISC-R. *Journal of Clinical Psychology*, 1983, *39*, 141–144.

Hays, J. R., & Smith, A. L. Comparison of the WISC-R and culture-fair intelligence tests for three ethnic groups of juvenile delinquents. *Psychological Reports*, 1980, *46*, 931–934.

Hays, J. R., Solway, K. S., & Schreiner, D. Intellectual characteristics of juvenile murderers verses status offenders. *Psychological Reports*, 1978, *43*, 80–82.

Hecht, I. H., & Jurkovic, G. J. The Performance-Verbal discrepancy in differentiated subgroups of delinquent adolescent boys. *Journal of Youth and Adolescence*, 1978, *7*, 197–201.

Heilbrun, A. B., Jr. Psychopathy and violent crime. *Journal of Consulting and Clinical Psychology*, 1979, *47*, 509–516.

Henning, J. J., & Levy, R. H. Verbal-Performance IQ differences of white and negro delinquents on the WISC and WAIS. *Journal of Clinical Psychology*, 1967, *23*, 457–463.

Higgins, J. P., & Thies, A. P. Problem solving and social position among emotionally disturbed boys. *American Journal of Orthopsychiatry*, 1981, *51*, 356–358.

Hodges, K. Factor structure of the WISC-R for a psychiatric sample. *Journal of Consulting and Clinical Psychology*, 1982, *50*, 141–142.

Holland, T. R., Beckett, G. E., & Levi, M. Intelligence, personality and criminal violence: A multivariate approach. *Journal of Consulting and Clinical Psychology*, 1981, *49*, 106–111.

Hubble, L. M., & Groff, M. WISC-R profiles of adjudicated delinquents later incarcerated or released on probation. *Psychological Reports*, 1980, *47*, 481–482.

Hubble, L. M., & Groff, M. Magnitude and direction of WISC-R Verbal-Performance IQ discrepancies among adjudicated male delinquents. *Journal of Youth and Adolescence*, 1981, *10*, 179–184. (a)

Hubble, L. M., & Groff, M. Factor analysis of WISC-R scores of male delinquents referred for evaluation. *Journal of Consulting and Clinical Psychology*, 1981, *49*, 738–739. (b)

Hubble, L. M., & Groff, M. G. WISC-R Verbal Performance IQ discrepancies among Quay-classified adolescent male delinquents. *Journal of Youth and Adolescence*, 1982, *11*, 503–508.

Hudgins, W., & Prentice, N. M. Moral judgments in delinquent and nondelinquent adolescents and their mothers. *Journal of Abnormal Psychology*, 1973, *82*, 145–152.

Jurkovic, G. J. The juvenile delinquent as a moral philosopher: A structural-developmental perspective. *Psychological Bulletin*, 1980, *88*, 709–727.

Jurkovic, G. J., & Prentice, N. M. Relation of moral and cognitive development to dimensions of juvenile delinquency. *Journal of Abnormal Psychology*, 1977, *86*, 414–420.

Kagan, J., Rosman, B. L., Day, D., Albert, J., & Phillips, W. Information processing in the child: Significance of analytic and reflective attitudes. *Psychological Monographs*, 1964, *78* (Whole No. 578).

Kaufman, A. S. Verbal-Performance IQ discrepancies on the WISC-R. *Journal of Consulting and Clinical Psychology*, 1976, *44*, 739–744. (a)

Kaufman, A. S. A new approach to the interpretation of test scatter on the WISC-R. *Journal of Learning Disabilities*, 1976, *9*, 33–41. (b)

Kohlberg, L. Stage and sequence: The cognitive-developmental approach to socialization. In D. A. Goslin (Ed.), *Handbook of socialization theory and research*. Chicago: Rand McNally, 1969.

Kohlberg, L., Colby, A., Gibbs, J., & Speicher-Dubin, B. *Standard form scoring manual.* Cambridge, Mass.: Center for Moral Education, Harvard University, 1978.

Kunce, J. T., Ryan, J. J., & Eckelman, C. C. Violent behavior and differential WAIS characteristics. *Journal of Consulting and Clinical Psychology*, 1976, *44*, 42–45.

Miller, C. K., Zumoff, L., & Stephens, B. A comparison of reasoning skill and moral judgments in delinquent, retarded and normal adolescent girls. *Journal of Psychology*, 1974, *86*, 261–268.

Morris, J. D., Evans, J. G., & Pearson, D. R. The WISC-R subtest profile of a sample of severely emotionally disturbed children. *Psychological Reports*, 1978, *42*, 319–325.

Mosher, F. A., & Hornsby, J. R. On asking questions. In J. S. Bruner, R. R. Olver, & P. M. Greenfield (Eds.), *Studies on cognitive growth*. New York: Wiley, 1966.

Nasby, W., Hayden, B., & DePaulo, B. M. Attributional bias among aggressive boys to interpret unambiguous social stimuli as displays of hostility. *Journal of Abnormal Psychology*, 1980, *89*, 459–468.

Nucci, L. P., & Herman, S. Behavioral disordered children's conceptions of moral, conventional, and personal issues. *Journal of Abnormal Child Psychology*, 1982, *10*, 411–426.

Offord, D. R., Poushinsky, M. F., & Sullivan, K. School performance, IQ and delinquency. *British Journal of Criminology*, 1978, *18*, 110–126.

Ollendick, T. H. Discrepancies between Verbal and Performance IQs and subtest scatter on the WISC-R for juvenile delinquents. *Psychological Reports*, 1979, *45*, 563–568.

Ossofsky, H. J. Endogenous depression in infancy and childhood. *Comprehensive Psychiatry*, 1974, *15*, 19–25.

Overton, W., & Newman, J. Cognitive development: A competence–activation/utilization approach. In T. Field, A. Huston, H. Quay, L. Troll, & G. Finley (Eds.), *Review of human development*. New York: Wiley, 1982.

Peterson, C. R., & Hart, D. H. Factor structure of the WISC-R for a clinic-referred population and specific subgroups. *Journal of Consulting and Clinical Psychology*, 1979, *47*, 643–645.

Piaget, J. *The child's conception of number*. New York: Norton, 1965 (Originally published, 1941).

Prentice, N. M., & Kelly, F. J. Intelligence and delinquency: A reconsideration. *Journal of Social Psychology*, 1963, *60*, 327–337.

Prior, M. R. Cognitive abilities and disabilities in infantile autism: A review. *Journal of Abnormal Child Psychology*, 1979, *7*, 357–380.

Quay, H. C. Measuring dimensions of deviant behavior: The Behavior Problem Checklist. *Journal of Abnormal Child Psychology*, 1977, *5*, 277–287.

Quay, H. C. Classification. In H. C. Quay & J. S. Werry (Eds.), *Psychopathological disorders of childhood* (2nd ed.). New York: Wiley, 1979.

Quay, H. C., & Parsons, L. B. *The differential behavioral classification of the juvenile offender* (2nd ed.). Washington, D. C.: U. S. Bureau of Prisons, 1971.

Quay, H. C., & Peterson, D. R. *Manual for the Behavior Problem Checklist*. New Brunswick, N. J.: School of Professional Psychology, Busch Campus, Rutgers State University, 1979.

Rest, J. R. *Manual for the Defining Issues Test: An objective moral judgment*. Unpublished manuscript, University of Minnesota, 1974.

Richard, B. A., & Dodge, K. A. Social maladjustment and problem-solving in school-aged children. *Journal of Consulting and Clinical Psychology*, 1982, *50*, 226–233.

Richman, L. C., & Lindgren, S. D. Verbal mediation deficits: Relation to behavior and achievement in children. *Journal of Abnormal Psychology*, 1981, *90*, 99–104.

Riddle, M., & Roberts, A. H. Delinquency, delay of gratification and the Porteus Maze Tests. *Psychological Bulletin*, 1977, *84*, 417–425.

Rosenthal, R., Hall, J. A., DiMatteo, M. R., Rogers, P. L., & Archer, D. *Sensitivity to nonverbal communication: The PONS Test*. Baltimore: Johns Hopkins University Press, 1979.

Rotenberg, M. Conceptual and methodological notes on affective and cognitive role-taking: An illustrative experiment with delinquent and nondelinquent boys. *Journal of Genetic Psychology*, 1974, *125*, 177–185.

Rutter, M. Intelligence and childhood psychiatric disorder. *British Journal of Social and Clinical Psychology*, 1964, *3*, 120–129.

Sattler, J. M. *Assessment of children's intelligence* (1st ed.). Philadelphia: Saunders, 1974.

Sattler, J. M. Learning disabled children do not have a Perceptual Organization deficit: Comments on Dean's WISC-R analysis. *Journal of Consulting and Clinical Psychology*, 1980, *48*, 254–255.

Sattler, J. M. *Assessment of children's intelligence and special abilities* (2nd ed.). Boston: Allyn & Bacon, 1982.

Schooler, D. L., Beebe, M. C., & Koepke, T. Factor analysis of WISC-R scores for children identified as learning disabled, educable mentally impaired, and emotionally disturbed. *Psychology in the Schools*, 1978, *15*, 478–485.

Seashore, H. G. Differences between Verbal and Performance IQs on the WISC. *Journal of Consulting Psychology*, 1951, *15*, 62–67.

Selman, R. L. Toward a structural analysis of developing interpersonal relations concepts: Research with normal and disturbed pre-adolescent boys. In A. Pick (Ed.), *Minnesota symposium on child psychology* (Vol. 10). Minneapolis: University of Minnesota Press, 1976.

Selman, R. L. *The growth of interpersonal understanding: Developmental and clinical analyses*. New York: Academic Press, 1980.

Selman, R. L., Lavin, D. R., & Brion-Meisels, S. Troubled children's use of self-reflection. In F. C. Serafica (Ed.), *Social-cognitive development in context*. New York: Guilford Press, 1982.

Shure, M. B. Interpersonal problem-solving: A cog in the wheel of social cognition. In F. C. Serafica (Ed.), *Social cognitive development in context*. New York: Guilford Press, 1982.

Shure, M., & Spivack, G. Means–ends thinking, adjustment and the social class among elementary school-aged children. *Journal of consulting and Clinical Psychology*, 1972, *38*, 348–353.

Smith, M. D., Coleman, J. M., Dokecki, P. R., & Davis, E. E. Intellectual characteristics of school labeled learning disabled children. *Journal of Learning Disabilities*, 1977, *10*, 352–357.

Staton, R. D., Wilson, H., & Brumback, R. A. Cognitive improvement associated with tricyclic antidepressant treatment of childhood major depressive illness. *Perceptual and Motor Skills*, 1981, *50*, 1163–1167.

Stedman, J. M., Lawlis, G. F., Cortner, R. H., & Achterberg, G. Relationships between WISC-R factors, Wide-Range Achievement Test scores, and visual-motor maturation in children referred for psychological evaluation. *Journal of Consulting and Clinical Psychology*, 1978, *46*, 869–872.

Vance, B., Singer, M. G., Kitson, D. L., & Brenner, O. C. WISC-R profile analysis in differentiating LD from ED children. *Journal of Clinical Psychology*, 1983, *39*, 125–132.

Van Horn, K. R., & Bartz, W. H. Information seeking strategies in cognitive development. *Psychonomic Science*, 1968, *11*, 341–342.

Waterman, J. M., Sobesky, W. E., Silvern, L., Aoki, B., & McCaulay, M. Social perspective-taking and adjustment in emotionally disturbed, learning disabled and normal children. *Journal of Abnormal Child Psychology*, 1981, *9*, 133–148.

Witkin, H. A., Dyk, R. B., Faterson, H. F., Goodenough, D. R., & Karp, S. A. *Psychological differentiation*. New York: Wiley, 1962.

Wolff, P. H., Waber, D., Bauermeister, M., Cohen, C., & Ferber, R. The neurophysiological status of adolescent delinquent boys. *Journal of Child Psychology and Psychiatry*, 1982, *23*, 267–279.

2   Television Violence and Aggressive Behavior

Leonard D. Eron and L. Rowell Huesmann

There can no longer be any doubt that television influences behavior, especially the behavior of children. Any mother who goes marketing in the supermarket with a young child sitting in the shopping cart or tagging along beside her can attest to that fact, especially when she gets to the checkout counter and sees all the sugar-coated cereals, boxes of cookies, and candy bars which in some mysterious fashion had found their way into the cart. The television networks are proud of the way in which they can influence behavior with commercials. It is ludicrous, therefore, for the networks to insist that watching violent displays on television has no relation to subsequent violent behavior of viewers. If they did not expect television to influence behavior, why would they be broadcasting commercials showing people using products they want the viewer to use? It is unlikely that one would ever hear a sales representative tell a prospective customer for television time that television does not influence behavior. That is, after all, what commercials are about and how the networks stay alive and prosper.

The research described in this chapter demonstrates quite conclusively that the repeated observation of television violence can cause aggressive behavior in children and has a lasting effect on their character and personality. Our own research consists primarily of three sets of data hereafter referred to as (1) the Rip Van Winkle Study, (2) the Chicago Study, and (3) the Cross-Cultural Study.

1. The Rip Van Winkle Study

We started our research on how children learn to be aggressive almost 25 years ago. At that time, television viewing was not considered

LEONARD D. ERON AND L. ROWELL HUESMANN • Department of Psychology, University of Illinois, Chicago, Illinois 60680. The research described here has been supported by the National Institute of Mental Health with grants 1726 and 34410 (L. D. Eron), Grants 28280 and 31866 (L. R. Huesmann), and Contract HSM 42-70-60 (M. M. Lefkowitz) and by the Office of Child Development with Grant CB364 (L. D. Eron).

an important factor in causing aggressive behavior in children. In fact, it was believed to be no different than fairy stories, fables, comics, or the movies. These were certainly violent, but they had been with us for years, especially fairy stories, and it had never been claimed that *Little Red Riding Hood, Jack the Giant Killer,* and *Goldilocks* made aggressive monsters of the youngsters who grew up listening to these stories and repeating them over and over to themselves. Thus, we were skeptical about what effect television might have on subsequent aggressive behavior.

At that time, we were interested primarily in relating child-rearing practices of parents to aggressive behavior of children in school (Eron, Laulicht, Walder, Farber, & Spiegel, 1961). Thus, we examined the rewards and punishments parents administered for aggressive behavior, the models of aggressive behavior that the parents themselves provided, and various sociocultural factors such as father's occupation, social class, education, mobility, religion, and frequency of church attendance. Our sample included 875 children, all of the third-grade school children in a semirural county in New York State in 1960, and 75% of their mothers and fathers.

The level of the child's aggression was measured by a peer nomination technique in which every child in the class rated every other child on a series of 10 specific items of aggressive behavior. The child's aggression score was the percentage of times he was nominated by his peers on the 10 items out of the total number of times he could have been nominated. The reliability and validity of this measure have been extensively documented (Eron, Walder, & Lefkowitz, 1971; Lefkowitz, Eron, Walder, & Huesmann, 1977; Eron, Huesmann, Brice, Fischer, & Mermelstein, 1983). A measure of the parents' child-rearing practices was obtained from a 286-item questionnaire described in *Learning of Aggression in Children* (Eron *et al.,* 1971). Among the questions asked of the parents were the names of the child's four favorite television programs and how many hours he or she watched television during the week and on weekends. The violence of the programs was rated reliably by two independent judges and the violence scores agreed with those of other researchers in the area (Eron, 1963; Greenberg, 1972). Much to our surprise, we found that *for boys* there appeared to be a direct positive relation between the violence of the programs they preferred and how aggressive they were in school. Since this was no more than a contemporaneous relation, we did not have too much confidence in the finding by itself. It was not possible to tell by these data alone whether aggressive boys liked violent television programs, whether the violent programs made boys aggressive, whether aggression and watching violent television were both due to some other third variable, or all of these.

However, because these findings fit in well with certain theories about learning by imitation (Bandura, Ross, & Ross, 1961) and cue relevance (Berkowitz, 1962, 1964), a cause-and-effect relation was certainly plausible.

Ten years later, however, in 1970, we were fortunate in being able to reinterview over half of our original sample. One of the most striking findings again was the positive relation between viewing of violent television at age 8 and aggression at age 19 in the male subjects (Eron, Huesmann, Lefkowitz, & Walder, 1972; Lefkowitz et al., 1977). Actually, the relation was even stronger than it was when both variables were measured at age 8. Further, there was no relation between a young man's aggression at age 19 and the amount of television violence he viewed at the time. It appears that by the time a boy is a young adult, the kinds of television programs he watches no longer affect his aggressive behavior.

By use of several multivariate statistical techniques it was demonstrated that the most reasonable interpretation of these data was that early viewing of violent television caused later aggression. For example, the correlation between television violence at grade three and aggression ten years later is significantly greater than the correlation between aggression at grade three and television violence ten years later. Further, if one controls for how aggressive boys are at age 8, the relation does not diminish. As a matter of fact, those boys who at age 8 were low aggressive but watched violent television were significantly more aggressive ten years later than boys who were originally high aggressive but watched nonviolent programs. Similarly, we controlled for every other possible third variable that might account for this relation—IQ, social status, parents' aggression, social and geographical mobility, and church attendance—and none of these variables had an appreciable effect on the relation between violence of programs preferred by boys at age 8 and how aggressive they were ten years later.

It seems plausible that there is a sensitive developmental period in a child's life at around age 8 when he is very susceptible to the influence of violent scenes on television. By the continued watching of aggressive programs, the young child comes to think that aggression is an appropriate way to solve life's problems, the way one acquires things one wants but does not have. In this regard, we evaluated how realistic the subjects thought television programs were. For example, they were asked, "How realistic do you think 'Gunsmoke' is in telling about how life in the West really was?" or "How realistic would you say 'Mod Squad' is in showing what police work is really like?" We found that scores on this scale were higher for subjects who preferred more violent shows, who watched more hours per week, and who were more aggressive. That is, the more realistic these 19-year-old young men thought television was, the more aggressive they were, the more they watched television, and the more violent were the programs they preferred. This is not unlike Gerbner's conclusions (Gerbner & Gross, 1976). He found strong associations between patterns of network dramatic content and conceptions of social reality among children and adolescents and concluded that television cultivated an exaggerated sense of danger and mistrust in steady viewers compared with similar groups of those who watched television less frequently. Also, children who watch a great deal of television are more likely to believe that the police frequently use force and that the average officer will shoot fleeing suspects.

Why is television different, one might ask, from the movies on which earlier generations were nurtured? Films produced in the 1930s and 1940s had much violence. Why did they not have such an effect on young people of that generation when they were growing up and were in this sensitive period? For one thing, youngsters in those days were not exposed as often—they would attend the movies on Saturday afternoons, perhaps, not every day and every night and four hours on Saturday morning. Also, it was not happening right in their own living rooms—or while they were having dinner. Furthermore, since few studies were done, we do not really know whether these movies had any effect.

It should be emphasized that in this first study, a direct positive relation between violence of preferred programs and later aggression was found only for boys. Why should there have been this differential effect of television violence on boys and girls? First, boys were often encouraged and reinforced in the direct and overt expression of aggression. On the other hand, girls were trained not to behave aggressively in a direct manner and nonaggressive behavior was reinforced. Second, in 1960 there were far fewer aggressive females on television for a girl to imitate than there were aggressive males for a boy to imitate. When girls did appear in violent sequences on television, they were usually victims of aggression or at best passive observers. The more violent the programs that girls watched, the more they were exposed to female models as victims or passive observers, and the more they associated aversive consequences to aggression. Therefore, the less likely they were to be aggressive. Finally, girls did not think television was as realistic as boys did; for them, it was more a fantasy, an escape. They did not tend to think life was really this way. However, those girls who did think television was realistic were more aggressive than those who did not and also, interestingly enough, tended to resemble boys more in other attitudes and values as measured by the Masculinity–Femininity Scale of the

MMPI. Also, there was a strong positive relation between aggression of girls and the extent to which they watched contact sports on television (Lefkowitz, Walder, Eron, & Huesmann, 1973). For boys, there was no such relation. All boys watch contact sports, but it is primarily the aggressive girls who like to participate in this masculine ritual.

It has been contended by some skeptics (T. Cook, 1983) that although these studies may indicate a small effect of televised violence on subsequent behavior of youngsters, the type of behavior observed has nothing to do with the kind of real life violence that is of concern to most people. According to Cook, the peer-nomination measure of aggression which we developed reflects no more than youthful "boisterousness and incivility." However, the data indicate otherwise. The construct and empirical validity of this instrument as a measure of real-life aggression have been documented extensively over the years (Lefkowitz *et al.*, 1977). Recently obtained data are even more striking. In 1981, we reinterviewed 409 of the original subjects and 165 of their spouses. The modal age of the subjects was 30 years. During the interview, the subjects were administered the MMPI. The sum of scales F, 4, and 9 of this inventory have been demonstrated to be a valid indication of antisocial behavior (Huesmann, Lefkowitz, & Eron, 1978). The subjects were also asked a number of questions during this interview about how they punished their children. Spouses were asked about any physical aggression directed against them by the subjects. The latter questions were taken from the Strauss Home Violence Questionnaire (1979). In addition, we obtained data from the New York Division of Criminal Justice Services and the Division of Motor Vehicles as to the number and seriousness of crimes for which the subjects had been cited in New York State as well as the number of moving violations and convictions for driving while intoxicated. The correlations between the early peer-nominations and these later measures of aggression are shown in Table 1. It is apparent that over 22 years there is still moderately good predictability from early aggression to later aggression, especially in the case of males. Especially impressive is the correlation between aggression at age 8 and later encounters with the law as indicated by driving and criminal offenses. Since a disproportionate number of the original subjects who moved out of the state subsequent to the original testing were from high aggressive groups (Lefkowitz *et al.*, 1977), the range of aggression scores has been truncated and the correlations are probably a minimal estimate of the relation between aggression at age 8 and later antisocial behavior of the type that brings individuals into contact with the law. Further, as we mentioned before, the 1960 aggression score of males not interviewed was significantly higher than the aggression score of those males who were interviewed.

TABLE 1
*Correlations of Peer-nominated Aggression at Age 8 with
Aggression at Age 30*

Age 30 measures	Age 8 aggression	
	Males	Females
Aggression measures:		
MMPI Scales F + 4 + 9	.30***	.16*
Rating of subject by spouse	.27**	—
Punishment of child by subject	.24*	.24*
Criminal justice convictions	.24***	—
Seriousness of criminal offense	.21***	—
Moving traffic violations	.21***	—
Driving while intoxicated	.29***	—

*$p < .05$.
**$p < .01$.
***$p < .005$.

Another reason why the Pearson r may be an under estimation of
the true relation between variables presented here is that the distribu-
tions of many of the measures are skewed (e.g., peer-nominated aggression has a pile-up of scores at the low end of the scale). A more representative demonstration of the relations can be obtained by dividing the
subjects into low, medium, and high groups according to the original
peer-nomination measure and calculating mean scores on each of the
criterion variables separately for each of the three groups. These rela-

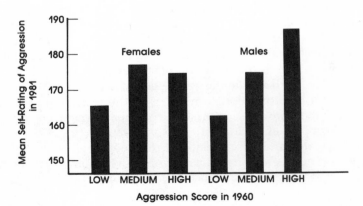

FIGURE 1. Mean self-rating of aggression (MMPI 4 + 9 + F) in 1981 according to subjects'
peer-nominated aggression score in 1960.

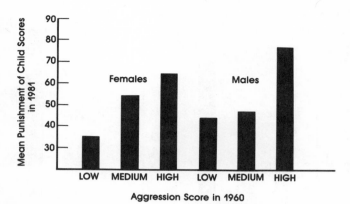

FIGURE 2. Mean punishment of child scores in 1981 according to subjects' aggression score in 1960.

tions are seen much more graphically in Figures 1, 2, 3, and 4. Figure 1 shows the relation between early peer-rated aggression and a self-rating of aggression 22 years later; Figure 2 refers to another self-disclosure measure, how severely the subject punishes his or her own child 22 years later. Figure 3 demonstrates the relation on the left between peer-rated aggression of boys at age 8 and how aggressive they were towards their wives, as rated by their wives, when they are age 30. On the right is the relation of the number of criminal convictions in the past 10 years to peer-rated aggression at age 8. And finally, in Figure 4, we have the

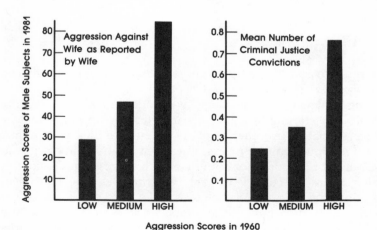

FIGURE 3. Aggression scores of male subjects in 1981 according to aggression scores in 1960.

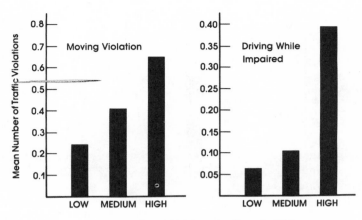

Male Subjects' Aggression Score in 1960

FIGURE 4. Mean number of traffic violations in New York State until 1981 according to male subjects' aggression score in 1960.

relation to moving traffic violations and convictions for driving while impaired. When tested by analysis of variance, the differences among the means on each of the criterion variables are highly significant, again especially in the case of males.

It is obvious that although the peer-nomination items, on their face, may refer to no more than "boisterousness or incivility," they do indeed predict the kinds of aggressive and violent behavior which are of interest to law enforcement officials, social agencies, and concerned citizens.

2. The Chicago Study

In order to investigate the hypothesis that there is a sensitive period around age 8 when youngsters are especially vulnerable to the effects of observing violence on television, we undertook a three-year long-itiudinal study starting in 1977, 17 years after the Rip Van Winkle study had been initiated. Another purpose of this study was to determine what are the intervening processes between observation of violence on television and the acting out of the viewer's aggression. Obviously, not all children are affected. What are the crucial events, attitudes, and feelings in some children's lives which make them especially vulnerable to television? To determine the answers, we studied 758 children in Oak Park, Illinois, and the inner city of Chicago. Half of these youngsters were in the first grade, 6 years old, when we started and half were in the third grade. We followed these subjects for three years. Thus, the two cohorts overlapped in the third grade. This gave us the opportunity in studying developmental trends to separate age effects from cohort effects. In each of the three years, we observed the children's aggressive behavior in school and investigated their television habits. Also, in the first year of the study, we interviewed the children's parents.

We found (Eron *et al.*, 1983) that as youngsters get older, from age 6 to 10, their aggression increases; but their viewing of television as a whole, as well as their viewing of violence specifically, increases from age 6 to 8 and then decreases from age 8 to 10. Their belief that television violence is realistic decreases continually from age 6 to 10. The trends are exactly the same for boys and girls, although girls in general are less aggressive, watch television less, and do not believe so strongly that television is realistic. However, as girls get older, their preference for boys' games and activities increases while their preference for girls' games and activities decreases. Boys, on the other hand, never like girls' games and their preference for boys' games remains high. These developmental trends are represented in Figures 5 to 8.

It is this convergence of developmental trends that indeed, as we suspected, makes the child around age 8 especially vulnerable to the

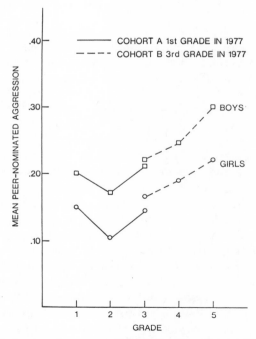

FIGURE 5. Increase in peer-rated aggression from first to fifth grade.

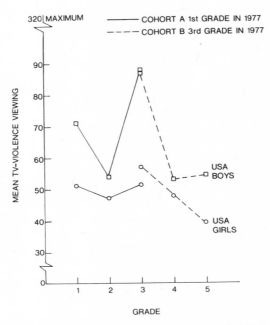

FIGURE 6. Extent of violence viewing from first fo fifth grade.

effect of violent television. We also found that the effect is cumulative. The correlations between television violence and aggression increase somewhat from grades 1 through 5—in other words, the relation becomes a little stronger as the children get older (Table 2).

In the Chicago Study, we found one striking difference from our earlier results. Now, in the study carried on in the late 1970s, we found that the effect of television violence on behavior was no longer restricted to boys; girls also appeared to be affected. In fact, the relation between television violence and subsequent aggression was even stronger now for girls than for boys. For both boys and girls, the relation was exacerbated by the frequency with which the violent programs were watched. For boys, the strength of the relation was increased by the degree to which they identified with television characters; not so for girls.

What could be the reason for the strong relation between television violence and aggression in girls in the late 1970s when there was no such relation in 1960? The first hypothesis that comes to mind is that there are now more violent and aggressive females on television whose behavior little girls can model. In the late 1970s we had "Mod Squad," "Police Woman," "The Bionic Woman," "The Girl from Uncle," and others. However, we found that girls, as they grow older, tend to identify more

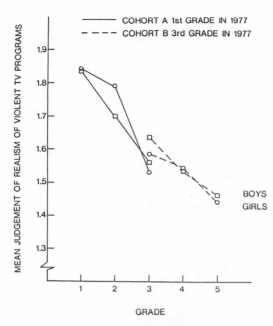

FIGURE 7. Decrease is judgment of television realism from first to fifth grade.

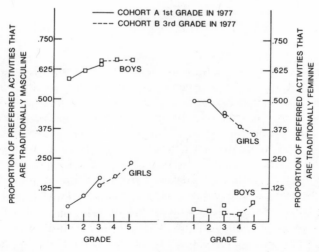

FIGURE 8. Changes in preference for sex-typed activities from first to fifth grade.

Table 2

Correlations between Television Violence Viewing and
Peer-nominated Aggression

	Males	Females
USA (N = 758)		
1st Grade	.160*	.210**
2nd Grade	.204*	.245***
3rd Grade	.191*	.205*
4th Grade	.184*	.260***
5th Grade	.199**	.294***
Finland (N = 220)		
1st Grade	—	.139
2nd Grade	.266*	—
3rd Grade	—	.192
4th Grade	.381***	−.158
5th Grade	.278*	
Poland (N = 237)		
1st Grade	.296**	—
2nd Grade	.170	.179
3rd Grade	.259**	.236*
4th Grade	.185	.127
5th Grade	—	.277**
Australia (N = 290)		
1st Grade	—	—
2nd Grade	—	.223*
3rd Grade	.175	.244*
4th Grade	.329***	.213*
5th Grade	.207**	.236*

*$p < .05$.
**$p < .01$.
***$p < .005$.

with aggressive male characters on television than with female characters, although they are also affected to some degree by the aggressive female characters (Huesmann, Lagerspetz, & Eron, in press). We have to look elsewhere for reasons why girls are now affected. We hypothesize that the reason has to do with the fact that aggression is now becoming a more acceptable activity for women. The recent emphasis on the need and desirability for women to be assertive has probably caused girls to have fewer inhibitions about performing the aggressive behaviors they observe on television whether performed by female or male characters. Girls are now encouraged to be assertive and aggressive and to engage in large-muscle activities. Their attitudes about what is appropriate for girls to do and how to act have changed. And although much of this is good for society, there are also some negative effects, as we now see.

Another change from the earlier findings is that path analyses with the Chicago data suggested a bidirectional cause-effect relation, in which the viewing of violence engenders aggression and aggression leads to increased viewing of violence. Again, however, there was no evidence that the relation between television violence and aggressive behavior on the part of the young viewer can be accounted for by the child's previous level of aggression, intelligence, social class, or parents' level of aggression (Huesmann *et al.*, in press). Whereas for boys the television variables were better longitudinal predictors of aggression than aggression was of the television variables, the process actually appears to be circular for both sexes. Television violence viewing for girls and violence viewing catalyzed by identification with television characters for boys leads to heightened aggressiveness which in turn leads to more television violence viewing.

Two mediating variables that appear to play a role in this cycle are the child's academic achievement and social popularity. Those children who are less successful in school watch more television, perhaps because they find it more satisfying than schoolwork. They prefer the more violent shows; they identify more with television characters; and they believe that the violence they observe on television reflects real life. They are exposed to more violence and have more opportunity to learn aggressive acts. Since their intellectual capacities are more limited, the easy aggressive solutions they observe may be incorporated more readily into their behavioral repertoire. In any case, the heavy viewing isolates them from their peers and gives them less time to work toward academic success. Similarly, children who behave aggressively are less popular. Perhaps because their relations with their peers tend to be unsatisfying, less popular children watch more television and view more violence. The violence they see on television may reassure them that their own behavior is appropriate or teach them new coercive techniques which they then attempt to use in their interactions with others. Thus, their aggressive behavior makes them even less popular, and this social isolation drives them back to television. The cycle continues with aggression, academic failure, social failure, and violence viewing mutually reinforcing each other.

A number of other variables may have similar circular relations to television violence viewing and aggression. Although none of these interacted significantly with violence viewing to affect aggression, they correlated with both variables. For example, it was found that the more a parent believes television violence to be realistic, the more the child believes it to be realistic; and the more a child believes this, the more the child views violence and acts aggressively. The violence the child views and the aggression the child commits may combine to increase the child's belief in the reality of violence, which in turn would increase the likelihood of the child's behaving aggressively. Similarly, a child's frequency of aggressive or active-heroic fantasy was correlated with the child's aggression and with violence viewing among girls. Thus, the hypothesis that aggressive fantasizing serves as a rehearsal process for aggressive acts is plausible. Finally, children of either sex who preferred less strongly sex-typed activities were less aggressive and watched less violence.

An interesting unexpected finding was that parental violence viewing did not correlate with child violence viewing despite many other parent–child viewing similarities. Furthermore, those parents who had had more education and higher status jobs and had achieving children watched somewhat more violence. Only speculative reasons can be offered for these parents' preferences for violent programs; however, the obtained data demonstrate that their children usually were not watching the same violent programs, either because of parental controls or other factors. This result, coupled with the failure of the sociocultural variables to explain the television violence/aggression relation, reinforces our conviction that television violence can affect children from all strata of society. Singer and Singer (1981) found the same positive relation between violence viewing and aggressive behavior in middle-class as well as lower-class preschoolers.

3. Cross-National Studies

The Chicago study has now been replicated in five other countries with over 1,400 subjects. These countries include Australia ($N=289$), Finland ($N=220$), Israel ($N=198$), the Netherlands ($N=469$) and Poland ($N=237$). Although data analyses for all the countries are not yet complete, comparisons between Finland and the United States have now been reported (Huesmann et al., in press). As in the United States, peer-nominated aggression increased from Grades 1 through 5 whereas television violence viewing peaked at around Grade 3. Boys were also consistently more aggressive than girls and also watched significantly more violence on television than did girls. As for the correlation between violence viewing and aggression, these are presented in Table 2. Although less consistent than in the United States, the correlations are usually positive and replicate the United States results, especially for boys. As in this country, there was no evidence that IQ, social class, previous aggression level, or parents' aggression affected the relation between violence viewing and aggressive behavior. However, a number of other variables did. In both countries, the child most likely to be aggressive would be one who watches violent programs most of the time they are on, who believes these shows portray life "just like it is," who identifies strongly with the aggressive characters in the shows, who frequently has aggressive fantasies and who, if a girl, prefers boys' activities.

4. Interventions to Lessen Television's Influence on Aggressive Behavior

Is there anything that can be done to mitigate the demonstrated effect of television violence on the aggressive behavior of children? Singer and Singer (1981), who have found effects of watching violent programs on the behavior of preschoolers similar to what we have found with older children, have not been successful in their attempts to devise interventions that parents can employ to reduce the effect of violence (Singer & Singer, 1981). They have instead developed a series of 30 lesson plans that teachers can use "to stimulate cognitive skills, imagination and prosocial behavior in children" (p. 153) with the hope that this will replace aggressive behavior.

On the basis of our own previous findings and in conjunction with the three-year longitudinal Chicago study, we intervened with groups of children to ameliorate the relation between television violence and subsequent aggressive behavior (Huesmann, Eron, Klein, Brice, & Fischer, 1983). We took 170 youngsters, both boys and girls, who were already high violence viewers and divided them randomly into an experimental and control group. Over the course of two years, the experimental subjects were exposed to two treatments designed to reduce the likelihood of their imitating the aggressive behaviors they observed on television. The control group received comparable neutral treatments.

The procedures we developed for the experimental group were based on the assumption that aggression is facilitated by the youngster's attitudes about aggression as an acceptable way of solving problems. Thus, the youngster is apt to copy the aggressive behavior he sees on television if he perceives the television violence as realistic, if he identifies closely with the characters, and if he believes society approves of aggressive ways of solving problems. If a child perceives that the problem-solving strategy used by the actor is unrealistic and ineffective in the real world or cannot identify with the actor or believes an aggressive response is unacceptable, then the child might be less likely to remember the sequence and act that way when he is in a similar situation or one in which he believes that such a response would be effective. On the other hand, even if the child remembers such a sequence, he will be less likely to respond in that way if he believes that kind of action to be unrealistic and unacceptable.

Thus, we believed that we could reduce the effect of violence on television by changing children's attitudes both about television and about aggression. We proposed to do this by teaching them first that television is an unrealistic portrayal of the real world; second, that aggressive behaviors are not as universal and acceptable in the real world as they would appear on television; and third, that it is just not good to behave like the aggressive characters on television.

The subjects in the study were approximately among the top 20% of violence viewers among the 700 children in the 1st year of the 3-year longitudinal study. At the beginning of the 2nd year of this study, they received either three training or three placebo sessions over a period of 6 to 8 weeks. Children were trained in groups of three to eight, in sessions separated by at least 2 weeks. The training sessions for the experimental subjects were designed to teach children three principles that, if learned, would be expected to reduce the modeling of aggressive behavior: (1) that the behaviors of the characters on these shows do not represent the behaviors of most people, (2) that camera techniques and special effects are giving the illusion that the characters are really performing their highly aggressive and unrealistic feats, and (3) that the average person uses other methods to solve problems similar to those encountered by the characters.

In the first experimental session, same-sex groups were shown violent television segments to introduce them to "super-hero" shows. The girls were shown segments from "The Bionic Woman" and boys were shown parts of "The Six-Million Dollar Man." After viewing the television segment, experimental subjects participated in a structured discussion about television realism. First, experimental subjects heard a standardized story line in which the "super-hero" character used violence to solve a problem. The experimenter then retold the story, this time emphasizing how "ordinary people" would solve the problem. Subsequently, a new plot containing a dilemma was outlined by the experimenter. Experimental subjects were then asked to think of realistic ways in which the Bionic Woman or Six-Million Dollar Man could solve the problem. Experimenters were prepared to ask leading questions and to provide the opportunity for every child to talk in the event that any children had difficulty in providing answers. Similar procedures were used for the second and third training sessions. For the second session, subjects of both sexes met in same-grade groups to discuss "The Road

Runner," which was not judged to be gender-specific. Boys watched and discussed "Starsky and Hutch" in the third session, and girls met separately to examine "Charlie's Angels."

For the placebo group, television programs were also shown and the same amount of time was spent in discussion as in the experimental group sessions. However, the shows were nonviolent, and there was no instruction as to the realistic nature of television. The first session consisted of excerpts from a program on Bali folk dance, followed by a discussion of different folk dances. The second session began with a segment from the show "Lavern and Shirley," after which subjects were encouraged to tell jokes and riddles they knew. In the third session, part of the show "Happy Days" was shown, and subjects were led in a discussion of nicknames.

Nine months later, we conducted a second intervention with the same groups of subjects. A more formal attitude and behavior change approach was adopted for the second experimental intervention. Although altering children's perceptions of television realism was still one goal of the intervention, the training also attempted to teach children directly that watching television violence was not desirable and that they should not imitate violent television programs. The design included several elements of counterattitudinal advocacy research which have been shown to produce enduring behavior changes (Cook & Flay, 1978).

Training occurred under the pretense of producing a film to alter the attitudes of school children in Chicago. Over the course of two sessions, children in the experimental groups developed arguments about the negative aspect of television violence, wrote their arguments out, were videotaped reading their paragraphs, and viewed the videotapes of themselves and their classmates reading the paragraphs. The placebo group performed identical tasks except that the topic for their paragraphs was their hobby and the purported purpose for the procedure was to introduce children in Chicago to new hobbies. The two training or placebo sessions were administered within a 2-week period by pairs of experimenters. Subjects met in groups of 4–10 children comprised primarily of children from their own classrooms. Other members of the group came from the same grade.

The experimental group's training sessions employed techniques which have produced behavior changes of some duration in attitude change experiments (Cook & Flay, 1978). These procedures included crediting the children for possession of the attitudes we wished them to adopt, inducing behaviors that would lead to the self-attribution of these attitudes, inducing perceptions of personal responsibility for an outcome related to the attitudes (e.g., Chicago school children's behaviors), inducing the perception of participation out of free choice, and promoting the perception that the consequences of their behaviors were important. In particular, the experimenters asked the children to volunteer to help in making a film to show to children in Chicago who had been "fooled by television or harmed by television violence or got into trouble because of imitating it." The experimenter introduced the self-labeling by saying that "of course you know better than to believe what you see on TV and you know that imitating what you see may be bad, but other children do not know this." As expected, all of the experimental subjects volunteered to produce the film.

Four months after this second intervention, the children were again tested along with all the other children during the regular procedures of the longitudinal study, and both their television-viewing habits and their aggressive behavior were evaluated in the same way as in the previous 2 years of the study. Although there was no difference in the amount of television violence viewed in the experimental and placebo groups, the subjects in the experimental groups were significantly less aggressive than those in the control group (Huesmann et al., 1983). Furthermore, the relation between television violence viewing and aggression had disappeared in the experimental group.

What brought about this dramatic change in the aggressive behavior of the experimental group? Two analyses of the data provide a reasonably likely explanation. In one analysis, a multiple regression analysis predicting aggression for the experimental and control groups from a number of television viewing variables, it was shown that in the experimental group the relation between violence viewing and aggressive behavior disappeared whereas in the placebo group the relation was the same as in the no-treatment group. What did relate to aggression in the experimental group was identification with television characters; not so in the placebo or no-treatment groups. In the latter groups, it was simply the amount of television violence which predicted to aggression. A second regression analysis explained why identification with television characters was an important predictor. Before the start of the experiment, all children were asked about their attitudes toward television (e.g., How much of what kids see is fake? Will watching a lot of shows make a kid meaner? Are TV shows with a lot of hitting harmless for kids?). They were administered the same questions after the experiment and a change score was calculated. It was found that the more closely the youngsters identified with television characters, the less likely their attitudes were to change as a result of the intervention; also, the more realistic they judged television to be, the less likely they were to change their attitudes. Furthermore, the lowering of aggressive behavior brought about by these straightforward attitude-change procedures, conducted in the classroom with groups of children by experimenters who were strangers to the children, was effected independently of such seemingly crucial antecedent variables as the parents' own level of aggression and severity of punishment for aggression (Eron, 1982).

Thus, in this experiment, conducted within the framework of the larger longitudinal field study, we demonstrated that it is possible to reduce the real life aggressive behavior of children who are high violence viewers by changing their attitudes about television. Not only does this result have implications for what can be done to counteract television's deleterious effects on our children, but it also bolsters the argument that children learn to be aggressive by watching violence on the television screen.

5. Conclusion

We believe that it has been demonstrated conclusively both by us and by others that heavy exposure to televised violence is one of the causes of aggressive behavior, crime, and violence in society. The evidence comes from both the laboratory and real-life studies. Television violence affects youngsters of all ages, of both genders, at all socioeconomic levels and all levels of intelligence. The effect is not limited to children who are already disposed to being aggressive and is not restricted to this country. We have demonstrated that children in at least five other countries, Finland, Poland, Israel, Australia, and the Netherlands, countries with different political and economic systems and varying in degree of control over television programming, are also affected in their aggressive behavior by the violence they observe on television. The fact that we get this same finding of a relation between television violence and aggression in children in study after study in one country after another, cannot be ignored. The causal effect of television violence on aggression, even though it is not very large, exists. It cannot be denied or explained away. We have demonstrated this causal effect outside the laboratory in real-life among many different children. We have come to believe that a vicious cycle exists in which television violence makes children more aggressive and these more aggressive children turn to watching more violence to justify their own behavior. Statistically this means that the effect is bidirectional. Practically it means that if media violence is reduced, the level of interpersonal aggression in our society will be reduced eventually.

What are the implications of these findings for public policy, for society, and for individual parents? How can the deleterious effects of television violence be curtailed and/or controlled? The most obvious response is to compel the networks to cut down drastically on the presentation of violence, especially gratuitous violence which is not necessary for the story line, has no esthetic purpose or socially redeeming value, but is included merely because of its sensational, attention-getting quality. Television executives have consistently denied that there is an effect of viewing television violence on aggressive behavior, although, illogically, they do not maintain there is no effect of viewing television commercials on consumer behavior. Violence is a cheap and easy way to attract and maintain viewers' attention. Network executives claim that viewers prefer programs with heavy doses of violence. Thus, it is highly unlikely that they will voluntarily reduce the heavy violence content of daily television fare. Whenever government censorship is suggested, a tremendous hue and cry is raised about First Amendment rights. Personally, we are in favor of freedom of expression and abhor the prospect of censorship. But the situation has now assumed the proportions of a massive public health problem. If the networks do not voluntarily impose some controls on the producers of their programs, the public will ultimately demand that the government intervene. Many democratic countries limit the amount of violence shown on television— for instance, England, Finland, and the Netherlands. This has not been seen as a threat to the democratic rights of their citizens.

But what can we do until the networks show some restraint or restraint is imposed on them by some government agency? Parents cannot absolve themselves completely of responsibility for monitoring what their children watch, although it is very difficult for most parents to exercise complete control over their children's viewing habits. However, a number of aids have been developed to help parents cope with these problems (see, for example, the work of Singer & Singer, 1981). In this chapter we have also demonstrated that it is possible to reduce the deleterious effect of television violence on children's aggressive behavior by teaching them that the violence they see is unrealistic, that there are productive ways to solve life's problems, that aggression and violence have serious irreversible consequences, and that too much television is, very simply, bad for children. It is the responsibility of educators, media experts, child-welfare workers, and the researchers themselves to see that such findings are disseminated widely so that parents will know what television is doing to their children and what they can do about it.

6. References

Bandura, A., Ross D., & Ross, S. A. Transmission of aggression through imitation of aggressive models. *Journal of Abnormal and Social Psychology*, 1961, *63*, 575–582.

Berkowitz, L. *Aggression: A social psychological analysis.* New York: McGraw-Hill, 1962.

Berkowitz, L. Aggressive cues in aggressive behavior and hostility catharsis. *Psychological Review,* 1964, *71,* 104–122.

Cook, T. *Testimony before Subcommitte on Crime of House Committee on Judiciary.* Washington, D.C., April 13, 1983.

Cook, T. D., & Flay, B. R. The temporal persistence of experimentally induced attitude change: An evaluative review. In L. Berkowitz (Ed.), *Advances in experimental social psychology* (Vol. 2). New York: Academic Press, 1978.

Eron, L. D. Relationship of TV viewing habits and aggressive behavior in children. *Journal of Abnormal and Social Psychology,* 1963, *67,* 193–196.

Eron, L. D. Parent–child interaction, television violence, and aggression of children. *American Psychologist,* 1982, *37,* 197–211.

Eron, L. D., Laulicht, J. H., Walder, L. O., Farber, I. E., & Spiegel, J. P. Application of role and learning theories to the study of the development of aggression in children. *Psychological Reports,* 1961, *9,* 291–334. *Monograph Supplement* 2=V9.

Eron, L. D., Walder, L. O., & Lefkowitz, M. M. *Learning of aggression in children.* Boston: Little, Brown, 1971.

Eron, L. D., Huesmann, L. R., Lefkowitz, M. M., & Walder, L. O. Does television violence cause aggression? *American Psychologist,* 1972, *27,* 253–263.

Eron, L. D., Huesmann, L. R., Brice, P., Fischer, P., & Mermelstein, R. Age trends in the development of aggression, sex typing, and related television habits. *Developmental Psychology,* 1983, *19,* 71–77.

Gerbner, G., & Gross, L. Living with television: The violence profile. *Journal of Communication,* 1976, *26,* 173–199.

Greenberg, B. S. Televised violence: Further explorations. In G. A. Comstock, E. A. Rubinstein, & J. P. Murray (Eds.), *Television and social behavior: Vol. 5. Television's effect: Further explorations.* Washington, D.C.: U.S. Government Printing Office, 1972, pp. 1–21.

Huesmann, L. R., Lefkowitz, M. M., & Eron, L. D. Sum of MMPI Scales F, 4 and 9 as a measure of aggression. *Journal of Consulting and Clinical Psychology,* 1978, *46,* 1071–1078.

Huesmann, L. R., Eron, L. D., Klein, R., Brice, P., & Fischer, P. Mitigating the imitation of aggressive behaviors by changing children's attitudes about media violence. *Journal of Personality and Social Psychology,* 1983, *44,* 899–910.

Huesmann, L. R., Lagerspetz, K., & Eron, L. D. Intervening variables in the television violence-aggression relation: A longitudinal study. *Developmental Psychology,* in press.

Lefkowitz, M. M., Walder, L. O., Eron, L. D., & Huesmann, L. R. Preference for televised contact sports as related to sex differences in aggression. *Developmental Psychology,* 1973, 417–420.

Lefkowitz, M. M., Eron, L. D., Walder, L. O., & Huesmann, L. R. *Growing up to be violent: A longitudinal study of the development of aggression.* New York: Pergamon Press 1977.

Singer, J. L., & Singer, D. G. *Television, imagination and aggression: A study of preschoolers.* Hillsdale, N.J.: Erlbaum, 1981.

Strauss, M. A., Gilles, R. J., & Steinmetz, S. K. *Behind closed doors: Violence in the American family.* New York: Doubleday/Anchor, 1979.

3 Suicide and Attempted Suicide in Children and Adolescents

KEITH HAWTON AND MADELINE OSBORN

In embarking on a review of suicidal behavior among children and adolescents, one encounters several difficulties. The first results from the extremely diverse nature of research in this field. A second difficulty, and a very important source of confusion in the literature, is that the group of young people who kill themselves is frequently studied with the group who commit self-damaging acts but do not die, as if they were a single population. Among adults, this second group, for whom we will use the term *attempted suicide*, shows some characteristics in common with completed suicides (Stengel & Cook, 1958) but also shows characteristics that are markedly different from those of successful suicides. The same appears to be true among children and adolescents. For this reason we propose to consider these two groups separately.

The following review contains two main sections: the first dealing with suicide among young people and the second dealing with attempted suicide. In each section we propose to consider several different aspects of each syndrome, namely, the findings of epidemiological research, the characteristics of the behavior, the factors which may be of etiological significance, and the factors which may help to predict the behavior. In addition, we will discuss the management and prevention of suicidal behavior in children and adolescents.

1. Suicide

1.1. Epidemiology

In trying to determine the extent of suicide among children and adolescents, major problems of case identifications arise. These prob-

KEITH HAWTON AND MADELINE OSBORN • University Department of Psychiatry, Warneford Hospital, Oxford, OX3 7JX, England.

lems, which may lead to inaccuracies in the suicide rates among young people, are similar to those which beset the researcher in the field of adult suicide.

1.1.1. Problems of Ascertaining the Extent of Suicide

It has been suggested that deaths from suicide may be under-reported to a considerable extent, and that official suicide statistics therefore fail to represent the real incidence of suicide (Douglas, 1967). However, estimates of the extent of the discrepancy between real and official rates of suicide vary from country to country. For example, in the United States, Dublin (1963) estimated that the real suicide rate was almost a third greater than the official figure. In the Scottish city of Edinburgh, Ovenstone (1973) suggested that official suicide statistics represented only half the true rate. In Ireland, an even greater gap between real and official figures was estimated by McCarthy and Walsh (1975), who suggested that the probable suicide rate in Dublin was about four times higher than the official rate. In a study comparing the report-ing of suicide in Denmark and England, Brooke and Atkinson (1974) cast doubt on the value of suicide statistics as a basis for international epi-demiological research. They found that, using the same case material, Danish coroners reported more cases of suicide than did their English counterparts, and they concluded that differences in the suicide rates between the two countries might arise from differences in the criteria used to determine suicide, rather than differences in the number of individuals killing themselves. In addition, Atkinson, Kessel, and Dalgaard (1975) suggested that criteria within a single country may also vary. Among deaths by poisoning in different districts of England and Wales, they showed a considerable variation in the proportions which were reported as accidental, suicidal, or given an open verdict. Howev-er, in spite of possible inaccuracies in national official suicide rates, it does appear that these statistics reflect gross differences in the incidence of suicide and can be used as a basis for international comparisons. Sainsbury and Barraclough (1968), for example, found that suicide rates in first-generation immigrants of different nationalities were related to the suicide rates in their respective countries of origin.

1.1.2. Possible Factors Contributing to the Underreporting of Suicide in Children and Adolescents

Several factors may be associated with the underreporting of suicide among children and adolescents. First, the relative rarity of the event in this age group may make those responsible for determining the cause of death unlikely to consider suicide as an explanation. Atkinson (1975) pointed out that the kind of criteria that are used to determine whether a death is due to suicide are based on that particular society's assumptions about suicide (e.g., notions about what sort of people commit suicide, why they do it, what sort of methods they tend to use). When research workers subsequently study the characteristics of patients whose deaths have been reported as suicide, they may therefore elicit those factors that the society *believes* to be associated with suicide rather than factors with a real relationship to self-inflicted death. This may be a particular problem in studies of young people who kill themselves; for example, the widely held belief that small children rarely commit suicide may lead to deaths in this age group being mistakenly reported as accidental with the result that subsequent suicide statistics are likely to confirm the belief that suicide is uncommon in children.

Second, those responsible for reporting suicides may be, consciously or unconsciously, concerned to protect individuals or institutions from the distress that a verdict of suicide may cause. Parents are particularly likely to feel not only grieved but guilty about the suicide of a young son or daughter, and therefore the death may be reported as accidental or of undetermined cause in order to protect their feelings.

A third factor may be associated with the predominant religious beliefs of a country or society. For example, because the Roman Catholic Church regards suicide as a mortal sin, in predominantly Catholic countries, such as Italy and Ireland, officials may be less likely to believe that a young person has committed suicide than those in predominantly Protestant countries. On the other hand, because some non-Christian religions have a completely different philosophy about suicide, there may be more willingness to consider and report suicide as cause of death in countries practicing these religions.

Fourth, there is considerable international variation in the training of officials who ascertain the cause of death, in that some receive a medical training, others a legal training, and yet others a combination of the two. In determining the cause of death, it is likely that the training of the assessor will influence how he appraises evidence and reaches a decision. The variety of verdicts available to such an assessor may also influence the proportion of deaths categorized as suicide. For example, in England and Wales, an "open" verdict is available to coroners in addition to verdicts of accidental death and suicide. In some cases, this may be a compromise category for some deaths that would have otherwise been classed as suicide.

1.1.3. Recent Trends in Suicide Rates among Young People

In addition to possible inaccuracies in the identification of cases, the ways in which suicides are classified with respect to age often make it difficult to ascertain and compare suicide rates among young people. For example, the age groups within which suicide rates are reported not only vary from country to country, but may vary over time within the same country. Rates may be reported in 5-year age bands or 10-year age bands; this is a particular problem among adolescents, who are often combined with young adults for the purposes of suicide statistics.

Two further difficulties arise in trying to evaluate trends in these suicide rates. First, in some countries improved standards of medical resuscitation may lead to a decrease in suicide rates, though the incidence of children making serious suicide attempts may not have fallen. Secondly, fluctuations in suicide rates may be unreliable when few children commit suicide each year, as in countries with small populations such as Hungary and Austria.

Bearing in mind these difficulties of interpretation, we will now review the recent trends in child and adolescent suicide in three geographical areas: North America, Europe, and the Far East.

1.1.3.1. Recent Trends in North America. In the United States, as in other countries, the suicide rate among older adolescents has risen considerably in the past 20 to 30 years. Among young adolescents and children, however, the rate has remained low. Although suicide rates among older adolescents (aged 15–19) were high at the very beginning of this century (Seiden, 1969), they fell and stayed moderately low until the early 1960s. For example, in 1951–53 the rate among boys 15–19 years old was 3.9/100,000 and among girls of the same age it was 1.6/100,000 (Seiden, 1969).

Ten years later, although the age groups in which suicide statistics were reported were not completely comparable, there appeared to be a marked increase. Thus, among 15- to 24-year-olds, rates had risen to 9.3/100,000 for whites and 8.0/100,000 for nonwhites (Seiden, 1969). It was pointed out that this increase in suicide among older adolescents was not an isolated phenomenon, in that the incidence among the general population of the United States had risen at about the same rate (Seiden, 1969). More recently, however, the increase in the suicide rate among young people has outstripped that among the population at large. By the late 1960s and early 1970s, the increase in suicide among the 15–24 age group was eight times the increase among the general population. Thus, by 1974 the rate among young people (10.9/100,000) had almost caught up with the suicide rate of 12.1/100,000 in the population as a whole (Petzel & Cline, 1978). On the basis of these figures, it is tempting to assume that factors in modern society are leading more young people to commit suicide. However, before making such assumptions, we should note that the incidence of suicide among 15- to 24-year-olds in 1974 was very similar to the suicide rate in 1908–1912, 50 years previously (Seiden, 1969).

The 1974 suicide statistics (Petzel & Cline, 1978) show that the major increase in suicide had occurred among young adults (aged 20–24) rather than among older adolescents (aged 15–19). Nevertheless, although still outstripped by the rate amongst young adults, the suicide rate amongst 15- to 19-year-olds has continued to rise.

Shaffer and Fisher's (1981) survey of suicides committed in 1978 showed that the rate among 15- to 19-year-olds had risen to 7.64/100,000, suicide representing 7.95% of all deaths in this age group. In absolute terms, this meant that 1,686 adolescents between the ages of 15 and 19 had committed suicide in the United States during 1978. On the basis of these figures, Shaffer suggested that suicide was not "a major public health problem." In support of this assertion, he reported that, although adolescents aged 15–19 constituted 10% of the total population, they accounted for only 6.18% of all suicides. However, as adolescents are less likely to die from any cause than other age groups, a comparison of this sort does not appear to be an adequate method of evaluating the public health problem caused by suicide. The fact that it represents the third most common cause of death amongst American adolescents (Holinger, 1979) suggests that, although suicide is less common than among the rest of the population, within this age group it poses a serious problem.

Suicide rates among young adolescents (aged 10–14) have shown a small increase over recent years (Petzel & Cline, 1978) but are much lower than those among older adolescents. For example, in 1978, the incidence of suicide among 10- to 14-year-olds was 0.81/100,000, one ninth of the rate among 15- to 19-year-olds. In the younger age group suicide accounted for only 2.4% of deaths, and, although these young people represented 8.5% of the total population, they accounted for only .5% of all suicides in the United States (Shaffer & Fisher, 1981).

In summary, suicide rates among American adolescents appear to be increasing, having tripled between 1956 and 1975. It is now the third leading cause of death in young people, only accidents and homicide being more common (Holinger, 1979). However, it should be remembered that, in the United States at least, this is not the first time that the incidence of suicide among young people has undergone a dramatic increase, as the rates recorded at the beginning of this century amply demonstrate.

1.1.3.2. Recent Trends in Europe. At the turn of the century, in Europe as in the United States the suicide rate among young people was reported to have undergone a sharp increase, with rates equal to or in excess of those during much of the present century (MacDonald, 1906–1907). The incidence of suicide subsequently fell. However in recent years statistics from most European countries have suggested a similar increase to that found in the United States.

For example, Seiden (1969) reported that in England and Wales, between 1952 and 1954, the suicide rate among 10- to 14-year-olds was very low (0.2/100,000 for boys, and 0.1/100,000 for girls) with somewhat higher rates among 15- to 19-year-olds (2.9/100,000 and 1.1/100,000 respectively). Thereafter, rates remained fairly steady until the last three or four years. Recently there have been disturbing indications of a further rise in the incidence of suicide among boys. For example, in 1981, among boys aged 15–19, the rate was 4.2/100,000, an increase of almost 25% over the rate found five years previously. On the other hand, among girls of the same age, the rate was 1.4/100,000, which was actually slightly lower than that recorded five years previously. The increase among boys has paralleled the recent rise in suicide rates among the whole of the male population of England and Wales, which has been most marked in men under 45 years old. Among adolescents of both sexes aged less than 15, the rate has remained constant over the years at about 0.5/100,000 (Office of Population Censuses and Surveys, 1977–1981).

The reasons for this increase among older adolescent boys and young men are unclear. It may be associated with national economic difficulties and the increase in unemployment over the last few years. On the other hand, since 1981 was a census year (occurring once every decade), the updated population figures available in 1981 may account for the sharpness of the increase in the incidence of suicide. However, the *size* of the increase suggests it was unlikely to have been entirely due to the census survey.

Suicide rates in other European countries have shown a pattern similar to that of England and Wales, with the exception of a few countries. In 1962–1963, among males aged 15 to 24, Hungary had by far the highest suicide rate (29.7/100,000), followed by Austria and West Germany, which both had rates over 18/100,000. Belgium and France had rates of 10/100,000 or less, and Italy occupied the bottom of the league, with a rate of less than 4/100,000; this may have indicated that few young people killed themselves in this country or may have reflected the previously noted tendency of Catholic societies to underreport suicide. Compared with a decade previously, all these countries, with the exception of Austria and Italy, had suffered a substantial increase in the incidence of suicide.

Over the same period of time, suicide rates among young females showed a similar pattern, with most countries reporting substantial increases in rates. However, as in the case of males, the rates among Austria and Italian females decreased between the early 1950s and the early 1960s. Rates in West Germany also showed a decrease. Nevertheless, in 1962–1963, Austria and West Germany, together with Hungary, headed the list of suicide rates among girls; Italy again had the lowest rate (Seiden, 1969).

During the 1960s, the incidence of suicide in Europe continued to rise, but increases in the suicide rates were not so marked as those found found during the 1950s. International comparisons showed a pattern similar to the previous decade, with two Eastern European countries having the highest suicide rates among 15- to 24-year-olds, namely Hungary and Czechoslovakia. Rates in Austria and West Germany were also high, while Italy and other predominantly Catholic countries such as Ireland and Malta reported the lowest rates (Brooke & Atkinson, 1974).

1.1.3.3. Recent Trends in Eastern Countries. Japan is one of the few Eastern countries for which sequential suicide statistics are available. They show that, among both young males and young females, Japanese rates are similar to those of the European countries with the highest incidence of suicide. Thus, in 1962–1963 Japan's suicide rate was 23.9/100,000 among males aged 15–24 and 19.7/100,000 among females of the same age. Interestingly, however, these figures represented substantial reductions compared with the rates of ten years previously, the rate for males having fallen by 36% and for females by 19% (Seiden, 1969). The reasons for this decrease are unclear; it may have represented a real fall in the number of young people trying to kill themselves, or it may have reflected a postwar improvement in Japanese medical services, leading to the resuscitation of a greater proportion of attempted suicides.

There appear to be few suicide statistics available for other Far Eastern countries except Singapore, where, in 1977, the suicide rate among adolescents of both sexes aged 10–19 was reported to be 3.7/100,000, suicide constituting 5% of all male deaths and 7% of all female deaths in this age group (Chia, 1979).

1.1.4. Relationship of Suicide to Demographic Factors

1.1.4.1. Sex and Age. Like adults who commit suicide, adolescent suicides show a noticeable preponderence of males, the ratio of boys to girls varying between 1.4:1 and 3.6:1. This excess of males is seen in countries with both high and low suicide rates. In England and Wales, the tendency for boys to outnumber girls has continued as the suicide rate has increased in recent years (Office of Population Censuses and Surveys, 1977–1981).

As indicated in previous sections, there is a strong correlation between suicide and age. Suicide is rarely reported among children and young adolescents, whereas older adolescents have a much higher rate. Thus, among children under 5, suicide is practically never reported in any country. Among children between the ages of 5 and 10, only a handful of suicides are reported (Toolan, 1962). For example, in Russia, at the end of the last century, an average of three children under the age of 10 committed suicide each year; over 60 years later, the number of cases among American children of the same age was the same, three cases per year (Toolan, 1962). In early adolescence, suicide is not commonly reported in any country, although the incidence is consistently higher than that found in children under 10. For example, in the United States in 1969, 100 suicides were reported in children between the ages of 10 and 14. More recently, in England and Wales during 1981, only four children in this age group were reported to have committed suicide, a rate of 0.1/100,000 (Office of Population Censuses and Surveys).

Above the age of 14, as already indicated, the suicide rate rises sharply and has shown a marked increase over the past 20–30 years. For example, in England and Wales in 1981, suicide was 20 times more common between the ages of 15–19 than among young people aged 14 or less (Office of Population Censuses and Surveys, 1977–1981).

1.1.4.2. Race.   Information on the relationship between race and suicide comes mostly from the United States, where large populations of different ethnic origins live alongside each other. In the early 1960s, the suicide rate among nonwhite teenagers was reported to be lower than that among whites, the difference being particularly marked among boys. However, in recent years, the pattern has reversed. Thus, by 1972, the rate among nonwhites exceeded that among whites (Petzel & Cline, 1978). It has been suggested that, compared with whites, nonwhite adolescents who commit suicide tend to be suffering from more situational stress (Seiden, 1972). Other ethnic groups that have been studied include North American Indians. The suicide rate among both adolescents and adults in this group has been reported to be greater than the national average and to be on the increase (U.S. Department of Health, Education, and Welfare, 1973), exceeding the general rate among 15–24 year olds by a factor of five. Rates have been found to vary between different Indian reservations and to be strongly associated with the extent of social problems on these reservations (Petzel & Cline, 1978).

1.1.4.3. Season of the Year.   Among adults, there appear to be seasonal fluctuations in the incidence of suicide, with the maximum frequency occurring in the spring (Meares, Mendelsohn, & Milgrom-Friedman, 1981). However, there is no evidence to suggest that the same pattern exists in adolescents or children. This may be because the number of cases is too small to reveal seasonal variations.

1.1.4.4. Marital Status.   Although a small proportion of adolescents are married, they appear more likely to commit suicide than do other young people. For example, in 15- to 19-year-old boys the suicide rate is 1.5 times greater among the married than the unmarried. Married girls in the same age group have a rate 1.7 times higher than unmarried girls (Petzel & Cline, 1978). This contrasts strongly with the suicide rate among married persons in other age groups, which are, on the whole, lower than those for single or divorced people, though not for widows and widowers (Kreitman, 1977).

1.2. Methods of Suicide

Over the past three decades, there has been remarkably little change in the methods of suicide used by children and adolescents. In particular, young people do not appear to have followed the increasing trend of adults to commit suicide by drug overdoses. In a British survey of 357 suicides aged under 17, Mulcock (1955) found that, of the boys, half had used hanging or self-strangulation, while a third had poisoned themselves with coal gas. Of the girls, on the other hand, almost three-quarters had used coal gas, whereas none had hung or strangled herself. Among both sexes, the proportion using drug overdoses was extremely small. In attempting to explain the marked preference of boys for strangulation or hanging, Mulcock examined the statistics for accidental death in this age group. He found that, among accidental deaths from strangulation or hanging, boys outnumbered girls in a ratio of over 100:1. From this finding, he concluded that boys were more likely than girls to experiment with ropes and the like and thus more likely to choose these methods in committing suicide. A similar sexual pattern was found by Shaffer (1974); in a careful study of 30 British cases under the age of 15, five boys, but no girls, were found to have chosen hanging as the method of suicide. Overall, however, compared with Mulcock's findings, hanging had been supplanted by carbon monoxide poisoning as the most popular means of death. A small proportion of children (10%) had killed themselves with firearms; all these children lived in rural areas, where guns were easily available. Three children (10%) used ingenious mechanical methods of committing suicide, for example electrocution or decapitation on a railway line: they were all boys, and all appeared to be of superior intelligence. Shaffer attempted to determine the lethality of the method of suicide by estimating the rapidity with which death might have been expected to occur and the precautions that the child took against discovery. Using these two criteria, it was possible to decide whether lethality was high or low in 21 cases: 15 had used highly lethal methods; of these cases 14 were boys and only one was a girl (Shaffer, 1974).

A survey of the methods used in adolescent suicide in the United

States between 1949 and 1973 led Holinger (1978) to suggest that hanging or firearms and explosives were by far the most prevalent methods of committing suicide in this age group. Hanging appeared to be more common among younger adolescents (10- to 14-year-olds) than among older adolescents (15- to 19-year-olds). As in previous studies, boys were more likely than girls to use violent methods, and girls were more likely than boys to use poisons (Holinger, 1978).

However, sexual differences in the choice of method are by no means universally reported. For example, among 45 Indian suicides aged less than 15 notified to the Bangalore Police during a six-year period, Sathyavathi (1975) found no difference in the proportions of boys and girls using violent methods. Overall, burning and drowning were the most common methods of suicide, each accounting for 38% of cases; hanging was rare, accounting for only 9% of cases. One interesting finding in this study was that active methods of suicide (e.g., burning or hanging) and passive methods of suicide (e.g., poisoning and drowning) were used with equal frequency in this sample of young people. The use of active methods was far more common than among suicides in the general population.

The findings of this Indian study suggest that psychodynamic interpretations of boys' predeliction for violent methods of suicide (e.g., that they are exhibiting a higher aggressive drive than girls) may have only limited application. The findings of a recent study from Singapore suggested that children tend to used whatever methods of suicide are readily available (Chia, 1979). For example, jumping from high-rise flats was the commonest cause of death, followed by hanging (more frequent among boys than girls) and poisoning (more frequent among girls); insecticides were the most commonly ingested poisons. It is possible that, among boys, firearms and ropes are the most readily available means of suicide, because boys are more used to playing with or handling such objects. Compared with girls, they may be more able to assess their properties and thus more likely to use them if they decide to kill themselves.

In conclusion, children and adolescents use self-poisoning less often than do adult suicides, and violent or mechanical methods more often. Although in Western countries boys appear to use violent methods more often than girls, suggesting that aggression may play a different role in male suicide, this pattern is much less evident among non-Western cultures.

1.3. Possible Contributory Factors

Although there is a substantial literature on etiological factors in attempted suicide among children and adolescents, this is not the case for successful suicide. There have been very few studies which have carried out a detailed investigation of young people who have committed suicide. The reason for the paucity of research in this field may be partly the distress which such an enquiry may cause to the investigator and partly the methodological difficulties that arise.

1.3.1. Methodological Problems

In both young people and adults, the first problem encountered in attempting to study the etiology of suicide lies in the necessarily retrospective nature of such an investigation. Information has to be gleaned months or years after the suicide has occurred and may be inadequate in that, for example, aspects of the child's character, feelings, or educational ability may have gone unrecorded; or may be inaccurate, in that informants' recollections may be distorted by the passage of time and by the knowledge that the young person has committed suicide.

A second problem is the difficulty of using parents or siblings as informants. To get accurate and detailed information about the dead person it is obviously important to interview family members. However, it is likely to be extremely distressing for parents to answer questions about their dead son or daughter. They may be suffering from a heavy burden of guilt which may render them unwilling to remember certain aspects of the dead child's history or family relationships.

The difficulty of obtaining information from relatives means that data about young suicides must be elicited mainly from records held by various institutions, such as school authorities, family doctors, and social or public health agencies. This leads to a third problem of research method, namely, that these records may be lacking the sort of detail required for any comprehensive study of the young person's character traits, educational ability, worries and preoccupations, interpersonal relationships, or psychiatric symptoms. Any studies attempting to examine the relationship between suicide and psychiatric illness encounter a fourth methodological problem, in that, compared with adults, psychiatric illnesses in children and adolescents may be atypical. For example, depression in adolescence may present as a behavioral disorder, without the obvious features of low mood, sleep disturbance, loss of concentration, for instance, found in adult depressive illnesses (Toolan, 1962). Thus, in retrospective investigations, estimates of the extent to which psychiatric illness has contributed to suicide is largely a matter of guesswork.

We will now examine those factors which *may* have a causal relationship to suicide among children and adolescents. However, for the reasons discussed, the inferences drawn from research findings must be tentative. In considering possible contributory factors it is convenient to divide them into two main groups: background factors and problems immediately preceding suicide.

1.3.2. Background Factors

1.3.2.1. Family Background. Although the findings are somewhat conflicting, studies of successful suicide in young people suggest that a high proportion come from broken homes or unhappy families. For example, in a British study of 30 individuals who had committed suicide between the ages of 12 and 14, Shaffer (1974) found that seven had broken homes at the time of their death and in six further cases the parents had separated by the time of the survey (one to four years after the suicide). In an American study of ten adolescents between the ages of 11 and 19, Sanborn, Sanborn, and Cimbolic (1973) found that they were all living with their natural parents at the time of death, although it is unclear how many were living with one parent only. Eight of the adolescents were said to come from families described as unhappy. Of the 45 suicides aged under 15 studied by Sathyavathi (1975) in Bangalore, 80% were living with either one or both parents and 16% were living with families other than their own. Again, it is unclear from these findings what proportion of children had lost a parent through death, desertion, or marital breakdown.

It has been suggested by McAnarney (1979) that loosening or disruption of family ties may be an important determinant of the prevalence of suicide among young people in different societies. In support of this hypothesis, she compared the suicide rates in a number of different geographical areas, such as Seattle, Edinburgh, a Shoshonean Indian reservation, Denmark, and North Sudan. On the basis of this comparison, she suggested that the prevalence of suicide was related to the degree of geographical mobility and family disruption found in these societies. For example, the lowest suicide rate was found in North Sudan (1/100,000) where there was a structure of close Muslim family units; on the other hand, the highest suicide rate was found in the Indian reservation (98/100,000), where there was a lack of family stability. Half the suicides on this reservation were less than 25 years old; and when this group was compared with an age-matched control group, it was found that a higher proportion had had more than one caretaker in childhood (70% compared with 15% of controls) and a much higher proportion had suffered two or more losses by desertion or divorce (50% compared with 10% of controls). This finding may lend some support to the notion that a chaotic or disrupted upbringing may contribute to suicide among young people.

Another area of family background which may be important is that of psychiatric disorder or attempted suicide among relatives. In Shaffer's (1974) study, 16 of the 30 cases had a family history of psychiatric consultation with either a psychiatrist or a general practitioner, and nine parents were heavy drinkers. In addition, four first-degree relatives had made suicide attempts before the adolescent's suicide, and three had made subsequent attempts. These figures are roughly comparable to those found in studies of attempted suicide among young people (see Section 2.2.2).

1.3.2.2. Intellectual Level. There has been very little investigation of the intelligence of children and adolescents who commit suicide. We know of only one study in which intellectual performance was examined, namely, that of Shaffer (1974). Estimates of IQ were available in 28 of the 30 cases, and they revealed an excess of adolescents with an above-average IQ. For example, 14 of the 30 had an IQ of 115 or more and five had an IQ above 130.

1.3.2.3. Religion. On the basis of the low suicide rates in Catholic countries and among orthodox Jewish communities, McAnarney (1979) suggested that religious culture may influence the suicide rate. There has been little research into religious beliefs among adolescent or childhood suicides, with the exception of Sathyavathi's Indian study, in which 93% of the subjects were found to be Hindus, 4% Moslems and 2% Christians (Sathyavathi, 1975).

1.3.2.4. Physical Factors. A number of studies have suggested that a disproportionate number of adolescent suicide attempters have problems with their physical health (see Section 2.3.2.5), and similar though less striking findings emerge from studies of completed suicide. For example, Sathyavathi (1975) found that 29% of her series had some sort of physical illness (e.g., asthma, fits, tonsilitis), although these usually seemed to be associated with social problems. The author postulated that the physical illness constituted a predisposing factor rendering the child more vulnerable to distress caused by a social problem such as punishment by parents or school failure. Other studies have reported a smaller proportion with physical illnesses; for example, in a study of 137 suicides below the age of 20 in Singapore, Chia (1979) found that physical illness was a "dominant causative factor" in only nine, although it is unclear in what additional proportion it may have been a contributory factor rather than a dominant causal factor. Shaffer (1974) found only two of his 30 subjects to have chronic illnesses. He reported an interesting physical abnormality among the adolescents, in that a disproportionate number of those for whom a record of height was available were tall or very tall for their age.

1.3.2.5. Psychiatric Disorders. In spite of the difficulties of retrospectively identifying mental illness in young people, most studies of completed suicide in this age group suggest a fairly high prevalence of psychiatric disorder. For example, in Shaffer's study, 9 out of the 30 adolescents (8 boys and 1 girl) had been attending a psychiatrist or were on the waiting list for a psychiatric appointment; only 2 of these subjects had been referred because of a previous suicide attempt. Six further adolescents were recognized by school authorities as having conduct or emotional problems and had been seen by probation and welfare services. Thus, a total of half the sample had evidence of some sort of psychiatric disorder. When Shaffer tried to identify individual psychiatric symptoms in these children, he found that 22 had antisocial symptoms, such as bullying, stealing, or truancy, and 21 had emotional symptoms, such as depression, excessive fears, or school refusal; 17 children had a combination of both sorts of symptom. Almost half the sample had either discussed or actually attempted suicide before they successfully killed themselves (Shaffer, 1974).

Unlike Shaffer, who obtained information on psychiatric status from school, medical, and psychiatric records, Chia (1975) based his assessment of psychiatric disorder on information in the Singapore coroner's case files, which may have been less complete. Nevertheless, he considered that psychiatric disorder was the "dominant causal factor" in the death of 32 (23%) of his 137 subjects. Of these 32 adolescents, 24 were considered to be suffering from a psychotic illness, 4 from a personality disorder, 3 from psychosomatic illness, and 1 from acute alcoholism. A rather lower prevalence of mental illness was suggested by Sathyavathi (1975) on the basis of information in the Bangalore police records. Mental illness was identified in 12% of her sample, although no further details were given.

These estimates of the prevalence of psychiatric disorder correspond fairly well with those found in populations of adolescent suicide attempters (see Section 2.3.2.6).

1.3.3. Problems Immediately Preceding Suicide

Although it might be useful to separate background or predisposing etiological factors from more immediate or precipitating factors, most studies have not made this distinction. However, it is possible to get an impression from the literature of the sorts of problems which may immediately precede the act of suicide in young people.

For example, Shaffer (1974) found that a "disciplinary crisis" was the commonest problem, occurring in 36% of his sample. Other common problems included fights with peers (13%); disputes with boyfriends or girlfriends (10%); disputes with parents (10%); and interaction with a psychotic parent (10%). In a further 10% of the adolescents there was no obvious precipitant. The three adolescents who had a problem with a psychotic parent were a particularly interesting group, all of whom overtly expressed distress at having to live with a mad parent. Two of these teenagers killed themselves on the day that a psychotic parent was due to be discharged from psychiatric hospital. A further interesting finding was that seven of the 30 subjects died within two weeks of their birthdays; this was three times the proportion that would be expected by chance. In a further six adolescents, bereavement was mentioned at the inquest as a possible contributory factor; in two cases the loss involved parents, and in four it involved grandparents. However, there appeared to be no chronological relationship between the bereavement and the time of the subsequent suicide.

In her Bangalore study, Sathyavathi (1975) reported that, of the 35 adolescents for whom information was available, 43% had social problems, such as punishment by parents, ill-treatment, or fear of examinations, although it is unclear whether these were chronic difficulties or acute problems acting as precipitants. A similar difficulty in separating chronic from acute difficulties arises in evaluating the findings of Chia's (1979) Singapore study. The author considered that social problems were the "dominant causal factor" in 40 of the 137 cases, whereas interpersonal problems were the dominant factor in 56 cases. The most common social problems were those involving work, national service, and school or examinations. The most common interpersonal problems were being reprimanded, love problems, and marital problems.

1.4. Possible Predictive Factors

As indicated earlier, the currently available research findings provide an inadequate basis on which to identify precise predictors of suicide among young people. However, the literature provides sufficient evidence for us to identify broadly the individual at risk. From epidemiological studies we know that boys are more likely to kill themselves than girls, and young people over 14 are far more likely to commit suicide than those aged 14 or under.

From Shaffer's study of completed suicide, it is possible to identify background factors which, when taken in combination, may distinguish the adolescent at risk of suicide. These factors include superior intelligence; higher than average stature; a broken home or loss of a parent; the presence of psychiatric disorder, particularly if depression is a feature; and previous suicide attempts or talk of suicide (Shaffer, 1974). In addition, other studies have suggested that physical illness, when combined with these other factors, may predispose a young person to suicide (Sathyavathyi, 1975).

In an adolescent rendered at risk by these background factors, an acute interpersonal or social crisis may increase the chance of suicide. In Shaffer's study, the most commonly occurring precedent was a situation in which the adolescent knew that his parents were about to be told of some misdemeanor or loss of face outside the home. Disputes with peers and with boy- or girlfriends were also found to precede the suicide. Shaffer also noted that many suicides took place after a period of absence from school, a phenomenon which has been noted in studies of attempted suicide (Stanley & Barter, 1970).

We would suggest that family doctors are in a particularly good position to recognize children at risk, in that, unlike school authorities, they are more likely to know of a history of physical or psychiatric disorder or family disruption. Among adult suicides, three-quarters have been reported to consult their family doctor in the month before death (Barraclough, Bunch, Nelson, & Sainsbury, 1974), and the same is true among adolescent suicide attempters (Hawton, Cole, O'Grady, & Osborn, 1982). It is not yet clear whether young people who commit suicide behave in the same way, although it is reasonable to assume that they might. If this is so, it would provide an alert family doctor with a vital opportunity to intercede in the potentially tragic career of a would-be suicide. The help that could be offered to such a young person at this stage will be discussed in the second section of the chapter.

2. Attempted Suicide

2.1. Epidemiology

2.1.1. The Problem of Ascertaining the Extent of Attempted Suicide

In the attempt to establish the extent of nonfatal suicidal behavior among children and adolescents two major methodological issues face the investigator.

2.1.1.1. How the Behavior Is Defined. Considerable confusion abounds in the literature because some workers study suicidal thoughts and threats in combination with actual suicide attempts. Clearly the former are far more common than the latter, and there are likely to be important differences between young people who consider or threaten suicide and those who carry out acts of attempted suicide. In addition, some workers have distinguished two categories of suicide attempts on the basis of the apparent intention; thus, the "suicidal gesture" may be distinguished from the "serious suicidal attempt." This distinction is not useful for epidemiological purposes because it will necessarily be made on the basis of researchers' subjective judgment. In epidemiological studies it is preferable to define attempted suicide on the basis of behavior alone, rather than on inferences about intention. In several British investigations conducted in Oxford the following definitions of nonfatal suicidal behavior (Hawton & Catalan, 1982) have been found useful and appear to overcome this problem:

- *Deliberate self-poisoning.* The deliberate ingestion of more than the prescribed amount of medicinal substances, or ingestion of substances never intended for human consumption, irrespective of whether harm was intended.
- *Deliberate self-injury.* Any intentional self-inflicted injury, irrespective of the apparent purpose of the act.

2.1.1.2. How Cases Are Identified. Some studies of attempted suicide in young persons are based on cases admitted to psychiatric hospitals (e.g., Stanley & Barter, 1970). More usually, cases are identified on the basis of referrals to general hospitals. In one study of attempted suicide in all age groups, Whitehead and colleagues (1973) tried to identify all overdoses and self-injuries which occurred in a particular community by obtaining information not only on general hospital referrals but also on suicide attempts in psychiatric hospitals and jails, and on those identified by social and other health care agencies and not referred to hospital. The number of cases identified by these means represented an increase of more than 100% over the number identified *only* on the basis of general hospital referral. Therefore the perceived size of the problem of attempted suicide depends to a great extent on the way in which cases are identified.

2.1.2. Recent Trends

In the United Kingdom during the late 1960s and early 1970s there was a vast increase in the rates of attempted suicide among young people, especially girls. Thus Kreitman and Schreiber (1979) reported a 250% increase in the rate of attempts among 15- to 19-year-old girls between 1968–69 and 1974–75. After the mid-1970s further but less dramatic increases occurred. In the Oxfordshire region of the United Kingdom between 1974 and 1979 a 28% increase in rates of admissions for self-poisoning was found for 12–20 year olds (Hawton & Goldacre, 1982). The increase was more marked among those aged 12–15 years (35%) than among those aged 16–20 years (23%). During this period, admissions for self-poisoning accounted for 4.7% of all general hospital admissions among people aged 12–20 years. A similar increase in this behavior among young people was reported from various parts of the world (Weissman, 1974).

It appears that the development of the phenomenon of attempted suicide in children and adolescents has paralleled that found for adults throughout most of the Western world (Wexler, Weissman, & Kasl, 1978), with perhaps a more substantial increase in the behavior among *young* teenagers during the 1970s. We do not know why attempted suicide has increased as it has. The greater acceptance of the use of medication to deal with stress, fuelled by the increased prescribing of psychotropic drugs, may be one factor. It has also been suggested that young people now face greater social pressures, due perhaps partly to earlier expectation of adult behavior which is not matched by psychological maturity. It also seems likely that fashion has played a part in the development of self-poisoning, with imitation being a powerful factor.

The numbers of attempted suicides far outnumber completed suicides in this age group, particularly among girls. In France, for example, Choquet, Facy, and Davidson (1980) reported a ratio of 160:1 for girls and 25:1 for boys in the 15–24 age group.

2.1.3. Demographic Characteristics

2.1.3.1. Age and Sex. Attempted suicide is relatively rare under the age of 12 years, although suicidal thoughts and threats are fairly common among children seen in child psychiatry clinics. Thirteen (39%) out of 39 outpatient children aged 6–12 years seen at a clinic in New York had entertained suicidal ideas, made suicidal threats, or made actual attempts (Pfeffer, Conte, Plutchik, & Jerrett, 1980). There were five (13%) cases in the last category. Lukianowicz (1968) found these phenomena in approximately 8% of children referred to Child Guidance Clinics in Northern Ireland, with actual attempts in 4% of cases. In a series of 30 cases of attempted suicide in the age range 9–15 years in Scotland, 5 (17%) were aged 9–11 years (Haldane & Haider, 1967).

After the age of 12, the behavior becomes increasingly common, especially among girls. In a survey of 4,232 episodes of self-poisoning in teenagers in the Oxford region, the rates for girls steadily increased from age 12, reaching a peak at age 16 and then continuing at the same level until age 20. Among boys the rates increased much more slowly, the increase continuing throughout the teenage years (Hawton & Goldacre, 1982). Interestingly, the patterns of self-poisoning with increasing age for the two sexes found in this study were almost exactly replicated in a study in Western Australia using the same methodology (Goldacre, personal communication).

In virtually all studies of attempted suicide in children and adolescents, girls have outnumbered boys with the ratio usually being in the range 3:1 to 9:1 (Garfinkel, Froese, & Golombek, 1979; Hawton, O'Grady, Osborn, & Cole, 1982; Otto, 1972; Rohn, Sarles, Kenny, Reynolds, & Head, 1977; Tuckman & Connon, 1962; Walker, 1980; White, 1974). These ratios are different from those found in adults, where, although women do outnumber men, the ratio is usually found to be of the order of 1.5 to 2:1 (Wexler *et al.*, 1978). Three possible explanations for the great excess of young female attempters come to mind. The first is that girls may mature and face problems of adulthood, such as broken relationships with boyfriends, earlier than boys. Second, self-poisoning may be a more acceptable coping strategy in girls than boys, the latter only seeming to resort to suicidal behavior in the face of very severe difficulties (Hawton, O'Grady, Osborn, & Cole, 1982). Thirdly, boys may have alternative outlets for dealing with distress, such as indulging in aggressive behavior or heavy alcohol consumption. A small subgroup of girls who are at special risk of attempted suicide are teenage wives (Bancroft, Skrimshire, Reynolds, Simkin, & Smith, 1975; Kreitman & Schreiber, 1979). Often it appears that these girls may have taken flight from their unhappy families only to end up in disastrous marriages.

   2.1.3.2. Social Class.   There are conflicting findings concerning the social class backgrounds of young suicide attempters. In Sweden, Bergstrand and Otto (1962) found an association with lower social class, whereas in two studies in the United Kingdom adolescent suicide attempters have been found to have a social class distribution similar to that of the general population (Hawton, O'Grady, Osborn, & Cole, 1982; White, 1974). However, as we shall see later, it is the family backgrounds of these adolescents that most clearly distinguish them from other young people.

2.1.4. Season of the Year

   In some studies a seasonal effect on the incidence of attempted suicide among young people has been noted, with a peak number of cases occurring in the spring (Hawton & Goldacre, 1982; Jacobziner, 1965; Otto, 1972). However, this effect is not usually marked.

2.2. Background Characteristics

   We shall now examine some of the background factors which may contribute to attempted suicide in adolescents and children. Before doing so, we must emphasize that drawing causal inferences from findings concerning the backgrounds and problems of such young people can only be speculative. These findings by themselves are in no way sufficient to explain why this behavior occurs.

2.2.1. Broken Homes

A universal finding in all studies of attempted suicide in children and adolescents is the large number of cases in which there is a history of a broken home, with absence of one or both parents (Barter, Swaback, & Todd, 1968; Bergstrand & Otto, 1962; Choquet et al., 1980; Jacobziner, 1965; Rohn et al., 1977; Stanley & Barter, 1970; Tuckman & Connon, 1962; Walker, 1980; White, 1974). This impression has been confirmed in studies in which comparison has been made with other young people from the general population (e.g., Jacobs, 1971).

Here we shall briefly introduce a study carried out by ourselves and colleagues in the United Kingdom. We will draw on findings of this investigation at various points throughout the rest of this chapter. A consecutive sample of 50 adolescent self-poisoners in the age range 13–18 years were studied, all of whom had been admitted to a general hospital in Oxford following an overdose (Hawton, O'Grady, Osborn, & Cole, 1982). Half were in the range 13–15 years and half in the range 16–18 years. After the routine clinical interview by a member of the hospital psychiatric service, each adolescent was interviewed in depth by a research worker. Among many other aspects of the enquiry the adolescents were asked about their upbringing. Of the adolescents aged 13–15 years, we found that 36% were living with a single parent and 12% with neither parent, compared with figures of 5% and 11.4% respectively in a sample of adolescents in the general population (Fogelman, 1976). This finding is similar to that of a Toronto study, in which less than half of young attempters referred to the emergency service in a children's hospital were living with both parents, compared with 84% of children referred for reasons other than suicide attempts (Garfinkel et al., 1979). In many cases the children were being cared for in group homes.

An important question is to what extent are broken homes a feature of young suicide attempters, compared to other adolescents who develop psychiatric disorders? Although absence of parents appears to be just as common among the latter group (Mattsson, Seese, & Hawkins, 1969; Stanley & Barter, 1970), there is some evidence that suicide attempters may be distinguished by having more often suffered *early* loss of one or both parents (Stanley & Barter, 1970).

2.2.2. Family Psychiatric Disorder and Suicidal Behavior

In several studies a high incidence of psychiatric disorder has been found among other members of the families of young suicide attempters (e.g., Garfinkel *et al.*, 1979; Jacobs, 1971; Walker, 1980). A history of family psychiatric disorder was recorded for 52% of young suicide attempters in Toronto compared with 16% of controls (Garfinkel *et al.*, 1979). Alcoholism, neurotic disorders, and depression were the most common disorders. Among a small series of boys aged 14–18 who made suicide attempts, Margolin and Teicher (1968) noted that most of their mothers were psychiatrically disturbed and themselves entertaining suicidal ideas.

Suicidal behavior also appears to be quite common in other family members (Jacobs, 1971). This includes both completed suicide and nonfatal attempts. Garfinkel and colleagues (1979) found that a history of suicidal behavior was seven times as common among young suicide attempters' families as among the families of control subjects. Although this presumably reflects the high degree of family psychiatric disorder noted above, suicidal acts by other family members may serve as a model for an adolescent, so that a suicidal act becomes a more readily used method of coping at a time of severe stress. A clinical impression is that this behavior may even occur as a result of competition, particularly between a daughter and her mother, with an attempt by the latter being followed shortly afterward by the daughter's attempt.

2.2.3. Childhood Maltreatment

Childhood abuse and neglect may be associated with subsequent suicidal behavior. A higher incidence of self-destructive behavior (e.g., self-biting, self-cutting, self-burning, hair pulling, head banging, suicide attempts, and suicidal threats and gestures) was found by Green (1978) in 59 physically abused children (49.6%) and in 29 neglected children (17.2%) compared with 30 normal controls (6.7%). The author concluded:

> The abused child's sense of worthlessness, badness, and self-hatred as a consequence of parental assault, rejection, and scapegoating formed the nucleus for subsequent self-destructive behaviour. The transformation of the child's self-hatred into self-destructive behaviour was catalyzed by ego deficits and impaired impulse control.

In a study of child abuse families in the United Kingdom, Roberts and Hawton (1980) found that in 29% of the families one or both parents had made a suicide attempt. Thus, parental suicide behavior, child abuse and neglect, and suicidal acts by children may represent a continuing cycle of internally and externally directed aggression within families.

2.3. Problems Preceding Attempted Suicide

2.3.1. Methodological Issues

It is important, although sometimes difficult, to distinguish between the problems faced by young suicide attempters during the period leading up to their suicidal acts and the events which appear to precipitate the act itself. We will discuss the latter when considering the nature of the act. There are other obvious methodological issues involved in research into this aspect of suicidal behavior.

1. The method by which the information is obtained. In retrospective studies the information is usually gleaned from hospital case records. Such information is likely to be incomplete and may provide distorted findings when comparison is made with control subjects because of the very fact that a suicide attempt has occurred. For example, if suicide attempters are compared in this way with young people referred to hospital for physical illness, a clinician may be more likely to look for social and psychological difficulties in the former group than in the latter. Even in prospective studies, the question arises whether information obtained from the suicide attempters themselves is sufficiently reliable or whether further information should be sought from other sources such as family members, friends and health professionals. It could be argued that in some ways the subjects are the most relevant source because it is their perception of their difficulties which is most important.

2. How a problem is defined. It is probably impossible to draw up entirely satisfactory criteria, and the likely differences in operational definition of problems must be borne in mind when comparing the findings from different studies.

3. The difficulty of establishing a causal link between a set of problems and attempted suicide. It is most important to be clear that the association of particular types of problems with suicide attempts does not necessarily imply a causal connection. We should remind ourselves that there are likely to be many young people who have undergone similar experiences and have not resorted to suicidal acts or to what could be considered other maladaptive behavior. Later in this chapter we shall return to the fascinating if somewhat intangible issue of why some children and adolescents engage in suicidal behavior whereas others do not.

2.3.2. Nature of the Problems

It is clear that, compared with nonsuicidal children and adolescents, suicide attempters are generally facing more problems in their lives (Ja-

TABLE 1
Current Problems Identified for 50 Adolescent Self-Poisoners

Problem area	Percentage of subjects for whom each problem was applicable
Parents	76
School/work	58
Boyfriend/girlfriend	52
Social isolation	28
Sibling(s)	22
Physical health	22
Psychiatric symptoms	20
Sexual	16
Relationship with peers	14
Alcohol	14
Physical illness of family member	14
Financial	8
Psychiatric disorder of family member	6
Legal	2
Drugs	2

cobs, 1971). The nature of their problems has been investigated in several studies. In the Oxford study to which we referred earlier, the research interviewer recorded each patient's problems on a standard checklist. A problem was recorded only if it was judged to be causing difficulty for the subject, irrespective of whether it appeared to have a direct relationship to the overdose. A disturbance in a relationship or a mild physical complaint, for example, was listed as a problem only if it seemed to be causing distress or affecting normal functioning. A second assessment of the subject's problems was independently made by clinical interviewers using a similar check list.

The nature of the problems found by the research interviewers in this group of adolescents is summarized in Table 1. There was good agreement between the clinical assessors and research interviewers concerning the adolescents' problems (Kappa 0.58, $p < 0.001$). Problems with parents, with school or work, and with boyfriends or girlfriends were the most common. The order of frequency of problems found in this study is in keeping with findings of other studies both in the United Kingdom and the United States. We shall now examine more closely the different types of problems, both in terms of our findings and those from elsewhere.

2.3.2.1. Relationships with Parents. The majority of child and adolescent suicide attempters who are in contact with their parents appear to face substantial difficulties in their relationships with them. Certainly, compared with adolescents in the general population, these relationships are more disturbed, although the suicide attempters may not differ much in this respect from psychiatrically disordered individuals who have not made a suicide attempt (Stanley & Barter, 1970). The relationship which is most often disturbed is that with the parent of the opposite sex. In our Oxford sample, 90% of which were girls, the main area of difficulty was typically between the girl and her father. Walker (1980) made a similar observation. Most of the subjects felt totally unable to discuss any of their problems with their fathers, with whom they also had frequent quarrels. Among boys who made suicide attempts, Margolin and Teicher (1968) found that serious disturbances in the relationships with the mothers were common. These often arose because the boys found that they were expected to take over the role of the elder male in the household, usually because the father was absent, and at these times they felt nagged and unloved by their mothers.

2.3.2.2. *School or Work Difficulties.* Many young suicide attempters have problems at school (Table 1; Garfinkel *et al.*, 1979; Otto, 1972; Rohn *et al.*, 1977; White, 1974). These include both poor academic attainments and difficulties in relationships with teachers. For those who have left school, work problems are also common. In our study the unemployment rate among the 16–18 year old attempters was far in excess of the unemployment rate in other young people in the Oxford area at the time of the study. Only rarely did school or work problems appear to cause the attempt directly. More often they seemed to contribute to the adolescents' low self-esteem which, in turn, probably impaired their ability to cope with other life stresses, especially those of an interpersonal nature.

2.3.2.3. *Problems with Boy- or Girlfriends.* Difficulties in the relationship with a boy- or girlfriend commonly precede suicidal acts in young people (Bergstrand & Otto, 1962; Garfinkel *et al.*, 1979; Tuckman & Connon, 1962). The very high proportion of subjects with such problems (58%) in our study may be partly the result of the especially large female to male ratio, for it appears that girls who make suicide attempts are more likely to have problems in their relationships with members of the other sex than are boys who make attempts (Otto, 1972). Commonly, the young person appears to have no one to turn to in order to get support when in anguish about a deteriorating or disrupted relationship.

2.3.2.4. *Social Isolation.* Social isolation was a characteristic of a minority of subjects in our Oxford study (Table 1). For the majority of adolescents it was not that they lacked relationships but rather that their relationships were disturbed. Nonsupportive family relations appear to lead to excessively dependent relationships with members of the other sex; such dependence makes the individual vulnerable to overwhelming distress when the relationship is threatened or disrupted.

2.3.2.5. Physical Health. An excessive frequency of subjects with ill health is a common finding in several studies of young suicide attempters (Choquet *et al.*, 1980; Jacobs, 1971; Walker, 1980; White, 1974). This is reflected in both an excess of subjects who have had recent general hospital admissions for physical illness and a high proportion who have current physical disorders (e.g., asthma, dysmenorrhea). In our study, physical illness never appeared to be directly associated with an overdose, but it often appeared to be a factor which might have increased a person's vulnerability to other stresses.

A potentially important but, as far as we are aware, unreplicated finding was reported by Rohn *et al.* (1977), who claimed that more than half of a subgroup of adolescent attempters showed evidence of minimal brain dysfunction on psychological testing. Clearly this requires further examination.

2.3.2.6. Psychiatric Disorder and Personality Factors. It is difficult to get a clear idea of the extent of psychiatric disturbance in young suicide attempters for two reasons. First, in many studies it is unclear what criteria have been used to define psychiatric disorder. Second, there are the well-recognized difficulties surrounding the identification of possible depressive conditions in children and adolescents (Cantwell & Carlson, 1979; Toolan, 1962).

In general, relatively few young suicide attempters appear to suffer from psychiatric disorders. In our study, one in five subjects had psychiatric problems, usually in the form of relatively mild depression and/or personality difficulties. In addition, 14% had problems in the use of alcohol, although none of these adolescents could have been described as suffering from alcoholism. Far higher rates of alcohol abuse have been reported in some studies (e.g., Headlam, Goldsmith, Hanenson, & Rauh, 1979). Several reports have suggested that the majority of adolescent suicide attempts are related to adjustment reactions or adolescent crises (e.g., Mattson *et al.*, 1969; White, 1974). Psychiatric disorder appears to be more common among boys than girls. Thus Otto (1972) reported psychiatric disorder in 35.7% of boys and 14.2% of girls in his large series of young attempters. The most common conditions were neuroses and character disorders, with a few subjects suffering from schizophrenia.

Personality factors which might characterize groups of young suicide attempters have not been studied extensively. On the basis of the results of arithmetical and problem-solving tests, Levenson and Neuringer (1971) suggested that suicidal adolescents showed diminished problem-solving capacity compared with matched control subjects.

White (1974) produced evidence suggesting that adolescent suicide attempters showed greater neuroticism traits than the normal population. Hopelessness is a most important link between depression and suicidal behaviour in adults (Beck, Kovacs, & Weissman, 1975); we do not yet know if adolescent suicide attempters tend to experience hopelessness when faced by adversity more easily than nonattempters.

2.4. The Nature of the Act

2.4.1. Precipitants

In our study in Oxford, 64% of the overdoses appeared to have precipitated by a tangible event in the 48 hours preceding the act (Hawton, O'Grady, Osborn, & Cole, 1982). In half of the cases this consisted of disruption of a relationship with a parent or parents, and in a few cases a quarrel had occurred with a member of the adolescent's peer group. In other studies similar precipitants have been identified, although the relative frequency of each has varied (Jacobziner, 1965; Mattson *et al.*, 1969; White, 1974). It is interesting to note that discovery of unwanted pregnancy is only rarely a precipitant for adolescent suicide attempts (Hawton, O'Grady, Osborn, & Cole, 1982; Otto, 1972; White, 1974).

2.4.2. Methods Used in Attempts

2.4.2.1. Deliberate Self-Poisoning. Attempted suicide in young people most commonly involves deliberate self-poisoning. In the large series of cases studied in Sweden by Otto (1972), 86.9% involved drug ingestion. However, as with adult attempters, there is some degree of sex difference, with females tending to use drug overdoses more often than male attempters, whereas males more often use violent means such as jumping, hanging, or shooting (Mehr, Zeltzer, & Robinson, 1981; Otto, 1972).

Most overdoses by children and adolescents are taken very impulsively, often with little more than a few minutes of forethought. Therefore the drugs most often used are those most readily available, such as analgesics (e.g., aspirin and paracetamol) and psychotropic agents (Hawton & Goldacre, 1982). The majority of overdoses in this age group involve relatively little threat to life (Barter *et al.*, 1968; Hawton, Cole, O'Grady, & Osborn, 1982). However, there has been a recent trend in the United Kingdom for overdoses of paracetamol and para-cetamol-containing drugs to increase in number. These overdoses are associated with a significant risk of death due to liver toxicity (Davidson

& Eastham, 1966) and therefore this trend is causing concern. Gazzard and colleagues (1976) found that most people (many of whom were in the 12–20 age group) admitted to a liver unit following paracetamol overdoses did not know of the hepatic effects; nearly all said they would not have taken the drug if they had known that liver damage could develop after a delay of several days. In addition, distalgesic, a commonly available combination of paracetamol and dextropropoxyphene, which is frequently used in overdoses, carries serious risk of respiratory depression and death.

2.4.2.2. *Deliberate Self-Injury.* We have already noted that deliberate self-injury is a far less common method of attempted suicide by adolescents and children. Self-injuries can be divided into three broad categories (Hawton & Catalan, 1982).

• *Superficial self-cutting.* The cuts are usually made on the wrist or forearm, and most are associated with little or no suicidal intent. Young people who repeatedly cut themselves often come from broken homes, although this type of background may be no more frequent than among attempted suicide patients in general (Rosenthal, Rinzler, & Klausner, 1972). Some workers have emphasized that deprivation of parental warmth and physical contact are important factors (Simpson, 1976). Attention has also been drawn to the unexpectedly frequent history in these patients of hospitalization or surgery before the age of 5 and in some cases before the age of 18 months (Rosenthal *et al.*, 1972; Simpson, 1975).

Repeated self-cutting appears to be associated with eating disorders and with alcohol and drug abuse. Menstrual disturbances are also common (Rosenthal *et al.*, 1972; Simpson, 1975). These include negative reactions to the onset of menstruation, dislike of periods, and menstrual irregularity. There is conflicting evidence as to whether cutting is more likely during menstruation (Simpson, 1976).

The cuts are typically superficial, and the behavior is commonly repeated. As with overdoses, the usual precipitants are actual or threatened loss or an impasse in a personal relationship (Simpson, 1975). Often the behavior is preceded by feelings of tension, and the cuts may be made when the patient is experiencing depersonalization or dissociation. Thus the patient may suddenly become aware that she has cut herself, having experienced no pain. The sight of blood may provide the patient with a sense of relief, mingled with feelings of disgust or guilt.

Self-cutting sometimes occurs in an epidemic fashion in adolescent inpatient psychiatric units (Offer & Barglow, 1960; Simpson, 1975). Imitation and competition between the adolescents are likely to be important factors in such epidemics.

• *Serious self-injury.* This includes hanging, jumping from heights, shooting, and jumping in front of vehicles, as well as deep cutting of the throat and neck. These methods are used far more often by boys than by girls, and almost invariably are associated with serious suicidal intent.

• *Self-mutilation.* Such acts, which may include, for example, damage to the genitals or to the eyes, are rare in young people. They are usually the result of serious psychiatric disorder, including schizophrenia, in which the mutilation may occur as a consequence of a delusional belief or a hallucinatory command.

2.5. Motivation

The concept of motivation for attempted suicide is complicated. Essentially it refers to the intention behind the behavior. However, such intention is usually not directly accessible and is therefore difficult to study. Often the patient's intention appears to be unconscious; or, if it is conscious, the patient may find it difficult to admit his or her true intention because of fear of condemnation by clinical staff, family members, and friends. Surprisingly little research has been directed toward elucidating motivation for attempted suicide. This is unfortunate because such understanding would appear crucial if effective methods of prevention are to be devised.

Various methods can be used to try to unravel motivational aspects of the behavior:

1. Young people can be asked directly to account for their suicide attempt. One complication of this approach is that a patient's explanation may change within a short time of the attempt (Bergstrand & Otto, 1962; Leese, 1969; White, 1974). Another difficulty, as already indicated, is that an individual may be unable to explain the behavior spontaneously; this was the case in 54% of the adolescent self-poisoners studied by White (1974). One method of overcoming this problem, which is discussed below, is to ask the patient to choose reasons from a list of possibilities. Another approach is use of the repertory grid technique (Parker, 1981).

2. The circumstances of the behavior can be examined for clues about intention. This is probably most useful in determining the degree to which the person intended that the act should have a fatal outcome.

3. Other people, such as clinical staff, relatives, or friends, can be asked for their explanation of the behavior.

In Oxford, our method of investigating motivational aspects of deliberate self-poisoning in adolescents incorporated all three of these approaches (Hawton, Cole, O'Grady, & Osborn, 1982). We examined the feelings reported by adolescents to have preceded the overdose, the

TABLE 2

Feelings That 50 Adolescent Self-Poisoners Had at the Time of Their Overdoses (by Age Group)

Feelings	Age group		
	Under 16 (N = 25)	16–18 (N = 25)	Both (N = 50)
Angry with someone	15 (60%)	12 (48%)	27 (54%)
Lonely or unwanted	13 (52%)	14 (56%)	27 (54%)
Worried about the future	6 (24%)	14 (56%)*	20 (40%)
Failed in life	4 (16%)	10 (40%)	14 (28%)
Sorry or ashamed of something	2 (8%)	5 (20%)	7 (14%)

*$\chi^2 = 4.083$, $df = 1$, $p < 0.05$.

Note. From "Motivational Aspects of Deliberate Self-Poisoning in Adolescents" by K. Hawton, D. Cole, J. O'Grady, & M. Osborn, *British Journal of Psychiatry*, 1982, *141*, 286–291. Copyright 1982 by the British Journal of Psychiatry. Reprinted by permission.

circumstances in which it occurred, and the reasons chosen both by the adolescents themselves and clinical staff to explain the behavior; and, in addition, we inquired about the extent to which the act was premeditated.

2.5.1. Feelings Preceding Attempts

In our study the state of mind preceding the overdose was examined by asking the adolescents to select from a series of five printed cards those which best described how they had been feeling at the time of the attempt (see Table 2). They could choose more than one if necessary. Just over half the adolescents indicated that they had been angry with someone or feeling lonely or unwanted (Table 2). These feelings are congruent with the problems that, as we have already noted, commonly precede self-poisoning, for example, poor communication with parents and disruption in the relationship with a boy or girlfriend (they are also compatible with the reasons, as distinct from feelings, described below, to which the adolescents most commonly attributed their overdoses). Compared with the younger adolescents (13–15 years), significantly more of the older subjects (16–18 years) indicated that they had been feeling worried about the future. This may have been the result of the older adolescents' being more aware of the way in which their lives were developing.

2.5.2. Reasons Given to Explain Attempted Suicide

There appears to have been little in the way of systematic investigation of the explanations for this behavior in young people. Many authors have conjectured about likely reasons but have not subjected their theories to rigorous testing. Therefore in our study of adolescent self-poisoners we tried to look more closely at the reasons given by both the adolescents themselves and clinical staff involved in their care (Hawton, Cole, O'Grady, & Osborn, 1982). We will describe this investigation in some detail because it sheds considerable light on an important aspect of attempted suicide in young people.

Adolescents were first asked about their suicidal intent at the time of the overdose by requesting each to select one from a series of three cards to indicate whether, at the time of the overdose, he or she had (a) wanted to die, (b) did not want to die, or (c) did not mind whether he or she lived or died. The member of the clinical service who had carried out the routine clinical assessment of each case was also asked to indicate his or her impression of the subject's suicidal intent in the same way. More of the adolescents indicated that they had wanted to die (34%) than were judged by the clinicians to have felt this way (14%). Similarly, more of the adolescents indicated that they had been ambivalent or did not mind whether they lived or died (42%) than were so judged by the clinical staff (18%). The clinical assessors considered that the majority of the adolescents had *not* wanted to die (68% compared with only 24% of the adolescents). Complete agreement between the adolescents and the clinicians was found in all cases in which the patients indicated no suicidal intent at all, but the clinicians only agreed with five (29%) of the adolescents who said they had wanted to die. The difference between the adolescents' pattern of choices and that of the clinical assessors was highly significant ($\chi^2 = 19.49$, $df = 2$, $p < .001$). The interesting discrepancy between the choices of the adolescents and those of the clinical staff is discussed below.

In order to investigate further explanations of the behavior (other than the wish to die), each adolescent was asked to select from a series of eight printed cards those which best described his or her reasons for taking the overdose. The reasons are listed in Table 3. As many reasons could be chosen as thought necessary to explain the act. Again, the clinical assessor in each case also selected reasons he or she thought best explained the behavior by choosing from the same list of eight that was offered to the adolescents.

The frequency with which the adolescents and the clinical assessors chose these other reasons to explain the overdoses is shown in Table 3. The reasons most often chosen by the patients (a, b, and c) suggested that the adolescents were in a distressed state and/or a very stressful situation prior to the overdose. The clinical assessors also frequently selected the first two reasons (a and b), but chose the third reasons (c) somewhat more frequently than the adolescents.

TABLE 3

Reasons (Other than Suicidal Intent) Selected by Adolescents and Clinical Assessors to Explain Overdoses

Reasons	Selected by the adolescents ($N = 50$)	Selected by the clinical assessors ($N = 50$)	Comparison of the numbers of clinical assessors' and adolescents' choices[a]
a. Get relief from a terrible state of mind	21 (42%)	20 (40%)	n.s.
b. Escape for a while from an impossible situation	21 (42%)	18 (36%)	n.s.
c. Make people understand how desperate you were feeling	21 (42%)	30 (60%)	n.s.
d. Make people sorry for the way they have treated you, frighten or get your own back on someone	16 (32%)	28 (56%)	$\chi^2 = 8.103, p < 0.01$
e. Try to influence some particular person or get them to change their mind	13 (26%)	28 (56%)	$\chi^2 = 4.911, p < 0.05$
f. Show how much you loved someone	13 (26%)	8 (16%)	n.s.
g. Find out whether someone really loved you or not	12 (24%)	9 (18%)	n.s.
h. Seek help from someone	9 (18%)	19 (38%)	$\chi^2 = 4.018, p < 0.05$

[a]n.s. = not significant.

Note. From "Motivational Aspects of Deliberate Self-Poisoning in Adolescents" by K. Hawton, D. Cole, J. O'Grady, & M. Osborn, British Journal of Psychiatry, 1982, 141, 286–291. Copyright 1982 by the British Journal of Psychiatry. Reprinted by permission.

One striking difference between the adolescents' choices and those of the clinicians was that the latter far more frequently selected the punitive and manipulative reasons (d and e) than did the adolescents. This discrepancy was also found, though to an even more marked extent, in a similar study of adult self-poisoning patients (Bancroft *et al.*, 1979). The difference between the reason chosen by the adolescents and those selected by the clinicians may have arisen because many adolescents recognized that admitting to punitive or manipulative reasons was likely to evoke unfavorable attitudes from hospital staff (Hawton, Marsack, & Fagg, 1981; Ramon, Bancroft, & Skrimshire, 1975). However, we believe that a more likely explanation is that many overdoses with punitive or manipulative explanations are an unconscious expression of externally directed hostility that is unrecognized by the patient. Indeed, the large number of cases in which suicidal intention is claimed by the adolescent but not apparent to the clinician suggests that "wanting to die" often provides the only reason for taking an overdose which seems credible to the patient. Thus, adolescent self-poisoners may feel so distressed at the time of taking the overdose that they feel as if they want to die, but death is not the intended outcome of the act. "Wanting to die" may be the individual's way of legitimizing the suicide attempt. However, it is also essential to realize that in some cases suicidal intention will be serious and will be the main reason for the act.

In this study, another important difference between patient and clinician was that the clinical assessors more often judged the overdose to be a means of obtaining help (reason h) than did the adolescents. The "cry for help" hypothesis for many suicide attempts was first put forward by Stengel and Cook (1958). However, this may be a misleading explanation because it implies that the suicide attempter may be trying to seek professional help. We would concur with White (1974) who, when commenting on Stengel and Cooke's idea, said of adolescent overdoses, "Today, some self-poisoning episodes may still have an appeal function, but the appeal is more often interpersonal than directed to any outside helping agency. The patient wishes to modify the outlook of those close to her." This may explain why many adolescent self-poisoners initially reject any offer of professional help. Unfortunately, this rejection is often misunderstood by clinicians, who may consequently be annoyed by the patient's initial failure to accept this help, thus further alienating the patient and making engagement in constructive treatment highly unlikely. A successful treatment alliance would more readily be established if the clinician first acknowledged that the attempt was not made in order to get professional help and then went on to explore with the patient how he or she might be assisted in dealing with the difficulties that led to the overdose.

TABLE 4
Circumstances of 50 Adolescents' Overdoses

Circumstance	(N = 50)
1. Evidence of any planning for the overdose	10 (20%)
2. Left a suicide note	6 (12%)
3. Precautions taken to prevent discovery and intervention by other people	3 (6%)
4. Overdose timed so that intervention was very likely	39 (78%)
5. Someone present or nearby (e.g., in the next room)	43 (86%)
6. Notified potential helper after the overdose	43 (86%)

Note. From "Motivational Aspects of Deliberate Self-Poisoning in Adolescents" by K. Hawton, D. Cole, J. O'Grady, & M. Osborn, *British Journal of Psychiatry*, 1982, *141*, 286–291. Copyright 1982 by the British Journal of Psychiatry. Reprinted by permission.

A final point that needs to be made about the results of our study is that the motivation for attempted suicide is usually complex. This is evidenced by the finding that in most cases both the adolescents and the clinicians attributed the overdose to more than one reason.

A further study which is of relevance to this aspect of self-poisoning is Parker's (1981) comparison of the perception of overdoses between young people with low suicidal intent and those with high suicidal intent, using the repertory grid technique. Whereas the high-intent group perceived "an overdose" and "suicide" in quite similar terms, the low-intent group perceived an overdose as similar to "being alone and crying" and "getting drunk" and construed it almost exclusively as an escape from tension. In fact, the low-intent group perceived an overdose as second only to getting drunk as an easy course of action. Other possible actions, such as seeking professional help, or talking to a key person, were perceived as very much less easy. Parker concluded that for many young self-poisoners, especially those with low suicidal intent, an overdose serves a "respite" function, allowing the person to escape, albeit temporarily, from distressing circumstances. This is in keeping with two of the three reasons chosen most frequently by the adolescents in our study, namely to "get relief from a terrible state of mind" and to "escape for a while from an impossible situation."

2.5.3. The Circumstances of the Act

Important clues as to the intention involved in an overdose or self-injury are to be found in the circumstances in which the act occurs. In our Oxford study, the circumstances surrounding the overdoses rarely suggested that the act was seriously intended to result in death. As can be seen from Table 4, it was unusual to find evidence that the overdose had been planned, and it usually occurred in circumstances which ensured that the adolescent would be discovered and receive medical attention. In most cases someone was in the vicinity, often in a nearby room.

However, although the majority of overdoses may occur in similar circumstances, this should not obscure the fact that in a few cases attempts are made in circumstances in which discovery is unlikely. In these adolescents the suicidal intent is likely to be high.

2.5.4. Premeditation

Several authors have commented on the highly impulsive nature of many overdoses and self-injuries by young people (Jacobziner, 1965; Walker, 1980; White, 1974). In our study, over half of the adolescent self-poisoners reported thinking seriously about the act for less than a quarter of an hour and 16% for a period between 15 min and 1 hr. Only 8% had contemplated taking the overdose for more than 24 hours. There was little difference in the reported duration of premeditation between the younger and older adolescents. Such figures do not mean that suicidal behavior had never been considered in the past. Indeed, as we shall suggest later, it is likely that some sort of cognitive rehearsal of the behavior may often occur long beforehand. However, in general it appears to be true that the longer a particular act has been contemplated the more serious the suicidal intent is likely to be.

2.5.5. Concluding Comments on Motivation

Before leaving the fascinating and important topic of motivation we would like to put forward some ideas about the factors which may contribute to the development of the at-risk individual and the eventual suicide attempt.

An important factor in understanding suicidal behavior in children and adolescents is the way in which the concept of death is developed. Awareness that death is a final event does not appear to begin to develop until between the ages of 7 and 11, and full awareness of the concept of death does not usually occur until adolescence. It has been suggested that suicidal children often view death as being temporary and also as being a pleasant state offering relief from pain. Such ideation may facilitate suicidal behavior when the child is under severe stress (Pfeffer, Conte, Plutchik, & Jerrett, 1979).

We have already noted that most suicide attempts by adolescents appear to be impulsive. However, we would suggest that considerable suicidal ideation may occur at other times of stress, possibly several years beforehand, and this may have served as a form of cognitive rehearsal which allows the concept of a suicidal act to be rapidly activated at a time of severe stress. Such ideation is typified in the common fantasy, "You will be sorry when I am dead. You will see how badly you treated me." Interestingly, this idea encapsulates the clinician's ideas about the motives for many adolescent overdoses, as discussed in the previous section. There is evidence from a survey by Bagley (1975) that suicidal ideas in young adolescents are relatively common. Among 112 boys and 128 girls in a comprehensive school in southern England, 4.5% of the boys and 9.4% of the girls admitted to having experienced relatively serious suicidal ideation at some time.

These findings lead to the tantalizing question of what factors distinguish the young person who crosses the threshold of entertaining suicidal thought to actually engaging in suicidal behavior from other young people who have entertained similar ideas but never put them into practice. First, it has been suggested that disturbed upbringing, which we have already noted to be a common factor among suicidal adolescents, may impair personality formation with a marked tendency to poor impulse control, lability of mood, and a defective sense of reality (Pfeffer et al., 1979). Second, suicidal behavior in other persons, especially other family members and friends, may provide a model of coping for the adolescent to copy. Third, when faced by stress, some adolescents may easily become hopeless, which, as we have noted, appears to be an important link between depressive feelings and suicidal behavior (Beck et al., 1975). Fourth, alcohol consumption, which immediately preceded the overdoses of 24% of older adolescents (16-18 years) in our Oxford study, may, for example, lead to disinhibition and contribute to impulsive behavior. Fifth, because prescribed or nonprescribed medication is readily available, the adolescent may not have to look beyond the bathroom cupboard for the means of an overdose; thus, there need be little delay between the decision to take an overdose and actually doing so. If drugs for the attempt were harder to come by, there might be more time for the planned action to be reappraised and, perhaps, avoided.

2.6. Outcome after Attempted Suicide

We will consider the outcome for young people who attempt suicide in terms of general adjustment, further suicide attempts, and completed suicide. However, mention should first be made of some of the methodological issues which are encountered in follow-up studies of outcome. A major difficulty in assessing adjustment, especially if there is a long delay between the initial attempt and the follow-up, is that the subjects may not wish to be interviewed (Nardini-Maillard & Ladame, 1980). In many cases this may be because the individual does not wish to be reminded of the act. It was for this reason that in Sweden Otto (1972) abandoned an interview-based follow-up study, using instead medical and social records to provide information about outcome. Some workers have used postal questionnaires for follow-up and have encountered extremely low response rates. For example, of 235 questionnaires sent out to adolescent suicide attempters and control subjects by Mehr and colleagues (1982), only 12.3% were returned. Findings from such an enquiry are likely to be highly misleading because the subjects who reply may differ in important respects from those who do not.

When studying repetition of attempts it is usual to identify individuals who re-present at hospitals within a given geographical area. Account should be taken of the high mobility in this group, which may mean that some at-risk subjects have moved away from the area. Thus, their further attempts might not be identified by this method. Information about suicidal deaths following attempted suicide is usually more complete in that most countries maintain a register of suicides. However, as discussed at the beginning of this chapter, all the factors influencing the identification of suicides are likely to affect the findings.

2.6.1. General Adjustment

In discussing the adjustment of adolescents who have made suicide attempts, we will review three studies in which the subjects were followed up for different periods of time: first, our Oxford study, in which follow-up took place 1 month after the overdose (Hawton, O'Grady, Osborn, & Cole, 1982; Hawton, Osborn, O'Grady, & Cole, 1982); second, White's (1974) study in Birmingham (U.K.), in which subjects were followed up one year afterwards; and third, a much longer term follow-up (10–15 years after the attempts) in Sweden, reported by Otto (1972).

All 50 adolescent self-poisoners in our Oxford study were interviewed one month after their overdoses. On the basis of a global rating of outcome made by the research interviewers, 33 (66%) of the adolescents were rated as improved, 16 (32%) as unchanged, and one as worse. Compared with the initial assessment, problems which tended to have most often improved one month after the overdoses were those concerning boyfriends and girlfriends, alcohol, peers, and finance. Problems with parents were improved in only half the cases. When the adolescents were asked whether the overdose had produced any positive changes in their problems, half the subjects said that it had.

A simple method was devised for classifying the adolescents in this study (Hawton, Osborn, O'Grady, & Cole, 1982). It consisted of three categories which were defined by the duration of the patient's problems and the presence or absence of behavioral disturbance:

> *Group 1: Acute.* The problems identified at the time of the overdose had persisted for less than 1 month; there was no behavioral disturbance.
>
> *Group 2: Chronic.* The problems identified at the time of the overdose had persisted for 1 month or more; there was no behavioral disturbance.
>
> *Group 3: Chronic with behavior disturbance.* The problems identified at the time of the overdose had persisted for one month or more; there had been recent behavioral disturbance (e.g., repeated truancy, stealing, drug-taking, heavy drinking, fighting, being in trouble with the police).

When the global ratings of adjustment 1 month after the overdose were examined in terms of the categories to which the adolescents had been allocated, a clear difference was found between the three groups. Thus, 90% of subjects in Group 1 were rated as improved, compared with 75% in Group 2 and only 25% in Group 3.

This study demonstrated that in adolescents the short-term outcome following an overdose is good in the majority of cases. However, approximately a third of the adolescents were still facing serious difficulties four weeks after their overdoses. At the time of the overdose, those who were in this position were most likely to have had problems lasting more than one month and also to have shown disturbed behavior.

White (1974) was able to follow up 40 out of 50 adolescent self-poisoners (aged 13–19 years) one year after their overdoses. It is not entirely clear from his report how the follow-up enquiry was conducted. Twenty-eight subjects (56%) were rated as improved at follow-up, and in 12 (24%) there had been no change or they were worse. The 10 subjects who were not available for follow-up had either changed their address or were not known to their family doctors. White suggested that they comprised an unstable group and were unlikely to have shown less morbidity than those who were available for follow-up. He concluded that at least a quarter of adolescent self-poisoners are found to be experiencing continuing disturbance a year after their overdoses.

As noted above, Otto (1972) followed up 1,547 adolescent suicide attempters in Sweden 10–15 years after their attempts, using medical and social records available in that country. Compared with an age-, sex-, and nationality-matched control group, the overall death rate was three times higher among the suicide attempters, the difference being greater among boys than girls. The suicide attempters of both sexes had a significantly lower rate of marriage and a higher rate of divorce than the controls. Emigration from Sweden, preventive detention, entry in the criminal register, imprisonment, and probation orders had all occurred more frequently among the suicide attempters, and they had more sick leave for both psychiatric and physical reasons. In general, more of the boys than the girls showed evidence of mental ill health.

2.6.2. Repetition of Suicide Attempts

In considering repetition of attempted suicide, we must first have some idea of the proportion of young suicide attempters who have made previous attempts. The incidence of known previous attempts has been variously estimated as: 14% (White, 1974); 18% (Rohn et al., 1977); 22% (Headlam et al., 1979); 30%, of which only 12% had resulted in hospital referral (Hawton et al., 1982); and 40% (Mattsson et al., 1969). Thus, very approximately, about a quarter of adolescent suicide attempters will have a history of previous attempts. Not surprisingly, given the shorter time that adolescents have been at risk, this is a lower figure than is found among adult attempters (Bancroft & Marsack, 1977).

It appears that approximately 1 in 10 adolescent suicide attempters will make further attempts within 1 year (Hawton, O'Grady, Osborn, & Cole, 1982). Haldane and Haider (1967) found a similar repetition rate during a follow-up period ranging from 6 months to 5 years. During a 22-month follow-up study, Barter et al. (1968) found a much higher repetition rate (42%) in a sample of adolescent suicide attempters admitted to a psychiatric hospital. As found in adult suicide attempters (Bancroft & Marsack, 1977), the most likely time for a repeat attempt is in the three months after the previous episode (Goldacre & Hawton, submitted for publication).

Several studies have investigated the characteristics which distinguish repeaters from nonrepeaters. For convenience, these have been summarized in Table 5. Clearly there is a good deal of overlap between items on this list.

In order to develop properly a scale for the prediction of repeat attempts, a study is required which identifies factors which appear to distinguish repeaters from nonrepeaters in the same cohort, then reduces the number of factors by some statistical method such as multiple regression analysis, and finally validates these factors in a prospective

TABLE 5
*Characteristics Probably Associated with Increased Risk of
Further Attempts*

1. Sex: male (Choquet *et al.*, 1980; Goldacre & Hawton, submitted for publication)
2. Previous attempts (Hawton, O'Grady, Osborn, & Cole, 1982)
3. Psychiatric or personality disorder (Choquet *et al.*, 1980)
4. Coming from a large family (Choquet *et al.*, 1980)
5. Alcoholism in family (Choquet *et al.*, 1980)
6. Disturbed relationships with family members (Choquet *et al.*, 1980)
7. Not living with parents (Stanley & Barter, 1970)
8. Chronic problems and behavior disturbance (Choquet *et al.*, 1980; Hawton, Osborn, O'Grady, & Cole, 1982)
9. Alcohol or drug abuse (Headlam *et al.*, 1979)
10. Social isolation (Stanley & Barter, 1970)
11. Poor school record (Stanley & Barter, 1970; Choquet *et al.*, 1980)
12. Depressive tendencies (Choquet *et al.*, 1980)

study of more than one cohort of subjects. This kind of investigation has been carried out among adults (Buglass & McCulloch, 1970; Buglass & Horton, 1974), but not among adolescents, as far as we know. Only Choquet and colleagues (1980) in France have made any progress in the development of a predictive scale for adolescents. They found a high risk of repetition when psychiatric or personality disorder was associated with at least three out of five other factors (4, 5, 6, 11, and 12 in Table 5).

One further factor likely to be relevant to the risk of immediate repetition is the extent to which the young person's problems appear to have altered as the result of the attempt. Clearly this is a clinical judgment and as such is difficult to quantify.

2.6.3. Completed Suicide

We know of only one sizeable study of child and adolescent attempters in which subsequent deaths by suicide have been examined. This is Otto's (1972) Swedish investigation, previously described. Of 1,547 subjects, 84 died during the follow-up period, in 67 cases (80%) by suicide. The proportion committing suicide (4.3% of the total sample) was far higher among the boys (10%) than the girls (2.9%). The suicide rate was highest during the first 2 years of follow-up. Although boys were at greatest risk of suicide, girls who had made active attempts (e.g., hanging) were at greater risk of subsequent suicide than those who had used passive means (e.g., drugs).

2.6.4. Concluding Comments on Outcome

For the majority of adolescent suicide attempters, the outcome following attempts is relatively good, with improved adjustment occurring in many cases within a month of the attempt. However, a substantial minority of such adolescents continue to have major difficulties following their attempts, as evidenced by high rates of psychiatric and physical disorder, poor marital adjustment, and elevated rates of criminality, as well as repeat attempts. Several factors have been associated with repetition of attempted suicide among adolescents; however, a fully validated predictive scale has not yet been developed. The risk of suicide in adolescent attempters is, in the long-term, substantial and, judging by the results of the one major study which has been carried out (Otto, 1972), not much less than the risk in adult attempters (Kreitman, 1977). Boys who make attempts are at particular risk of subsequently taking their own lives. Otto's study was based on adolescents who made attempts in the 1950s, and a more up-to-date investigation is required to determine the current suicide risk among adolescent attempters of both sexes.

2.7. Management

The management of young persons who have taken overdoses or deliberately injured themselves very often appears to be grossly inadequate. The initial assessment after hospital referral may be a rushed and superficial affair, undertaken by busy and sometimes unsympathetic emergency room staff (Jacobs, 1971; Ramon et al., 1975), their primary aim, understandably, being to deal with the physical complications of the suicide attempt. The patient may then be discharged without adequate plans for further care.

Ideally, the young suicide attempter should be admitted to a general hospital bed to allow time for a full assessment. Where shortage of hospital beds, or the triviality of the attempt, makes admission inappropriate, a full psychiatric and social assessment should be carried out and appropriate after-care plans made before the patient is discharged. In all cases, the initial assessment should, if possible, include interviews with relatives and any professionals involved in the patient's care, as well as discussion with the family doctor. The patient's relatives, especially parents, or close friends, may feel guilty or angry about the attempt. The clinician should allow them the opportunity to ventilate these feelings, as well as obtaining their account of the patient and the attempt.

After discharge from the medical ward, treatment must be tailored to the needs of the individual. This is not the place for detailed descriptions of methods of assessment and treatment; these are available elsewhere (Hawton & Catalan, 1982). We will instead provide an outline of the essential features of the management of children and adolescents who have made suicide attempts.

2.7.1. Assessment

The family doctor is often the first professional person to be confronted by a young person who had made an attempt. He will have to appraise the physical effects and likely complications of the act. However, it is recommended that he should always try to arrange immediate referral to a local general hospital. This is important, first, to obtain appropriate physical treatment, particularly as the extent of the overdose may have been concealed by the patient, and, second, to allow adequate time for a full psychological and social assessment. Any information the doctor can provide because of his special knowledge of the patient and his or her family will be invaluable. He should encourage a family member, usually a parent, to go to the hospital with the patient. If hospital referral is judged to be undesirable, he should request an urgent assessment either by a psychiatrist or other mental health professional in his surgery or in the patient's home.

The issue then arises of who is best trained to carry out the assessment of the young suicide attempter when in hospital. Ideally the patient should be seen by a member of the local child or adolescent psychiatric service. This may not be immediately possible, in which case the assessment can be made by a member of the adult service.

Young suicide attempters often appear diffident when an assessment interview is initiated. This may be because they are anxious about the hospital surroundings or because the assessor is viewed as an authority figure who is not to be trusted. We have already noted that the patient may initially reject professional offers of help because the act was carried out to change the attitudes of family or friends rather than to alert helping agencies. Compared with an older assessor, a young person may be able to form a better relationship with the patient, who can more readily identify with him or her.

In the case of self-poisoning, the assessor should first establish that the patient has fully recovered from the physical effects of the overdose; otherwise he or she may be confused and give unreliable information. In addition, the toxic effects of an overdose may prevent an adequate assessment of the individual's mental state. However, once full physical recovery is established, any delay before the assessment interview may allow defensive covering up of important facts and feelings (Connell, 1965).

The interview should always be carried out in privacy and, unless unavoidable, never on an open medical ward. The interviewer should not launch straight into a series of questions; the aim should be first to establish a sense of trust and rapport with the patient. Thus, a warm accepting and friendly approach should be employed, without there being any suggestion of condemnation of the patient.

Once the interviewer feels that rapport has been established with the patient, he should then try systematically to obtain information on the following points:

1. *The events that preceded the act.* A useful beginning is to ask the patient to provide a detailed sequential account of events that occurred during the few days before the act.

2. *Degree of suicidal intent, and other reasons for the act.* The interviewer should try to develop an understanding of the apparent reasons for the attempt, including both the circumstances in which it occurred and the explanations given by the patient. Features that suggest high suicidal intent are as follows (Beck *et al.*, 1974):

   a. The act was carried out in isolation.
   b. It was timed so that intervention was unlikely.
   c. The patient took precautions to avoid being discovered.
   d. Preparations were made in anticipation of death (e.g., arranging for the care of pets; saying farewell to friends).
   e. The patient talked about suicide beforehand.
   f. The act had been considered for hours or days beforehand.
   g. A suicide note was written.
   h. The patient failed to alert others during or after the act.

Violent methods are usually associated with serious suicidal intent. However, in overdoses, the amount of the substance taken or its likely lethality is only weakly correlated with suicidal intent (Fox & Weissman, 1975), except when an adolescent has special knowledge of the danger of the drugs used.

3. *The patient's current problems.* The range of such problems has already been elaborated. Considerable information about the individual patient's problem will usually be gained from a sequential account of the events preceding the attempt. However, the interviewer should also

check through a list of other possible problem areas, since this may elicit further difficulties (see Table 1).

4. *The possible presence of psychiatric disorder.* As mentioned earlier, psychiatric illness in young people may have an atypical presentation (Cantwell & Carlson, 1979; Toolan, 1962). Loss of interest in hobbies and friends, poor concentration, irritability, lack of energy, and hypersomnia may be prominent features, but they may be elicited only by careful enquiry of both the patient and relatives. Sometimes there may be recent changes in school performance. Psychiatric illness should always be suspected if the interviewer is unable to understand the act in terms of the patient's life and current circumstances.

5. *Family and personal history.* Much of this information will have to be obtained from the parents or a sibling. Enquiry should be made about any family history of psychiatric disorder, attempts by other family members, and the young person's upbringing and development. Particular attention should be paid to any suggestion of violence or sexual abuse involving the patient. The interviewer should try to gain a clear impression of the nature of the patient's family and whether the family relationships are stressful for the patient.

6. *History of previous psychiatric disorder, or of suicide attempts.*

7. *The risk of a further attempt, and of completed suicide.* Factors associated with risk of a further attempt were discussed earlier. Because completed suicide among the young is a rare event, and because the risk will depend on a complex interaction of factors in the individual patient, accurate detection of those most at risk of taking their own lives can be very difficult. However, apart from the known high risk among boys and those suffering from psychiatric disorder, further clues to risk can be provided by the degree of suicidal intent and whether or not there is any immediate prospect of the patient's circumstances altering to his or her advantage.

8. *The nature of the patient's coping resources and supports.* Assessment of coping resources, especially in young people, is often difficult. First, previous methods of coping should be determined. This can be done by asking how important life changes, such as a death in the family, moving home, or leaving school, have been dealt with. Second, the patient's current resources might be assessed by asking for suggestions as to how the present difficulties might be tackled. The patient's supports can be assessed by asking who he or she turns to when in trouble, whether there is a confidant, and whether there are professional sources of help to whom the patient has access and would turn if necessary.

2.7.2. Subsequent Treatment

Some young suicide attempters require no special after-care; these include adolescents who have been leading relatively normal lives, without previous suicide attempts, but who take an overdose in response to an acute crisis which resolves as a result of the act. Such patients are usually best returned to the care of their family doctor (White, 1974).

Only a small minority of children and adolescents who make suicide attempts appear to require admission to an inpatient psychiatric unit (Hawton, Osborn, O'Grady, & Cole, 1982; White, 1974). They are patients who either are at risk of an immediate repetition or need further psychiatric assessment and treatment. The clinician should not assume that suicide attempts will always be prevented by inpatient admission because, as we noted earlier, outbreaks of suicidal behavior are not uncommon in hospital, particularly in adolescent units (Hawton, 1978; Offer & Barglow 1960). This is not surprising because, first, many hospitalized patients have a history of previous attempts; second, their high level of personal distress may increase the risk of an attempt; and third, the behavior often has a contagious quality, perhaps because of modeling. Such outbreaks are probably best dealt with by removing the patient who appears to be fueling the epidemic and then holding open discussions of the phenomenon between the patients and staff members.

Treatment in the inpatient setting usually includes family therapy and group therapy with other patients. Psychotropic drugs should be used according to the usual indications.

Outpatient treatment seems to be the treatment of choice for the majority of young suicide attempters. Sometimes treatment is more appropriately conducted in the patient's home; this arrangement makes it easier for family members to be included. Family therapy, focusing particularly on disturbed communication between family members, is the treatment of choice in many cases (Richman, 1979). Evening clinics may make it easier for the father and for other family members to attend treatment sessions (Connell, 1965). It is usually imperative that at some stage patient and relatives should be encouraged to express their feelings about the attempt and give their explanation for the act. This can serve as a useful means of highlighting faulty communication between family members and may assist in prevention of further attempts.

Individual therapy is appropriate in many cases, especially those in which separation from the family has already occurred or parents are unwilling to cooperate with treatment. A brief problem-oriented approach is often useful (Hawton & Catalan, 1982). This usually involves agreement between therapist and patient on tasks the patient can carry out between sessions in order gradually to overcome the problems that have been identified as important targets. Some arrangement for telephone access to the therapist can be a useful facility at times of further crisis.

Psychotropic drugs have only a limited role in the management of young suicide attempters, particularly because of the risk of further self-poisoning. The most common indication is an affective illness, in which case antidepressants may be used. The number of tablets available should be restricted, and it may be wise to put them in the charge of another family member.

The treatment of child and adolescent suicide attempters has not been systematically evaluated. We do know that the proportion of young patients who drop out of outpatient care is high (White, 1974). This may be the result of discouragement by the patient's family and is more common among those with chronic behavior problems (Mattsson et al., 1969).

The repetitive wrist-cutter poses considerable management problems which do not appear to have been successfully addressed. Two lines of approach are indicated in most cases. The first includes helping the patient develop alternative means of reducing feelings of tension, such as by muscle relaxation; and the second involves psychotherapeutic measures directed toward improving the patient's self-esteem and ability to communicate feelings and needs. The pursuit of analytical insights into the reasons for cutting is probably unhelpful (Simpson, 1976).

3. Prevention of Suicidal Behavior by Children and Adolescents

Several suggestions have been made about the primary prevention of suicidal behavior in young people (British Medical Journal, 1981). However, there appears to have been little in the way of implementation of these suggestions, and even less in the way of evaluation. Suggested measures include social support to poorly functioning families; improvement in the diagnosis and treatment of depression and other psychiatric disorders in childhood; an increase in educational programs in child and adolescent psychiatry for family doctors and hospital and community physicians; and courses aimed at helping parents, teachers, and social workers become more aware of the problems of young people. It has also been suggested that more cautious prescribing of psychotropic drugs for young people may prevent overdoses (British Medical Journal, 1981; Morgan, 1979; White, 1974). However, it is important to remember that young adolescents often take overdoses of nonprescribed drugs (Hawton & Goldacre, 1982). Finally, educational measures aimed at modifying the attitudes of school children to self-poisoning have also been proposed (Morgan, 1979) and the use of the media for this purpose is a possibility.

In recent years a large number of voluntary agencies concerned with the prevention of suicidal behavior have appeared, some of which are designed specially for young people, but their effectiveness is unclear. In adults, the results of studies evaluating the prevention of suicide by such agencies have been disappointing (Bridge *et al.*, 1978; Lester, 1974).

In adolescent overdoses, the lack of a "help-seeking" motive and the impulsiveness of the behavior suggest that prevention may not be feasible once the act has been seriously considered; help should be available at a much earlier stage when problems are beginning to develop. Perhaps the best hope for prevention lies in educational changes, which are already beginning to appear, so that some time in the school curriculum is devoted to helping young people consider problems that they may face in the future and to developing methods of coping with them.

4. Concluding Comments

In spite of the difficulties of obtaining reliable statistics about suicide in young people, sufficient evidence is available to suggest that among children completed suicide is very rare, whereas among adolescents the incidence of suicide is a significant problem, with rates increasing markedly throughout the teenage years. Although the numbers of suicides are relatively small, especially compared with adults, suicide is one of the major causes of death in this relatively healthy population. In recent years the rates of suicide among adolescents in many countries have shown a disturbing increase. In all countries for which data are available, suicide rates among boys outnumber those among girls.

Attempted suicide is also relatively rare in children under the age of 12. Thereafter the rates increase steadily with age, especially among girls, who grossly outnumber boys. During the late 1960s and early 1970s attempted suicide increased to almost epidemic proportions among adolescents, and the incidence has continued to rise although less dramatically during the middle and later 1970s. A considerable amount is known about the characteristics of adolescent suicide attempters, especially the disturbed upbringing and family relations experienced by the majority. We know much about their problems and the factors that precipitate their suicide attempts, but we are only just beginning to understand the motivational aspects of their behavior. Although the outcome in the majority of cases is good, a significant number make repeat attempts; and there is some evidence to suggest that the long-term risk of death by suicide is relatively high, especially among boys. If we are to prevent the morbidity and mortality in this minority of individuals, a better understanding of the motives that drive them seems essential.

Unfortunately, the management of young people who make attempts often appears to be inadequate. We have emphasized the need for a very careful assessment in each case, preferably in the general hospital, and the importance of interviewing relatives and friends. Arrangements for after-care need to be flexible, taking the adolescent's expressed needs firmly into account. A few cases will require inpatient psychiatric hospital treatment. Substantially more may benefit from outpatient or home-based counseling, in which other family members are involved where appropriate. Some cases can be returned to the care of their family doctor without special other after-care arrangements.

There is obviously considerable room for further research into suicidal behavior among young people. First, more must be known about the motivational aspects; for example, it is unclear whether adolescent suicide attempters differ from other adolescents in their coping responses to stressful events. Second, there is a remarkable absence of research into the effectiveness of different forms of after-care following suicide attempts by young people. Third, more information is required about both the short- and long-term outcome of suicide attempts, especially the subsequent social adjustment and psychiatric morbidity, and the incidence of repeated attempts and eventual suicide. Finally, in terms of prevention of both attempted suicide and completed suicide by children and adolescents, we appear to be only at the stage of conjecturing about possible strategies rather than being able to offer firm guidelines based on research findings.

ACKNOWLEDGMENTS

Results of our own research included in this chapter were obtained in investigations carried out with other colleagues, namely, Deborah Cole, Michael Goldacre, John O'Grady, and Joan Fagg, whose collaboration we gratefully acknowledge. We also thank the editor of the *British Journal of Psychiatry* for kind permission to publish Tables 2, 3, and 4.

5. References

Atkinson, M. W. *Ethnomethodology: A new perspective in the sociological analysis of suicide and crisis intervention.* Paper presented at 8th International Congress on Suicide Prevention, Jerusalem, 1975.

Atkinson, M. W., Kessel, W. I. N., & Dalgaard, J. B. The comparability of suicide rates. *British Journal of Psychiatry*, 1975, *127*, 247–256.

Bagley, C. Suicidal behaviour and suicidal ideation in adolescents: A problem for counsellors in education. *British Journal of Guidance and Counselling*, 1975, *3*, 190–208.

Bancroft, J., & Marsack, P. The repetitiveness of self-poisoning and self-injury. *British Journal of Psychiatry*, 1977, *131*, 394–399.

Bancroft, J., Skrimshire, A., Reynolds, F., Simkin, S., & Smith, J. Self-poisoning and self-injury in the Oxford area: Epidemiological aspects 1969–1973. *British Journal of Preventive and Social Medicine*, 1975, *29*, 170–177.

Bancroft, J., Hawton, K., Simkin, S., Kingston, B., Cumming, C., & Whitewell, D. The reasons people give for taking overdoses: A further enquiry. *British Journal of Medical Psychology*, 1979, *52*, 353–365.

Barraclough, B., Bunch, J., Nelson, B., & Sainsbury, P. A hundred cases of suicide: Clinical aspects. *British Journal of Psychiatry*, 1974, *25*, 355–373.

Barter, J. T., Swaback, D. O., & Todd, D. Adolescent suicide attempts: A follow-up study of hospitalized patients. *Archives of General Psychiatry*, 1968, *19*, 523–527.

Beck, A. T., Schuyler, R. D., & Herman, J. Development of suicidal intent scales. In A. T. Beck, H. L. P. Resnick, & D. J. Lettieri (Eds.), *The prediction of suicide*. Illinois: Charles Press, 1974.

Beck, A. T., Kovacs, M., & Weissman, A. Hopelessness and suicidal behaviour. An overview. *Journal of the American Medical Association*, 1975, *234*, 1146–1149.

Bergstrand, C. G., & Otto, U. Suicidal attempts in adolescence and childhood. *Acta Paediatrica*, 1962, *51*, 17–26.

Bridge, T. P., Potkin, S. G., Zung, W. W. K., & Soldo, B. J. Suicide prevention centres: Ecological study of effectiveness. *Journal of Nervous and Mental Diseases*, 1977, *164*, 18–24.

British Medical Journal. Children and parasuicide. 1981, *283*, 337–338.

Brooke, E., & Atkinson, M. W. Ascertainment of deaths from suicide. *Public Health Paper No. 38*. Geneva: World Health Organization, 1974.

Buglass, D., & Horton, J. A scale for predicting subsequent suicidal behaviour. *British Journal of Psychiatry*, 1974, *124*, 573–578.

Buglass, D., & McCulloch, J. W. Further suicidal behaviour: The development and validation of predictive scales. *British Journal of Psychiatry*, 1970, *116*, 483–491.

Cantwell, D. P., & Carlson, G. Problems and prospects in the study of childhood depression. *Journal of Nervous and Mental Disease*, 1979, *167*, 523–529.

Chia, B. H. Suicide of the young in Singapore. *Annals of the Academy of Medicine*, 1979, *8*, 262–268.

Choquet, M., Facy, F., & Davidson, F. Suicide and attempted suicide among adolescents in France. In R. D. T. Farmer & S. Hirsch (Eds.), *The suicide syndrome*. London: Cambridge University Press, 1980.

Connell, P. H. Suicidal attempts in childhood and adolescence. In J. G. Howell (Ed.), *Modern perspectives in child psychiatry*. Edinburgh: Oliver and Boyd, 1965.

Davidson, D. G. D., & Eastham, W. N. Acute liver necrosis following overdose of paracetamol. *British Medical Journal*, 1966, *2*, 497–499.

Douglas, J. D. *The social meanings of suicide*. Princeton: Princeton University Press, 1967.

Dublin, L. J. *Suicide: A sociological and statistical study*. New York: Ronald, 1963.

Fogelman, K. *Britain's sixteen year olds*. London: National Children's Bureau, 1976.

Fox, K., & Weissman, M. Suicide attempts and drugs: Contradiction between method and intent. *Social Psychiatry*, 1975, *10*, 31–38.

Garfinkel, B. D., Froese, A., & Golombek, H. Suicidal behaviour in a paediatric population. In *Proceedings of the 10th National Congress for Suicide Prevention and Crisis Intervention*, 1979, 305–312.

Gazzard, B. G., Davis, M., Spooner, J., & Williams, R., Why do people use paracetamol for suicide? *British Medical Journal*, 1976, *1*, 212–213.

Goldacre, M., & Hawton, K. Repetition of self-poisoning and subsequent death in adolescents who take overdoses. Submitted for publication.

Green, A. H. Self-destructive behavior in battered children. *American Journal of Psychiatry*, 1978, *135*, 579–582.

Haldane, J. D., & Haider, I. Attempted suicide in children and adolescents. *British Journal of Clinical Practice*, 1967, *21*, 587–589.

Hawton, K. Deliberate self-poisoning and self-injury in the psychiatric hospital. *British Journal of Medical Psychology*, 1978, *51*, 253–259.

Hawton, K., & Catalan, J. *Attempted suicide: A practical guide to its nature and management.* Oxford: Oxford University Press, 1982.

Hawton, K., & Goldacre, M. Hospital admission for adverse effects of medicinal agents (mainly self-poisoning) among adolescents in the Oxford region. *British Journal of Psychiatry*, 1982, *141*, 166–170.

Hawton, K., Marsack, P., & Fagg, J. The attitudes of psychiatrists to deliberate self-poisoning: Comparison with physicians and nurses. *British Journal of Medical Psychology*, 1981, *54*, 341–347.

Hawton, K., Cole, D., O'Grady, J., & Osborn, M. Motivational aspects of deliberate self-poisoning in adolescents. *British Journal of Psychiatry*, 1982, *141*, 286–291.

Hawton, K., O'Grady, J., Osborn, M., & Cole, D. Adolescents who take overdoses: Their characteristics, problems and contacts with helping agencies. *British Journal of Psychiatry*, 1982, *140*, 118–123.

Hawton, K., Osborn, M., O'Grady, J., & Cole, D. Classification of adolescents who take overdoses. *British Journal of Psychiatry*, 1982, *140*, 124–131.

Headlam, H. K., Goldsmith, J., Hanenson, I. B., & Rauh, J. L. Demographic characteristics of adolescents with self-poisoning. A survey of 235 instances in Cincinnati, Ohio. *Clinical Pediatrics*, 1979, *18*, 147–154.

Holinger, P. C. Adolescent suicide: An epidemiological study of recent trends. *American Journal of Psychiatry*, 1978, *135*, 754–756.

Holinger, P. C. Violent deaths among the young: Recent trends in suicide, homicide and accidents. *American Journal of Psychiatry*, 1979, *136*, 1144–1147.

Holinger, P. C. Self-destructiveness among the young: An epidemiological study of violent deaths. *International Journal of Social Psychiatry*, 1981, *27*, 277–282.

Jacobs, G. *Adolescent suicide.* New York: Wiley–Interscience, 1971.

Jacobziner, H. Attempted suicides in adolescence. *Journal of the American Medical Association*, 1965, *161*, 101–105.

Kreitman, N. (Ed.), *Parasuicide.* London: Wiley, 1977.

Kreitman, N., & Schreiber, M. Parasuicide in young Edinburgh women, 1968–75. *Psychological Medicine*, 1979, *9*, 469–479.

Leese, S. M. Suicide behaviour in twenty adolescents. *British Journal of Psychiatry*, 1969, *115*, 479–480.

Lester, D. Effect of suicide prevention centres on suicide rates in the United States. *Health Services Reports*, 1974, *89*, 37–39.

Levenson, M., & Neuringer, C. Problem-solving behaviour in suicidal adolescents. *Journal of Consulting and Clinical Psychology*, 1971, *37*, 433–436.

Lukianowicz, N. Attempted suicide in children. *Acta Psychiatrica Scandinavica*, 1968, 415–435.

Margolin, N. L., & Teicher, J. D. Thirteen adolescent male suicide attempts. *Journal of the American Academy of Child Psychiatry*, 1968, *7*, 296–315.

Mattsson, A., Seese, L. R., & Hawkins, J. W. Suicidal behavior as a child psychiatric emergency. *Archives of General Psychiatry*, 1969, *20*, 100–109.

McAnarney, E. R. Adolescent and young adult suicide in the United States—A reflection of societal unrest? *Adolescence*, 1979, *14*, 765–774.

McCarthy, P. D., & Walsh, D. Suicide in Dublin: I. The under-reporting of suicide and the consequences for national statistics. *British Journal of Psychiatry*, 1975, *126*, 301–308.

McDonald, A. Statistics of child suicide. *Publications of American Statistical Association Publications, New Series*, 1906/7, *10*, 260–264.

Meares, R., Mendelsohn, F. A. O., & Milgrom-Friedman, J. A sex difference in the seasonal variation of suicide rate: A single cycle for men, two cycles for women. *British Journal of Psychiatry*, 1981, *138*, 321–325.

Mehr, M., Zeltzer, L. K., & Robinson, R. Continued self-destructive behaviors in adolescent suicide attemptors: Part 1. *Journal of Adolescent Health Care*, 1981, *1*, 269–274.

Mehr, M., Zeltzer, L. K., & Robinson, R. Continued self-destructive behaviors in adolescent suicide attemptors. Part II: A pilot study. *Journal of Adolescent Health Care*, 1982, *2*, 183–187.

Morgan, H. G. *Death wishes? The understanding and management of deliberate self-harm.* Chichester: Wiley, 1979.

Mulcock, D. Juvenile suicide: A study of suicide and attempted suicide over a 16-year period. *The Medical Officer*, 1955, 155–160.

Nardini-Maillard, D., & Ladame, F. G. The results of a follow-up study of suicidal adolescents. *Journal of Adolescence*, 1980, *3*, 253–260.

Offer, D., & Barglow, P. Adolescent and young adult self-mutilation incidents in a general psychiatric hospital. *Archives of General Psychiatry*, 1960, *3*, 102–112.

Office of Population Censuses and Surveys. *Mortality Statistics: Cause.* London: Her Majesty's Stationery Office, 1977–1981.

Otto, U. Suicidal acts by children and adolescents. *Acta Psychiatrica Scandinavica*, 1972, Supplement 233.

Ovenstone, I. M. K. A psychiatric approach to the diagnosis of suicide and its effect upon the Edinburgh statistics. *British Journal of Psychiatry*, 1973, *123*, 15–21.

Parker, A. The meaning of attempted suicide to young parasuicides: A repertory grid study. *British Journal of Psychiatry*, 1981, *139*, 306–312.

Petzel, S. V., & Cline, D. W. Adolescent suicide: Epidemiological and biological aspects. *Adolescent Psychiatry*, 1978, *6*, 239–266.

Pfeffer, C. R., Conte, H. R., Plutchik, R., & Jerrett, I. Suicidal behaviour in latency-age children. *Journal of the American Academy of Child Psychiatry*, 1979, *18*, 679–692.

Pfeffer, C. R., Conte, H. R., Plutchik, R., & Jerrett, I. Suicidal behaviour in latency-age children: An out-patient population. *Journal of the American Academy of Child Psychiatry*, 1980, *19*, 703–710.

Ramon, S., Bancroft, J. H. J., & Skrimshire, A. M. Attitudes towards self-poisoning among physicians and nurses in a general hospital. *British Journal of Psychiatry*, 1975, *127*, 257–264.

Richman, J. The family therapy of attempted suicide. *Family Process*, 1979, *18*, 131–142.

Roberts, J., & Hawton, K. Child abuse and attempted suicide. *British Journal of Psychiatry*, 1980, *137*, 319–323.

Rohn, R. D., Sarles, R. M., Kenny, T. J., Reynolds, B. J., & Head, F. P. Adolescents who attempt suicide. *Journal of Pediatrics*, 1977, *90*, 636–638.

Rosenthal, R. J., Rinzler, C., & Klausner, E. Wrist-cutting syndrome: The meaning of a gesture. *American Journal of Psychiatry*, 1972, *128*, 1363–1368.

Sainsbury, P., & Barraclough, B. M. Differences between suicide rates. *Nature*, 1968, *220*, 1252.

Sanborn, D., Sanborn, C., & Cimbolic, P. Two years of suicide: A study of adolescent suicide in New Hampshire. *Child Psychiatry and Human Development*, 1973, *3*, 234–242.

Sathyavathi, K. Suicide among children in Bangalore. *Indian Journal of Paediatrics*, 1975, *42*, 149–157.

Seiden, R. H. Suicide among youth. *Supplement to the Bulletin of Suicidology*, 1969.

Seiden, R. H. Why are suicides of young Blacks increasing? *H.S.M.H.A., Health Report*, 1972, *87*, 3–8.

Shaffer, D. Suicide in childhood and early adolescence. *Journal of Child Psychology and Psychiatry*, 1974, *15*, 275–291.

Shaffer, D., & Fisher, P. The epidemiology of suicide in children and young adolescents. *Journal of the American Academy of Child Psychology*, 1981, *20*, 545–565.

Simpson, M. A. Self-mutilation in a general hospital setting. *Canadian Psychiatric Association Journal*, 1975, *20*, 429–433.

Simpson, M. A. Self-mutilation. *Hospital Medicine*, 1976, *16*, 430–438.

Stanley, E. J., & Barter, J. T. Adolescent suicidal behavior. *American Journal of Orthopsychiatry*, 1970, *40*, 87–96.

Stengel, C., & Cook, N. G. *Attempted suicide: Its social significance and effects.* Maudsley Monography Number 4. London: Oxford University Press, 1958.

Toolan, J. M. Depression in childhood and adolescents. *American Journal of Orthopsychiatry*, 1962, *32*, 404–415.

Tuckman, J., & Connon, H. E. Attempted suicide in adolescents. *American Journal of Psychiatry*, 1962, *119*, 228–232.

U.S. Department of Health, Education, and Welfare. *Suicide and homicide and alcoholism among American Indians: Guidelines for help.* Publication No. (ADM) 74-42. Rockville, Md.: Author, 1973.

Walker, W. L. Intentional self-injury in school age children. *Journal of Adolescence*, 1980, *3*, 217–228.

Weissman, M. M. The epidemiology of suicide attempts, 1960 to 1971. *Archives of General Psychiatry*, 1974, *30*, 737–746.

Wexler, L., Weissman, M. M., & Kasl, S. V. Suicide attempts 1970–75: Updating a United States study and comparisons with international trends. *British Journal of Psychiatry*, 1978, *132*, 180–185.

White, H. C. Self-poisoning in adolescents. *British Journal of Psychiatry*, 1974, *124*, 24–35.

Whitehead, P. C., Johnson, F. G., & Ferrence, R. Measuring the incidence of self-injury: Some methodological and design considerations. *American Journal of Orthopsychiatry*, 1973, *43*, 142–148.

4   The Legacy of Parental Divorce

A Nationwide Study of Family Status and Selected Mediating Variables on Children's Academic and Social Competencies

JOHN GUIDUBALDI, JOSEPH D. PERRY,
AND HELEN K. CLEMINSHAW

1. Introduction

The impact of parental divorce on children has recently become an area of primary concern for a variety of professionals in psychology and education. This interdisciplinary consensus has been generated in part by alarming census descriptions of changing adult lifestyles (e.g., Bronfenbrenner, 1979; Guidubaldi, 1980). For example, recent reports indicate that the divorce ratio has more than doubled from 1970 to 1981 and more than tripled since 1960. Since these figures do not account for those who were divorced and remarried at the time of the survey, they actually underestimate the total incidence of divorce in our society (U.S. Bureau of the Census, 1982b). Similarly, the incidence of single-parent child rearing has also increased markedly from 11.9% in 1970 to 20.1% in 1981. Again, these figures do not include those who have previously

Excerpts of this report were presented at the fifteenth annual convention of the National Association of School Psychologists (NASP), March, 1983, Detroit, Michigan, and published previously in NASP's *School Psychology Review* (Summer, 1983).

JOHN GUIDUBALDI • Department of Early Childhood Education, Kent State University, Kent, Ohio 44240.   JOSEPH D. PERRY • Department of Pediatrics, Tod Babies and Children's Hospital, Youngstown, Ohio 44501; and Department of Psychiatry, Northeastern Ohio Universities College of Medicine, Rootstown, Ohio 44272.   HELEN K. CLEMINSHAW • Department of Home Economics and Family Ecology, University of Akron, Akron, Ohio 44304. This research has been jointly supported by the National Association of School Psychologists, Kent State University, and the William T. Grant Foundation.

experienced a single-parent situation but are now living in reconstituted two-parent families. In fact, the Census Bureau estimates that in 1977, 10% of children living with two parents were living in a household with a stepparent. Single-parent families resulting specifically from divorce or separation have increased by 111% since 1970, and 90% of one-parent families are now headed by mothers. However, the percentage of father-custody households has not increased in the past decade (U.S. Bureau of the Census, 1979, 1982a, 1982b). Projecting future trends, Glick and Norton (1979) estimate that if these levels of divorce continue, 40% of current marriages will end in divorce, and Hetherington (1979a) reports a projection that 40% to 50% of children born in the past decade will spend some time living in a single-parent family.

Practitioners have also been sensitized by first-hand experience in clinics and schools where maladaptive child behaviors appear disproportionately among children from divorced-family households. Professionals in these applied settings have, however, received very limited help from researchers, who have only recently begun to study the relationship between divorce and subsequent child adjustment. Moreover, those studies reported in the literature have routinely been criticized for serious methodological weaknesses.

2. Previous Research Findings

In an *Advances in Clinical Child Psychology* review article 2 years ago, Atkeson, Forehand, and Rickard (1982) note that their chapter entitled "The Effects of Divorce on Children" might be considered premature given the limited set of research studies available. However, they appropriately suggest that critical examination of existing studies may correct the misguided assumption that prevailing conclusions are well supported by research. The Atkeson *et al.* review, as well as others done recently (Clingempeel & Reppucci, 1982; Emery, 1982; Hetherington, 1979b; Kurdek, 1981, 1983; Levitin, 1979; Shinn, 1978), conclude that existing studies are flawed by limited data-gathering procedures, biased sample selection inadequate or nonexistent controls, and other serious methodological weaknesses. Considering the magnitude of this change in family stability and the historical centrality of nuclear family structure as the basis for socialization of children, it is surprising that so little has been done to provide an empirical understanding of the impact of parental divorce on children.

Two major longitudinal studies are typically cited as having contributed the most to our understanding of children's adjustment to divorce (Hetherington, Cox, & Cox, 1978, 1979a, 1979b, 1982; Kelly & Wallerstein, 1976; Wallerstein & Kelly, 1974, 1975, 1976, 1980a, 1980b). More recently, an additional series of multidimensional longitudinal research has been reported (Kurdek & Berg, 1983; Kurdek, Blisk, & Siesky, 1981; Kurdek & Siesky, 1980a, 1980b). The impressive consensus of these studies is that divorce results in negative stresses for both children and parents. These major studies are emphasized here since the intent of the present investigation is to focus on children's adjustment specifically due to divorce rather than father absence or single-parent status, which can be caused by such other factors as unmarried mothers, death of a parent, or separation (see Biller, 1976; and Lamb, 1981, 1982, for reviews of father-absence literature).

The often cited longitudinal work of Wallerstein and Kelly (1974, 1975, 1976, 1980a, 1980b) suggests that children of divorce adjust and respond differentially by age level. Their original study was based on a sample of 131 children aged 2½ through 18 years of age from 60 divorced families residing in California. The primary assessment of the children's responses to divorce was made through the interviewing of family members conducted just after the separation and then 1 and 5 years following the divorce. Their basic initial findings (1974, 1975, 1976) in terms of characteristic responses and behavioral changes were as follows: (a) young preschoolers (2½–3¼ years) demonstrated regressive behavior; (b) middle preschoolers (3¾–4¾ years) displayed irritability, aggressive behavior, self-blame, and bewilderment; (c) oldest preschoolers (5–6 years) showed increased anxiety and aggressive behavior; (d) younger latency-aged children (7–8 years) responded with sadness, grieving, fear, fantasies of responsibility and reconciliation, anger, and loyalty to both parents; (e) older latency-aged children (9–10 years) portrayed feelings of loss, rejection, helplessness, loneliness, shame, anger, and loyalty conflicts; and (f) adolescents (11 years and over) illustrated sadness, shame, embarrassment, anxiety about future and marriage, worry, individuation from parents, and withdrawal.

A follow-up study on the preschoolers by Wallerstein and Kelly (1975) found that much of this negative behavior ended a year later in those children whose caregiver environments were stable. However, 44% of the children in this age group experienced a deteriorated psychological condition at follow-up. In particular, girls were especially vulnerable to depressive reactions and/or developmental delays.

Although intensive feelings had abated for younger latency-aged children at one year after divorce, 23% of this group were evaluated as in a deteriorated psychological condition (Wallerstein & Kelly, 1976). By comparison, 50% of older latency-aged children at 1-year follow-up appeared to have achieved equilibrium in their lives and accepted the divorce with some sense of finality; however, 50% still displayed troublesome, depressive behavior patterns. With regard to a 1-year follow-up for adolescents, Wallerstein and Kelly (1974) report that by contrast to latency-aged children, adolescents were able to avoid loyalty conflicts, often by distancing themselves from both parents.

Perhaps the most interesting results are presented by the 5-year follow-up study done by Wallerstein and Kelly (1980b). Basically, seven variables were identified as having a positive effect on children's adjustment to divorce. They include: (a) parental ability to resolve postdivorce conflict and anger; (b) ability of the custodial parent to resume the parenting role successfully; (c) ability of the noncustodial parent to keep a mutually satisfying relationship with the child; (d) personality characteristics of the child and the ability to develop coping skills; (e) ability of the child to find and use support systems; (f) diminished depressive or angry responses by the child; and (g) age and sex of the child. These researchers further report that boys from divorced families appear to need a positive relationship with their fathers more than do girls of divorce.

In an attempt to compensate for the weaknesses and methodological problems found in the Wallerstein and Kelly research (1974, 1975, 1976), Hetherington, Cox, and Cox (1978) employed a more comprehensive, multivariate 2-year study concerning the impact of divorce on children. Their research included a sample of 48 divorced and 48 intact middle-class families and their preschool-aged children. The families were matched by age, sex, birth order, and nursery school attendance of the child, and by parents' age, education, and length of marriage. The assessment devices included parental interviews, structured diary records, laboratory and home observations of parent-child interactions, observations of child–teacher and child–peer interactions in school, checklists and ratings of the child's behavior by parents and teachers, and personality tests and self-report ratings by parents. Finally, child development measures were utilized which assessed sex-role typing, cognitive performance, and social development.

Essentially, the results illustrate the severe stress and disorganization experienced by families during the first year following divorce (Hetherington, Cox, & Cox, 1978, 1979a, 1979b, 1982). Coping patterns of parents, interpersonal relationships and parenting approaches were analyzed. In general, divorced parents were less able to cope with their parenting tasks. They made fewer maturity demands on their children and illustrated less consistency in disciplining, reasoning, and communicating with their children. They also demonstrated less interaction and affection toward their children. Children from these divorced families displayed higher levels of dependent, disobedient, aggressive, demanding, unaffectionate, and whining behavior as compared to children from intact families. Mother–son interactions were especially affected by a decline in the mother's parenting skills, in that increased aggressive behavior was associated with increased coercive parental behavior, which in turn increased sons' negative behavior and mothers' feelings of helplessness and incompetence.

The results of the Hetherington, Cox, and Cox (1978) 2-year follow-up study indicated that most of the initial debilitating effects of divorce were abated. They further cited low postdivorce conflict between parents and general agreement with regard to child-rearing techniques as the major factors associated with less profound and less prolonged disorganization and stress for parents and children. Thus, it appeared that by the 2nd year following divorce, both adjustment and equilibrium were being established.

More recently, Kurdek and associates conducted ongoing studies of 70 children from divorced homes, emphasizing the importance of children's social and cognitive skills that moderate divorce adjustment (Kurdek & Berg, 1983; Kurdek, Blisk, & Siesky, 1981; Kurdek & Siesky, 1980a, 1980b). Children who view consequences as within their locus of control and who accurately comprehend interpersonal relations were found more likely to accomplish a positive divorce adjustment. The home environment factors related to positive divorce consequences were low interparental stress and quality of relationship between the child and noncustodial parent. Characteristics of mothers who were successful custodial parents included effective use of support systems, reduced stress level, and positive adjustment relative to divorce. These studies have consistently indicated that younger children experience greater divorce-related problems than older children.

Other recent studies with a more restricted scope have identified further data about parent–child relationships and family conditions that influence the impact of divorce on children. In brief, children's divorce adjustment was found to be facilitated by authoritative management style of the custodial parent (Santrock & Warshak, 1979); residing with a custodial parent of the same sex (Warshak & Santrock, 1983); availability of the noncustodial parent and positive relations between parents (Hess & Camara, 1979; Rosen, 1977); parent–child discussions of divorce-related topics (Jacobson, 1978a, 1978b); low interparental hostility prior to separation (Berg & Kelly, 1979; Jacobson, 1978a, 1978b, 1978c); and more time with father after separation (Jacobson, 1978a, 1978c). These studies have also provided general corroborative findings that divorce presents significant stressors for children and their parents.

It should be noted that several studies have produced contradictory results which further complicate the issues. Whereas the above studies report a negative impact, others report no difference and even positive effects of divorce on children's adjustment (Bernard & Nesbitt, 1981; Colletta, 1979; Kurdek & Siesky, 1980b; Reinhard, 1977; Rosen, 1977). This may be due to the limited scope of criterion measures employed in these studies, which included only child questionnaire and interview data. Further, these studies did not include a control group of intact-family children to investigate effects of divorce more directly. Kurdek *et al.* (1981) found discrepancies between the reports of children's divorce-related adjustment by custodial parents and children. A caution concerning the utilization of children's self-report data was recorded by Warshak and Santrock (1983): "Can the failure to report negative perceptions be the result of defensive responding?" (p. 32).

3. Limitations of Previous Research

The principal methodological limitation of these major studies, as well as other related studies, is restricted samples. Sample selections have been small, based on ambiguous criteria, and limited to specific settings or geographic areas rather than representing the general population. For example, related studies have samples described as follows: 96 families from a white, middle-class preschool center in Virginia (Hetherington *et al.*, 1978, 1979a, 1979b, 1982); 30 families from a mental health center in Los Angeles (Jacobson, 1978a, 1978b, 1978c); 74 families from a Dayton, Ohio chapter of Parents Without Partners (Kurdek *et al.*, 1981); and 60 families from Marin County, California (Wallerstein & Kelly, 1975, 1976, 1980a). Samples almost exclusively represent Caucasian, middle- and upper-class families wherein the mother had child custody. These studies have utilized samples described as nonclinical, although selection was based on such biased criteria as volunteers from clinics or agencies. Other related studies include only clinical populations (e.g., Kalter, 1977; McDermott, 1970; Westman, 1972). Emery (1982) suggests that unknown mediating variables may account for children's divorce-related problems in clinic samples. There is a general lack of control groups, and the one employed by Hetherington *et al.* (1978, 1979a, 1979b, 1982) was matched to a possibly biased divorced group sample. Considering such severe sampling limitations, results of previous studies cannot be generalized to the total population of divorced families. More importantly, the many potential environmental mediating variables indicated to be critical for understanding children's divorce adjustment are not adequately controlled. That is, the middle-class populations of previous research lack variability in such factors as community social support systems, school environments, ethnic background, socioeconomic status, and culture that impinge on the experience of divorce and its impact on children.

The few related large-scale studies also have serious limitations. The study of 18,000 students from 14 states conducted jointly by the National Association of Elementary and Secondary Principals and The Kettering Foundation (Brown, 1980; Lazarus, 1980; Zakariya, 1982) indicated impaired school performance of children from one-parent, in comparison to two-parent, families. This study utilized global school criteria such as grade point average, attendance, suspensions, truancy, and referral for discipline problems rather than more specific measures of academic or social competencies. A further limitation is that one-parent families were defined as resulting from multiple factors, and two-parent families included remarried family units. Similarly, data based on 7,119 children included in a Health Examination Survey in 1963–1965 reported that father-absent children have lower Wechsler Intelligence Scale for Children (WISC) and Wide Range Achievement Test (WRAT) performance than father-present children when socioeconomic status (SES) and divorce were not controlled (Svanum, Bringle, & McLaughlin, 1982). Socioeconomic measures were found to be important intervening variables in both of these studies but were either based on data from the 1960s (Svanum et al., 1982) or defined as children's participation in supported lunch programs (Brown, 1980). Hence these studies were poorly controlled and cannot be considered an assessment of children's adjustment specifically due to divorce.

Data from another large-scale study, not specifically designed to assess the impact of divorce, provide evidence of differences in the reported incidence of biosocial and developmental problems between children from divorced and intact families (Task Force on Pediatric Education, 1978). This study was based on a nationwide survey of 1,201 mothers. For school-aged children, 26% of divorced mothers in comparison to only 7.8% of married mothers reported emotional problems. Differences in other child problem areas reported by mothers from divorced versus intact homes include 23% versus 14.9% for behavior disorders, 23% versus 13.8% for learning difficulties, and 19.7% versus 8.9% for impaired social relationships with peers, teachers, and parents. For divorced versus married mothers of preschool children, differences include 28.2% versus 13.4% for impaired growth and development, 15.5% versus 9.6% for behavioral problems, and 19.7% versus 6.5% for learning difficulties. The consistent pattern of differences indicates that children from divorced homes continue to experience difficulties from infancy through 20 years of age. It should be emphasized that these results were supplemental findings without control for mediating variables and with confounding of the definition of divorce by inclusion of remarried mothers.

A second major limitation of previous research is the lack of psychometrically adequate indices of school-aged children's cognitive and social competencies used to document their divorce adjustment. In relation to preschool children, Hetherington *et al.* (1982) had utilized multiple evaluative procedures (i.e., observations, ratings, and psychometric assessments) and multigroup input (i.e., child, parent, and teacher). However, typically, measures used to illustrate school-aged children's divorce adjustment were clinical impressions, interview and rating data which generally lack standardization as well as established reliability and validity (Jacobson, 1978a, 1979b, 1979c; Kelly & Wallerstein, 1976; Kurdek & Berg, 1983; Kurdek *et al.*, 1981; Kurdek & Siesky, 1980a, 1980b; Wallerstein & Kelly, 1980b). Achenbach (1978) criticized existing clinical assessments, indicating that there is currently no adequate classification system for children's mental disorders. Kurdek (1983) further emphasized that the clinical interview may not be sensitive to developmental levels of children since it typically is employed to elicit criteria for disorders, with implications for mental health intervention rather than school-related intervention.

Closely related is the scarcity of data concerning how the school climate may moderate adverse effects of divorce. Hetherington (1979) notes that "the role of extra-familial supports, peers, schools, neighborhoods, the church, and social groups such as clubs or athletic groups has barely been touched on" (p. 36, manuscript). Clearly, school-based support for children of divorce is a priority intervention, but we currently lack a detailed understanding of school-related criteria and school environments that may promote positive adjustment.

A further methodological problem has been the failure of many previous studies to control simultaneously for SES, age, and sex (McDermott, 1968; Morrison, 1974; Sugar, 1970; Tucker & Regan, 1966; Westman *et al.*, 1970). To add to the difficulties of interpretation, inconsistent findings have been reported concerning age and sex differences. For example, Kurdek *et al.* (1981) and Reinhard (1977) have not found sex differences, whereas other studies have found boys from divorced homes to experience greater difficulty both socially and cognitively (Hetherington *et al.*, 1982; Kurdek & Berg, 1983; Wallerstein & Kelly, 1980a, 1980b).

Age at time of divorce and length of time expired since divorce are two additional issues for which confusion exists. Wallerstein and Kelly (1980b) indicate that divorce is related to negative adjustment at all age levels studied (preschool through adolescence) though the manifested behaviors differ depending on age at the time of the divorce, and reactions are most acute at the youngest ages. Reinhard (1977), on the other hand, indicates that 12- to 18-year-olds do not demonstrate divorce-related maladjustment, and Kurdek, Blisk, and Siesky (1981) conclude that older children are better adjusted to their parents' divorce. However, the interaction of duration of time expired since divorce with age at time of divorce was not controlled in any of these studies. In reference to the former issue, Hetherington, Cox, and Cox (1982) conclude that adjustment is a function of both sex and duration of time since divorce, with girls making earlier adjustments while negative effects for boys are "more pervasive and long lasting" (p. 261). Further confusion emanates from Wallerstein and Kelly (1975) who, on the basis of a very small sample of preschoolers, contend that girls display more adverse effects than boys at a one-year follow-up evaluation.

The major studies, unfortunately, have also been unable to determine whether children's adjustment was merely a reaction to decreased family income, since families were almost exclusively from the middle social class. Other studies have indicated that declining SES accounts for the deleterious impact of single-parent status resulting from a divorce (Colletta, 1979; Svanum et al., 1982). Hence, there are many critical questions yet to be answered concerning children's divorce adjustment.

In order to provide more definitive conclusions about the impact of parental divorce on children and to unravel the complex effects of potential mediating factors such as social class, sex, age, and family support systems, methodological refinements are clearly needed. The current study employs improved sampling techniques, a nationwide sample, a carefully selected control group, and multifactored assessments conducted by highly trained evaluators in an attempt to promote a more comprehensive understanding of this critical mental health issue.

4. Involvement of the National Association of School Psychologists

The senior author designed and initiated this study during his term as president of the National Association of School Psychologists (NASP). Initial reports of the major findings of the study have therefore appeared in NASP publications (Guidubaldi, 1983; Guidubaldi, Cleminshaw, Perry, & Mcloughlin, 1983). Many of the 8,000 NASP members had been previously sensitized to the importance of this research issue because their caseloads included increasingly large numbers of divorced-family children. Similar to clinical child psychologists, this group of professionals was acutely aware that little conclusive research evidence existed to facilitate effective interventions for these children. Yet school psychologists were in optimal employment situations to perform such research on a nationwide basis. Relative to other professionals in education, they had unique assessment skills, better understanding of child development principles, and access to home environments. Relative to other psychologists, they had an understanding of school environments, greater support from school administrators, established relationships with teachers, and increased access to samples of normal children. Their employment in schools further provided the opportunity to implement data-based interventions in both home and school environments.

5. Methods

5.1. Sample Selection

In an attempt to develop a geographically stratified sample of evaluators, NASP members were randomly selected from the association's membership roster by state in proportion to state population. Of approximately 1,500 selected, 144 psychologists from 38 states agreed to participate in the study. Each of these evaluators randomly selected an elementary school within their school district and then randomly selected a total of six children from grade lists: two 1st-graders, two 3rd-graders, and two 5th-graders. One child from each grade level represented an intact-family situation (both biological parents present since birth of the child) and the other a currently divorced single-parent family. Some psychologists were unable to provide data on all subjects by the deadline for the study. Consequently, a total of 699 children were involved in the study as a function of grade level and marital status of parents. The geographic distribution of the sample is described in Table 1. Although close correspondence to census figures was not achieved in every region, this sample clearly is nationwide in scope and is matched within eight percentage points in seven of the nine regions. Demographic characteristics of the sample are described in Table 2. As indicated, the sample was quite evenly divided by marital status, grade, and school characteristics and fairly evenly divided by sex and race. Males were somewhat overrepresented in the divorced group, and Caucasians were somewhat overrepresented in the intact sample.

5.2. Assessments

This study employed a multimethod and multifactored approach to evaluating children's intellectual, academic, social-behavioral, and

TABLE 1
Sample Description by Census Region

Census region	Region population (mil.)	Percentage of U.S. population	N in sample	Percentage of sample
New England	12.2	5.4	39	5.6
Mid-Atlantic	36.9	16.3	44	6.3
East North Central	41.7	18.4	247	35.3
West North Central	17.3	7.6	74	10.6
South Atlantic	36.8	16.2	142	20.3
East South Central	14.7	6.5	43	6.2
West South Central	23.7	10.5	21	3.0
Mountain	11.4	5.0	44	6.3
Pacific	31.8	14.0	45	6.4
1980 Census Total Population	226.5			
Total N = 699				

adaptive characteristics, as well as family and school environments (see Nay, 1979). In addition to psychometric measures, assessments included teacher rating scales, child and parent interviews, and parent satisfaction assessment. Data collected from school records were grades, attendance, standardized group test scores, and special services provided to the child. In addition, school and community environment variables were included. Providers of direct psychological services in the schools administered assessments, conducted interviews, and coordinated ratings.

To compensate for the acknowledged scarcity of well-standardized social-emotional and adaptive behavior instruments, this multisource approach was deemed necessary to provide internal validity checks and increase confidence in findings. It also provided opportunity to examine the complex interactions among environmental conditions that typically have been neglected in previous research. Furthermore, the composite data base utilized here parallels legally mandated multifactored assessment procedures employed by psychologists in schools (see Guidubaldi, Kehle, & Murray, 1979).

5.2.1. Psychometric Assessments

The Wechsler Intelligence Scale for Children—Revised (WISC-R; Wechsler, 1974) and Wide Range Achievement Test (WRAT; Jastak, Jastak, & Bijou, 1978) were administered by participating school psychol-

TABLE 2
Sample Description

Variable	Total		Intact		Divorced	
	N	Percentage	N	Percentage	N	Percentage
Parent						
Marital status	699	100.0	358	51.2	341	48.8
Child sex						
Male	365	52.2	180	50.3	185	54.3
Female	334	47.8	178	49.7	156	45.7
Grade						
1	235	33.6	120	33.5	115	33.7
3	234	33.5	118	33.0	116	34.0
5	320	32.9	120	33.5	110	32.3
Race						
Caucasian	615	88.0	322	89.9	293	85.9
Black	52	7.4	21	5.9	31	9.1
Hispanic	16	2.3	9	2.5	7	2.1
Other	5	.7	1	.3	4	1.2
No response	11	1.6	5	1.4	6	1.7
School location						
Urban	165	23.6	84	23.5	81	23.8
Suburban	303	43.3	157	43.9	146	42.8
Rural	217	31.0	111	31.0	106	31.1
No response	14	2.0	6	1.7	8	2.3
Type						
Public	676	96.7	346	96.6	330	96.8
Private	3	.4	2	.6	1	.2
Parochial	11	1.6	6	1.7	5	1.5
No response	9	1.3	4	1.1	5	1.5

ogists to gain well-established measures of intellectual and academic functioning.

5.2.2. Social-Behavioral Assessment

Assessment in this domain was especially comprehensive, involving ratings by psychologists, teachers, and parents as well as selected items from the child and parent interviews. In addition to direct child assessments, characteristics derived from parent and teacher rating data have been found to be reliable and valid in both clinical child psychology and educational psychology research. For example, Archenbach and Edelbrock (1978, 1981) found two general maladaptive factors in childhood pathology that are included in present ratings. These are overcontrol characteristics involving anxiety–withdrawal and undercontrol factors involving aggressive acting out and conduct disorders. It has also been well established that attentive, task-oriented behavior as well as positive social relationships predict academic success and adjustment in school (Bloom, 1976; Perry, Guidubaldi, & Kehle, 1979; Stevenson, Parker, Wilkinson, Hegion, & Fish, 1976). Therefore, parent and teacher measures incorporating these adaptive and maladaptive domains were included as primary assessments of social and behavioral competence. Instruments employed were the Hahnemann Elementary School Behavior Rating Scale (HESB) (Spivak & Swift, 1975), the Sells and Roff Peer Acceptance–Rejection Rating (PAR) (Sells & Roff, 1967), a locus of control measure derived from the Harvard Project on Family Stress (LC) (Belle, 1982), and an optimism–pessimism scale abridged from Stipek, Lamb, and Zigler (OPTI) (1981).

The Hahnemann Elementary School Behavior Rating Scale (HESB) is a 60-item scale with a scoring system for 16 subscales. The teacher rates either the frequency of occurrence of a behavioral item or the degree to which a given behavior describes the child. The 16 subscales include both task-related and interpersonal behaviors. Selection of this instrument was based in part on the relevance of the subscales for clustering into school-related and diagnostic clinical factors. The subscales related to school tasks are Originality, Independent Learning, Involvement, Productivity with Peers, Inattention, and Academic Achievement. The domains considered here to be associated with undercontrol or conduct disorders include Negative Feelings, Critical–Competitive, Social (Over) Involvement, and Unreflectiveness. Overcontrol or anxiety–withdrawal characteristics are defined as the profile pattern comprised of Failure Anxiety, Holding Back–Withdrawn, Intellectual Dependency, and low frequencies of Productivity with Peers.

The HESB was developed by the authors of the Devereux Elementary School Behavior Rating Scale (DESB) (Spivack & Swift, 1967). It was developed as an updated, more comprehensive measure of school adjustment, expanded to 60 items rather than the 47 items included in the DESB. Spivack and Swift (1975) reported that factor analytic studies for item selection included academic achievement, age, sex, and criteria of childhood psychiatric disorders. The behavioral factors included in the DESB and HESB have received extensive research attention (Schaefer, Baker, & Zawel, 1975; Spivack & Swift, 1966, 1973, 1977; Spivack & Spotts, 1966; Spivack, Seift, & Prewitt, 1972; Swift & Spivack, 1969a, 1969b, 1973; Swift, Spivack, & Back, 1973; Willis, Smithy, & Holliday, 1979). Item validity studies by Willis et al. (1979) corroborated the subscales included in the DESB and HESB described in factor analytic studies by Swift and Spivack (1973). However, Schaefer et al. (1975) indicated that the 47 items of the DESB were not adequate for 11 subscales. Despite such limitations, Willis *et al.* (1979) stated, "The Devereux, although it is not ideal by any means, is probably one of the best available instruments of its type" (p. 334). Although there are adequate reliability and validity data on the DESB, there is presently a lack of reliability and validity data specifically relevant to the HESB. The standardization sample of the HESB includes 1,664 children from the United States, Canada, and England.

Peer status ratings were provided by both teachers and parents. The teacher rating scale includes seven levels describing the degree to which the child is accepted or rejected by peers (Sells & Roff, 1967). Roff, Sells, and Golden (1972) report reliability of .58 to .75 and a correlation of .57 between peer choice and teacher ratings. Roff *et al.* also report that peer status in middle childhood was a significant predictor of adolescent delinquency and incidence of school dropout. Perry, Guidubaldi, and Kehle (1979) found that peer status as a measure of social competence in kindergarten was a significant predictor of third-grade achievement and adjustment. The parent rating of peer status used in this report was based on a parent interview item comprised of three levels that described quality of interaction. Other items from the parent and child interviews also related to this issue but are not included in current analyses.

Two personality dimensions that affect behavioral outcomes are locus of control and optimism versus pessimism. These measures were selected to identify children who characteristically are proactive, risk-taking and confident versus those who are withdrawn, self-protective, and lacking in positive affect. The locus of control measure used in this study was derived from the Harvard University Stress and Families Survey (Belle, 1982). It is comprised of 18 questions that require either a yes or a no response from the child. The questions relate to children's perception of their control over what happens to them. The scores from each item are added to derive a total score. Low total scores indicate low perceptions of internal control, and high scores reflect perceptions of greater internal control over life events.

Optimism and pessimism are evaluated in this study by an abridged version of the Optimism–Pessimism Scale (OPTI Scale) developed by Stipek, Lamb, and Zigler (1981). Ten short unfinished stories are presented to children and they are asked to provide one of two alternative endings to each story. These endings are evaluated in terms of positive (scored as 1) and negative (scored as 0) outcomes. The scores achieved on all 10 stories are summed and higher total scores reflect greater optimism.

5.2.3. Adaptive Behavior

A standardization edition of the Vineland Teacher Questionnaire (VTQ) developed by Sparrow, Balla, and Chicchetti (1981) was used as a measure of adaptive behavior. Form A, used for first grade, included 240 items. Form B included 199 items and was used for third- and fifth-grade children. The items are rated by teachers on a three-point scale ranging from "never or very seldom performs the activity" to "satisfactorily and habitually performs the activity." The items are divided into four factors of adaptive behavior representing daily living skills, socialization, communication, and motor skills.

5.2.4. Child Interview

All children were interviewed by school psychologists. The interview instrument employed was adapted from the Harvard University Stress and Families Survey (Belle, 1982). Structured questions were developed to assess Peer Relations and Parent–Child Relationships. Other relationships were also evaluated in reference to activities and interactions including resident adult, sibling, friend, and other adult. The Peer Relations section assessed both school and neighborhood peer relations. Each question was scored separately, with a higher score indicating positive relations and a lower score suggesting negative or no relations.

5.2.5. Parent Interview

Parents from both intact and divorced families were interviewed by school psychologists. The interview instrument utilized was a structured questionnaire designed to ascertain relevant family data. Five major areas were evaluated as follows: Family Environment, Support Systems, Quality of Life, Childrearing, and Divorce Arrangements. The Family Environment domain dealt with information on residence, family composition, work and social arrangements, marriage, and home routines. Data pertinent to relatives, friends, organizations, and activities as well as school assistance were included in Support Systems. The Quality of Life area pertained to family health, income level, transportation, and life changes. The section on Childrearing was divided in terms of the developmental level of the child (e.g., perinatal period) and included assessments of parental approaches to discipline and parent–child relations. The last section, Divorce, was given only to parents with divorced status. Questions were related to custody arrangements, pre-

and post-divorce interactions, and adaptations and responses to the divorce for both parent and child.

5.2.6. Parent Satisfaction Scale

The Parent Satisfaction Scale (PSS) (Cleminshaw & Guidubaldi, 1981) was given to all prents to complete and return to the school psychologist. It is a 50-item, Likert-type instrument designed to assess the parent's perception of satisfaction in the parent role. The scale is composed of five separate factors including: Spouse Support, Child–Parent Relationship, Parent Performance, Spouse Discipline and Control, and General Parenting Satisfaction. A separate score is derived for each factor as well as a total score for the entire test. The higher the total score, the greater the perceived parent satisfaction.

5.2.7. School Environment

General school characteristics included size of school population, type of school population (ethnic and racial background), setting of school (urban, suburban, rural), type of school (private, public, parochial), school organization (neighborhood, consolidated, number of grades within school building), and transportation to school (walking or number of miles by bus). The classroom characteristics included structure (open or traditional) and size of classroom population. Additional school and classroom climate criteria were derived from the "effective schools" research movement (e.g., Brookover & Lezotte, 1977; Edmunds & Frederikesen, 1978). These were labeled as follows: safe and orderly environment, clear school mission, instructional leadership, high expectations, opportunity to learn and student time on task, frequent monitoring of student programs, home-school relations, and reinforcement practices. These dimensions were evaluated by the school psychologists on a five-point Likert scale.

6. Results

One of the common problems of past research on this topic is a restricted data base that precludes analyses of the complexity of relationships that mediate children's adjustment to parental divorce. The broad range of data available in the current study permits exploration of several potential mediating factors, leading to a more accurate description of divorce effects. However, because of this comprehensive array of information, analyses are ongoing and several important relationships have yet to be examined. Nevertheless, considering the critical importance of this issue for children's mental health and the general weakness of existing research literature, presentation of analyses performed to date (May, 1983) may contribute substantially to current understanding of this significant social phenomenon. Results are presented in two major sections. The first section offers evidence of differences in social and academic competence between children from intact and divorced families; the second section examines sex, age, and other differences in adjustment within the divorced-family sample, including correlational findings to document home and school environmental relationships with adjustment for divorced-family children. Since intelligence and socioeconomic status are well-documented predictors of adjustment, covariance analyses controlling for these characteristics serve as the primary evidence of group differences.

6.1. Differences between Children from Divorced and Intact Families

6.1.1. Analysis of Variance for Total Group

As displayed in Table 3, consistent differences were observed between intact and divorced groups on both social-emotional and academic-intellectual criteria. ANOVA results indicate that intact-family children performed better on 15 of the 16 Hahnemann classroom behavior ratings, as well as Vineland communication, daily living, and social scales. They were absent less frequently, had higher peer popularity according to both parent and teacher ratings, and demonstrated more internal locus of control, higher full-scale IQ and WRAT reading, spelling, and math scores. Grades in reading and math were higher, and they were less likely to repeat a school grade.

6.1.2. Covariance Controls for IQ

Substantial differences between intact- and divorced-family children were found on both social and academic competence criteria. As illustrated in Table 4, with WISC-R full-scale IQ controlled, intact-family children showed better performance on 15 of 16 Hahnemann teacher ratings of classroom behavior and Vineland teacher ratings of competence in communication and social interaction. They had less school absence, better WRAT reading and spelling subtest scores, higher assigned grades in reading and math, and higher teacher and parent ratings of peer popularity. They were also less likely to have repeated a school grade.

TABLE 3
Analysis of Variance by Sex, Grade, and Marital Status

Variable	Source	F	p
	Social-emotional		
Hahnemann Profiles:			
Originality	status	9.790	.002
	sex × grade	3.597	.028
Independent Learning	sex	12.946	.000
	status	29.022	.000
Involvement	status	12.608	.000
Productive with Peers	sex	12.471	.000
	grade	5.301	.005
	status	6.873	.009
Intellectual Dependency	status	15.759	.000
Failure Anxiety	grade	12.944	.000
	status	14.573	.000
	sex × grade × status	3.571	.029
Unreflectiveness	sex	17.665	.000
	status	23.034	.000
Irrelevant Talk	sex	24.328	.000
	status	25.711	.000
Social (Over) Involvement	sex	50.174	.000
	status	34.632	.000
Negative Feelings	sex	9.206	.003
	grade	16.251	.000
	status	23.605	.000
	sex × grade	3.664	.026
Holding Back–Withdrawn	sex	8.131	.004
	grade	5.117	.006
	status	20.363	.000
Critical/Competitive	sex	12.515	.000
	grade	5.559	.004
	status	18.896	.000
	sex × grade	3.787	.023
Blaming	sex	4.362	.037
	grade	9.972	.000
	status	30.954	.000
	sex × grade	3.752	.024
Approach to Teacher	sex	40.271	.000
	grade	2.960	.053
Inattention	sex	20.278	.000
	status	39.447	.000
Vineland Domains (z-scores):			
Communication	sex	4.492	.034
	grade	21.349	.000
	status	19.600	.000

TABLE 3 (*Continued*)

Variable	Source	F	p
	Social-emotional		
Daily Living	sex	5.017	.025
	grade	25.495	.000
	status	5.180	.023
Social	sex	7.486	.006
	grade	8.586	.000
	status	16.355	.000
Grade in Conduct	sex	19.343	.000
	sex × grade	4.183	.016
Absence	status	5.542	.019
Peer Rejection (teacher rating)	status	22.028	.000
Peer Popularity (parent rating)	status	12.515	.000
	sex × status	4.993	.026
Optimism	grade	7.022	.001
Locus of Control	grade	32.672	.000
	status	5.662	.018
Worry Scale	grade	4.054	.018
Peer Contact	status × sex	4.214	.041
	Academic-intellectual		
WISC-R Full-scale IQ	status	5.461	.020
Wide Range Achievement Test:			
Reading	sex	19.561	.000
	grade	6.439	.002
	status	10.433	.001
	status × sex × grade	4.138	.016
Spelling	sex	29.365	.000
	grade	6.297	.002
	status	9.780	.002
Math	sex	8.280	.004
	grade	96.134	.000
	status	7.255	.007
Grade in Reading	sex	11.644	.001
	status	8.366	.004
Grade in Math	sex	9.909	.002
	status	8.420	.004
Academic Achievement (teacher rating)	sex	11.179	.001
	grade	7.242	.001
	status	31.370	.000
Regular Class Placement	grade	6.243	.002
	sex × grade	3.034	.049
Repeated School Grade	sex	9.432	.002
	status	6.398	.012

TABLE 4
Analysis of Covariance by Sex, Grade, and Marital Status Controlling for WISC-R Full-Scale IQ

Variable	Source	F	p
	Social-emotional		
Hahnemann Profiles:			
Originality	status	4.631	.032
	sex × grade	5.083	.006
Independent Learning	sex	15.314	.000
	status	24.319	.000
Involvement	status	7.852	.005
Productive with Peers	sex	11.821	.001
	grade	4.018	.018
	status	3.822	.051
Intellectual Dependency	status	10.507	.001
Failure Anxiety	grade	11.301	.000
	status	10.758	.001
	sex × grade × status	3.979	.019
Unreflectiveness	sex	16.977	.000
	status	18.539	.000
Irrelevant Talk	sex	23.904	.000
	status	21.075	.000
Social (Over) Involvement	sex	48.356	.000
	status	28.394	.000
Negative Feelings	sex	7.293	.007
	grade	15.224	.000
	status	19.301	.000
Holding Back-Withdrawn	sex	7.405	.007
	grade	4.127	.017
	status	16.361	.000
Critical/Competitive	sex	11.055	.001
	grade	5.168	.006
	status	15.751	.000
Blaming	grade	9.007	.000
	status	25.934	.000
	sex × grade	3.107	.045
Approach to Teacher	sex	39.467	.000
	grade	3.050	.048
Inattention	sex	20.602	.000
	status	33.892	.000
Vineland Domains (z-scores):			
Communication	sex	6.168	.013
	grade	29.533	.000
	status	13.984	.000

TABLE 4 (*Continued*)

Variable	Source	F	p
Social-emotional			
Daily Living	sex	5.425	.020
Social	grade	27.094	.000
	sex	8.004	.005
	grade	9.588	.000
Grade in Conduct	status	11.244	.001
	sex	19.263	.000
Absence	sex × grade	3.270	.039
	status	5.341	.021
Peer Rejection (teacher rating)	status	18.401	.000
Peer Popularity (parent rating)	status	9.305	.002
	sex × status	3.873	.049
Peer Contact (child rating)	sex × status	4.031	.045
Optimism	grade	8.906	.000
	sex × grade	2.994	.051
Locus of Control	grade	35.360	.000
Worry Scale	grade	3.826	.022
Academic-intellectual			
Wide Range Achievement Test:			
Reading	sex	26.462	.000
	grade	6.253	.002
	status	5.433	.020
	sex × grade × status	5.927	.003
Spelling	sex	36.816	.000
	grade	6.452	.002
	status	5.300	.022
Math	sex	9.911	.022
	grade	122.954	.000
Grade in Reading	sex	12.679	.000
	grade	4.483	.012
	status	7.634	.006
Grade in Math	sex	12.219	.001
	status	5.821	.016
Academic Achievement (teacher rating)	sex	12.917	.000
	grade	6.605	.001
	status	27.455	.000
Regular Class Placement	grade	6.180	.002
Repeated School Grade	sex	9.602	.002
	status	3.756	.053

6.1.3. Covariance Controls for Family Income

Family socioeconomic status was defined separately by family income level (based on custodial household only in the case of divorced-family children) and by educational level and occupational classification of each parent. Table 5 describes analysis of covariance results for the family income index. With family income controlled, intact-family children performed better on 10 of the 16 Hahnemann ratings of classroom behaviors. Although one of these ratings pertained to academic achievement, no main effects of marital status were observed for academic criteria as defined by teacher grades or WRAT test scores. Once again, Full-Scale WISC-R IQ differences favored the intact group, as did teacher ratings of peer popularity.

6.1.4. Controlling for Parents' Educational and Occupational Levels

When the parent questionnaire respondent's educational level was controlled, intact-family children showed superior performance on 15 of

TABLE 5
Analysis of Covariance by Sex, Grade, and Marital Status Controlling for Family Income Level

Variable	Source	F	p
	Social-emotional		
Hahnemann Profiles:			
Originality	sex × grade	3.653	.026
Independent Learning	sex	12.108	.001
	status	3.760	.053
Involvement	sex	3.730	.054
Productive with Peers	sex	14.225	.000
	grade	6.189	.002
Intellectual Dependency	sex × grade × status	2.961	.053
Failure Anxiety	grade	9.897	.000
	status	4.136	.042
	sex × grade × status	3.273	.039
Unreflectiveness	sex	15.385	.000
	status	8.882	.003
Irrelevant Talk	sex	19.588	.000
	status	5.173	.023
Social (Over) Involvement	sex	42.614	.000
	status	11.559	.001
Negative Feelings	sex	6.667	.010
	grade	14.481	.000
	status	9.988	.002
Holding Back-Withdrawn	sex	7.867	.005
	grade	4.816	.008

TABLE 5 (*Continued*)

Variable	Source	F	p
Social-emotional			
Critical/Competitive	sex	9.939	.002
	grade	4.360	.013
	status	8.139	.004
	sex × status	5.411	.020
Blaming	grade	6.943	.001
	status	14.810	.000
Approach to Teacher	sex	41.321	.000
	grade	3.764	.024
Inattention	sex	17.913	.000
	status	8.268	.004
Vineland Domains (z-scores):			
Communication	sex	4.184	.041
	grade	17.456	.000
Daily Living	sex	5.558	.019
	grade	20.371	.000
Social	sex	7.693	.006
	grade	6.518	.001
Grade in Conduct	sex	22.936	.000
	sex × grade	3.525	.031
Peer Rejection (teacher rating)	sex	4.501	.034
	status	4.099	.043
Peer Popularity (parent rating)	sex × status	5.408	.020
Peer Contact (child rating)	sex × status	4.313	.038
Optimism	grade	6.719	.001
Locus of Control	grade	28.412	.000
Worry Scale	grade	3.206	.041
Academic-intellectual			
WISC-R Full-scale IQ	status	8.692	.003
Wide Range Achievement Test:			
Reading	sex	18.281	.000
	grade	7.891	.000
	sex × grade × status	4.656	.010
Spelling	sex	25.761	.000
	grade	6.670	.001
Math	sex	6.779	.009
	grade	87.453	.000
	grade × status	3.343	.036
Grade in Reading	sex	10.834	.001
Grade in Math	sex	8.697	.003
Academic Achievement (teacher rating)	sex	8.869	.003
	grade	7.675	.001
	status	5.389	.021
Regular Class Placement	grade	3.990	.019
Repeated School Grade	sex	8.386	.004

16 Hahnemann teacher ratings as well as Vineland communication and social scores. They were less likely to repeat a school grade, had higher grades in reading and math, and had better WRAT reading, spelling, and math scores. They were absent from school less often, had higher internal locus of control, and had better peer relations as judged by parent and teacher ratings.

When educational level of the child's other parent was controlled, intact-family children surpassed divorced-family children on 14 of 16 Hahnemman ratings as well as Vineland communication and social scores. They also had less school absence and higher popularity ratings.

Covariance controls for respondent's occupational level revealed differences in favor of intact-family children on 14 of 16 Hahnemann ratings, all four Vineland scores, absence frequency, peer popularity, WRAT reading and spelling scores, grades in math and reading, and regular versus special class placement.

With occupational level of the other parent as the control variable, intact-family children showed better performance on 13 of 16 Hahnemann ratings, Vineland communication and social scores, grade in reading, absence frequency, and peer rejection index.

6.1.5. Other Analyses

A number of other marital-status differences were examined through correlations and chi-square analyses. For example, intact-family parents scored higher on all five parent satisfaction scales included in the parent interview. Divorced-family children were far more likely to have been previously referred to a school psychologist ($\chi^2 = 17.58$, $p < .0001$), to be in programs for reading difficulties ($\chi^2 = 3.55$, $p < .050$), and to have repeated a school grade ($\chi^2 = 6.27$, $p < .010$).

6.2. Differences among Children of Divorced Families

6.2.1. Sex Differences

One of the most powerfully demonstrated findings of this study is that in divorced-family households girls consistently demonstrate better adjustment than boys. Table 6 illustrates that girls show superior performance on 11 of 16 Hahnemann measures; Vineland daily living score; peer popularity; the optimism–pessimism score; grades in reading, math, and classroom conduct; and WRAT reading, spelling, and math test scores. They were also less likely to be in special class placement or to have repeated a school grade.

Sex differences also persist when IQ is controlled in analyses of

TABLE 6

Analysis of Variance by Sex and Grade for Divorced-Family Children

Variable	Source	F	p
Social-emotional			
Hahnemann Profiles:			
Independent Learning	sex	7.196	.008
Productive with Peers	sex	8.858	.003
	grade	3.370	.036
Failure Anxiety	grade	7.289	.001
Unreflectiveness	sex	13.915	.000
Irrelevant Talk	sex	15.312	.000
Social (Over) Involvement	sex	28.127	.000
Negative Feelings	sex	5.843	.016
	grade	9.866	.000
	sex × grade	4.167	.016
Holding Back-Withdrawn	sex	8.858	.003
Critical/Competitive	sex	11.524	.001
	grade	3.596	.029
Blaming	grade	7.007	.001
Approach to Teacher	sex	14.542	.001
Inattention	sex	12.968	.000
Vineland Domains (z-scores):			
Communication	grade	13.869	.000
Daily Living	sex	5.277	.022
	grade	19.792	.000
Social	grade	3.791	.024
Grade in Conduct	sex	7.640	.006
	sex × grade	6.327	.002
Peer Rejection (teacher rating)	sex	4.203	.041
Peer Popularity (parent rating)	sex	8.247	.004
Optimism	sex	4.503	.035
	grade	3.782	.024
	sex × grade	4.651	.010
Locus of Control	grade	13.930	.000
Number of current child adjustment problems (parent rating)	grade	4.096	.018
Academic-intellectual			
Wide Range Achievement Test:			
Reading	sex	8.202	.004
Spelling	sex	14.976	.000
Math	sex	3.735	.054
	grade	38.891	.000
Grade in Reading	sex	11.744	.001
Grade in Math	sex	9.054	.003
Academic Achievement (Hahnemann teacher ratings)	sex	9.564	.002
	grade	3.973	.020
Regular Class Placement	sex	3.730	.054
	grade	6.465	.002
Repeated School Grade	sex	5.581	.019

covariance. Girls perform better on 10 of 16 Hahnemann ratings, Vineland daily living skills, grade in conduct, peer popularity (teaching rating), and optimism, as well as several academic criteria including WRAT reading and spelling, grades in reading and math, and history of repeating a school grade. When family income is controlled in covariance analyses, girls perform better than boys on 11 Hahnemann ratings; Vineland daily living and social skills; grades in conduct, reading, and math; WRAT reading and spelling subtest scores; peer popularity; optimism; and repeating a school grade.

Since girls generally perform better than boys at these age levels, point-biserial correlational analyses of marital status and criteria were performed separately for boys and girls (see Table 7). Results show more significant relationships between marital status and criteria for boys than for girls, especially in the area of academic achievement. For example, divorced status for boys was related to lower IQ, lower grades in reading and math, and more likelihood of special class placement and retention in school grade, whereas no relationships of these criteria to divorced status were apparent for girls.

T-tests on status performed separately for age–sex categories yielded further confirmation of substantial sex differences in the effects of parental divorce on children's adjustment. For example, at the 5th-grade level, divorced-family boys showed poorer performance than in-

TABLE 7

Criterion Mean Scores by Sex and Marital Status

Dependent variable	Divorced		Intact	
	Male	Female	Male	Female
Social-emotional				
Hahnemann Profiles:				
Originality	9.32	9.54	10.20	10.25
Independent Learning	19.96	21.63	22.40	23.88
Involvement	16.42	16.90	17.47	18.02
Productive with Peers	12.56	13.81	13.53	14.35
Intellectual Dependency	12.70	11.86	11.12	11.09
Failure Anxiety	12.56	12.22	11.23	10.99
Unreflectiveness	9.24	7.83	7.70	6.98
Irrelevant Talk	9.12	7.66	7.64	6.69
Social (Over) Involvement	12.87	10.27	10.68	8.65
Negative Feelings	9.28	8.21	7.73	7.15
Holding Back-Withdrawn	14.13	12.19	11.56	11.02
Critical/Competitive	9.12	7.81	7.61	7.11
Blaming	8.60	7.95	6.99	6.50
Approach to Teacher	14.46	16.07	13.72	15.93
Inattention	6.19	5.28	5.00	4.40

TABLE 7 (*Continued*)

Dependent variable	Divorced		Intact	
	Male	Female	Male	Female

Social-emotional

Dependent variable	Divorced Male	Divorced Female	Intact Male	Intact Female
Vineland (z-scores):				
Communication	−.25	−.08	.08	.26
Daily Living	−.21	.05	.03	.15
Social	−.25	−.06	.04	.28
Motor	−.01	−.12	.06	.08
Grade in Conduct	2.04	2.21	2.09	2.31
Absence	9.06	8.06	6.60	7.71
Peer Rejection (teacher rating)	3.84	3.59	3.36	3.31
Peer Popularity (parent rating)	2.19	2.37	2.43	2.42
Peer Contact	25.18	25.44	25.79	24.98
Optimism	6.19	6.65	6.48	6.45
Locus of Control	28.60	28.51	28.87	29.21
Worry Scale	11.10	11.14	11.25	10.79
Parent Ratings (divorced group only):				
Number of initial child adjustment problems	2.44	2.40		
Number of current child adjustment problems	.91	.86		
Number of initial parent adjustment problems	5.95	6.26		
Number of current parent adjustment problems	1.50	1.50		
Child's initial adjustment	2.77	2.95		
Child's second-year adjustment	3.07	3.24		
Child's current adjustment	3.26	3.22		

Academic-intellectual

Dependent variable	Divorced Male	Divorced Female	Intact Male	Intact Female
WISC-R Full-Scale IQ	104.94	106.61	108.49	108.05
Wide Range Achievement Test:				
Reading	108.42	110.80	109.40	120.76
Spelling	101.51	107.62	105.05	110.68
Math	98.87	101.43	100.99	103.46
Grade in Reading	1.98	2.21	2.18	2.28
Grade in Math	1.99	2.18	2.17	2.28
Academic Achievement (Hahnemann teacher ratings)	4.35	4.86	5.10	5.34
Regular Class Placement	1.90	1.95	1.95	1.95
Repeated School Grade	1.16	1.07	1.09	1.03

tact-family boys on 12 of 15 HESB teacher ratings of classroom behavior, Vineland social score, peer relations, grade in math and HESB teacher rating of overall academic achievement. Conversely, only one difference was noted for girls at this age level. Intact-family girls had higher HESB ratings of classroom involvement than divorced-family girls ($t = 1.98$, $p = .051$).

6.2.2. Current Age Differences

One commonly held assumption is that older children should make better adjustments to parental divorce since they generally have broader social networks and thus potentially greater social support systems. However, at the age levels examined in this study, this was not the case. As evidenced in Table 6, significant differences were found among the three age groups on six Hahnemann ratings, three of the Vineland ratings, optimism versus pessimism, locus of control, parents' ratings of number of current adjustment problems, WRAT math scores, and regular versus special class placement. On eight of these variables, younger children showed better adjustment than older children. These criteria included five HESB behavior ratings, HESB rating of academic achievement, WRAT math, and regular class placement. Fifth-graders had better scores on six measures: Vineland social, communication, and daily living, optimism, locus of control, and parent rating of number of current adjustment problems. These findings also occurred when analyses of covariance were performed controlling for IQ and family income. As an illustration of interaction effects, Figures 1, 2, and 3 present the interaction of age, sex, and marital status for three WRAT subtests.

6.2.3. Age at Time of Divorce

Considering differences of opinion reflected in previous research, separate analyses of child's age at time of parental divorce were performed. Inconsistent results were obtained by grade level and sex. For boys, earlier age at time of divorce was related to poorer classroom behavior in first grade. According to HESB teacher ratings, they exhibited more irrelevant talk ($r = .28$, $p = .054$), more negative feelings ($r = .28$, $p = .053$), more critical competitive behavior ($r = .41$, $p = .004$), and more blaming ($r = .33$, $p = .024$). For 3rd-grade boys, earlier age at time of divorce was related to higher optimism ($r = .28$, $p = .028$) and fewer current adjustment problems reported by parent ($r = .40$, $p = .001$). For 5th-grade boys only one current adjustment indicator, grade in math ($r = .32$, $p = .039$) was related, favoring children who were younger at time of parental divorce. For 1st-grade girls, earlier age at time of parental divorce was related to poorer performance on two vari-

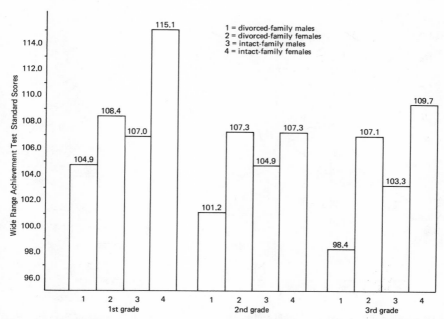

FIGURE 1. Comparisons by marital status, grade, and sex for wide range achievement—reading.

ables, HESB intellectual dependency ($r = .36$, $p = .012$) and Vineland social score ($r = .31$, $p = .039$), but to fewer current adjustment problems being reported by the parent ($r = .33$, $p = .020$). At third-grade level, girls who were younger at time of divorce performed better on three HESB variables, independent learning ($r = .35$, $p = .023$), involvement ($r = .44$, $p = .003$), and less intellectual dependency ($r = .38$, $p = .012$). They had lower Vineland daily living skills ($r = .33$, $p = .043$), higher WRAT reading ($r = .32$, $p = .038$), and higher WRAT spelling ($r = .34$, $p = .026$). Fifth-grade girls showed relationships similar in direction to first-grade girls. Girls who were young at time of divorce were higher in HESB critical-competitive scores ($r = .31$, $p = .039$), and lower in WRAT reading ($r = .36$, $p = .016$), spelling ($r = .31$, $p = .038$), and math ($r = .31$, $p = .038$) scores. They also had a higher rate of school absence ($r = .38$, $p = .026$).

6.2.4. Length of Time in Divorced Family

Since the child's age at time of parental divorce is a determinant of the length of time the child spends in a divorced household, results from

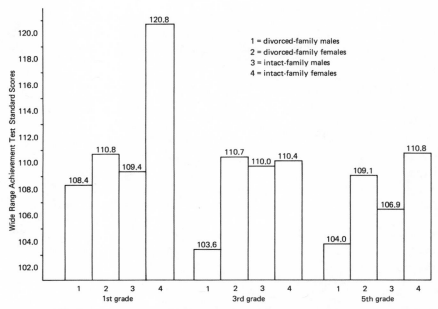

Figure 2. Comparisons by marital status, grade, and sex for wide range achievement—spelling.

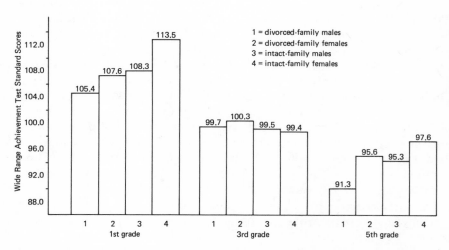

Figure 3. Comparisons by marital status, grade, and sex for wide range achievement—math.

analyses of the latter issue are also inconsistent. For boys, few relationships between this variable and criteria were noted. Those 1st-grade boys who spent a longer period of time in a divorced household displayed more irrelevant talk in classrooms ($r = .31$, $p = .027$) and had more peer rejection ($r = .29$, $p = .041$). Third-grade boys who lived in divorced households for longer lengths of time had higher Vineland daily living skills ($r = .31$, $p = .020$) but were more likely to have repeated a school grade ($r = .26$, $p = .046$). Fifth-grade boys with longer divorced household residence had higher Vineland daily living skills ($r = .29$, $p = .044$) and higher grades in math ($r = .31$, $p = .046$).

Girls in first grade displayed only one relationship between this variable and criteria. Those who had lived longer in divorced households had fewer current adjustment problems listed by the parent ($r = .29$, $p = .044$). In 3rd and 5th grades, however, several relationships were noted. Third-grade girls with longer residence in divorced homes had better HESB scores on independent learning ($r = .38$, $p = .011$), involvement ($r = .46$, $p = .002$), fewer negative feelings ($r = .31$, $p = .041$), less blaming ($r = .36$, $p = .015$), and less inattention ($r = .32$, $p = .034$). They also had better Vineland daily living skills ($r = .33$, $p = .038$). Fifth-grade girls with longer residence in divorced homes showed a markedly contrasting pattern with higher incidence of HESB critical-competitive scores ($r = .31$, $p = .038$) and poorer achievement scores on WRAT reading ($r = .34$, $p = .024$), spelling ($r = .30$, $p = .045$), and math ($r = .39$, $p = .008$). They were also more likely to have repeated a school grade ($r = .30$, $p = .049$).

6.2.5. Home Environment Differences

An extensive set of correlational analyses was also performed between criteria and individual items from the child and parent interviews and from the psychologists' ratings of school variables. Although these findings are too numerous to present in detail, a few central issues can be noted here. Twelve items from the Child Interview that reflected the quality of parent–child interactions were combined to form a summary index of parent–child relationships. This index was then correlated with criteria separately for divorced and intact groups. Whereas 19 of the criteria were predicted by the parent–child relationship index for the intact group, 27 criteria were significantly related to the index for the divorced group, and these criteria included classroom behavior, achievement, popularity, and general adjustment indices. In all cases, better performance on these 27 criteria was related to more positive custodial parents' relationships with the divorced-family children. Examination of divorced-parent childrearing style revealed that authoritarian custodial parents (who displayed such self-reported childrearing approaches as rejecting the child when he or she misbehaves) had children who were described on teacher ratings as higher on inattention, holding back-withdrawn behavior, and intellectual dependency and lower in originality, independent learning, involvement, productivity with peers, and academic achievement. They had lower scores on IQ tests, Vineland communication and daily living skills, and physical coordination and were more likely to have repeated a school grade.

The divorced-family child's positive relationship with the non-custodial parent was also related to better academic and social adjustment. For example, in response to the Child Interview question, "When you do something nice at school whom do you tell about it?" those divorced-group children who mentioned father, as opposed to those who did not, had higher IQ, WRAT reading, spelling and math scores, better grades in math, more likelihood of regular versus special class placement, and less likelihood of repeating a school grade. They also performed better on eight Hahnemann classroom behavior variables, three Vineland ratings, and parent's rating of popularity. It should be noted that for both sexes, poorer father–child relationships were related to divorced-family status ($r = .53$, $p = .001$ for boys and $r = .51$, $p = .001$ for girls).

6.2.6. Custody

The issue of parental custody is clearly one of the most emotional areas of divorce arrangements. Although this sample includes only 24 children in father-custody households and 27 children in joint-custody households, analyses of this issue may provide some clarification in this area of sparse research information. In analyses of variance of sex by custody, sex differences occurred on 24 of 41 criteria whereas no main effects were noted for custody and only two interactions of sex and custody were observed. These pertained to grade in conduct and parent rating of peer popularity. Girls in joint custody received the best conduct grades, whereas boys in joint custody and girls in father-custody situations received highest popularity ratings. Custody analyses of covariance, controlling for family income for divorced-family boys, yielded five significant main effects with joint-custody boys diplaying better scores on HESB ratings of holding back-withdrawn and inattention, as well as better parent ratings of peer popularity and higher grades in math. Mother-custody boys showed higher levels of involvement on the HESB scale. The same analysis performed for divorced-family girls yielded two significant main effects. Highest grades in conduct occurred in joint-custody households and highest locus of control scores were observed in mother-custody households.

6.2.7. School Differences

School characteristics related to successful functioning of divorced-family children included smaller school district population, which related to four of the Hahnemann factors, less absence, and not repeating a school grade; percentage of girls in the classroom, which related to better grades in reading and math; fewer miles bused to school, which related to less intellectual dependency, blaming, irrelevant talk, and fewer negative feelings; and traditional rather than open-classroom structure, which related to better WRAT reading, regular class placement, and less inattention. Through the use of psychologists' ratings of eight school climate dimensions, additional relationships to successful adjustment were observed. For example, "safe, orderly and predictable" school environments were related to higher WRAT math scores and greater likelihood to be in regular class placements; "higher expectations and high norms of achievement" predicted less failure anxiety, less inattention, a better conduct grade, and better current child adjustment as reported by the parent; "frequent monitoring of student progress" related to less failure anxiety and fewer negative feelings.

7. Discussion

The central purpose of this initial report has been to resolve contradictions and methodological weaknesses inherent in previous research concerning the impact of parental divorce on children's adjustment. Clearly, the inclusion of a large, nationwide sample of children randomly drawn from a normal population adds substantially to the generalizability of these conclusions. The inclusion of a randomly drawn control group from the same school classroom environments offers opportunity to differentiate those adjustment variations that result specifically from family disruption from those that are related simply to age, sex differences, and the like. The broad array of information obtained by highly qualified examiners provides additional confidence in these findings and offers opportunity to unravel some of the complexity of the divorce adjustment process.

Attempts to stratify the sample geographically by population of individual states failed because of the inability of many psychologists to participate in the study. Approximately 1,500 psychologists were sampled according to state census data, but school administrator refusals and heavy workloads resulted in a low acceptance rate. Nevertheless, the 144 psychologists who did participate provided a nationwide random sample of divorced children from 38 states with demographic characteristics including important variability in SES, race, school, and neighborhood characteristics. Additionally, by selecting a control group from the same classrooms, a variety of potential biases were minimized.

Space limitations preclude a more extensive display of results and a comprehensive discussion of findings and implications. Future publications will examine a variety of issues in greater depth, but two primary issues are elaborated here. These include findings relating to SES and sex and potential interventions by school psychologists.

7.1. SES

It is well established that SES is associated with children's intellectual, academic, and social functioning (e.g., Coleman, 1966; Jencks, 1972; Kagan, 1980), and it is also well documented that one-parent homes resulting from divorce have reduced SES (U.S. Bureau of Census, 1979, 1982a, 1982b). The percentage of divorced homes in the present study with incomes below $10,000 was 37.3, whereas only 3.7 of intact families had income at this level. Some studies have suggested that SES variables intervene to account for the negative impact of divorce on children (Colletta, 1979; Lazarus, 1980; Svanum et al., 1982; Zakariya, 1982). Conversely, the present results provide evidence that divorce accounts for a number of negative social and academic effects independent of well-defined SES measures, including income and educational and occupational levels of the parents.

Key factors that may account for the contradictory findings are differences in criteria and possible sampling bias of previous studies. Although the present study included multifactored criteria including specific cognitive, academic, social, and emotional adjustment variables, many other research studies on this topic employed restricted criteria. For example, in some studies criteria employed were only psychometric measures of IQ and achievement (Svanum et al., 1982), parent interview data (Colletta, 1979), and limited school measures such as referral for discipline problems (Lazarus, 1980; Zakariya, 1982). The current results support the repeated finding that variance in IQ is highly related to SES. However, current results also indicate that divorce accounts for a substantial amount of independent variance in nonintellectual measures of social and academic skills. These skills may be more malleable than global IQ scores, and environmental stressors such as divorce may have more impact on them. This is especially true for direct measures of classroom functioning and social skills which have been shown to be nonintellective correlates of school success (Perry, Guidubaldi, & Kehle, 1979). The particular measures of initiative, cooperation, and peer status have also been shown previously to be associated with positive adjustment to divorce (Hetherington, Cox, & Cox, 1979a).

In regard to sampling bias, the present sample is more representative of the general population of divorced families since it was randomly selected from across the nation. Samples from other studies comparing SES with marital status were selected from the National Center on Health Statistics in the 1960s of nonhandicapped children (Svanum *et al.*, 1982), 72 families from preschool centers in Buffalo, New York (Colletta, 1979), and two-parent homes that included remarried families (Lazarus, 1980; Zakariya, 1982).

7.2. Sex Differences

A major finding of the present study is the consistent pattern of sex differences in children's divorce-related adjustment. Boys from divorced families were found to experience greater behavioral, social, and academic difficulties in comparison to both girls from divorced families and boys from intact families. This is generally consistent with related studies (Hess & Camara, 1979; Hetherington *et al.*, 1982; Kurdek & Berg, 1983; Santrock & Warshak, 1979; Wallerstein & Kelly, 1980). Yet, these extensive differences between elementary school boys from divorced and intact families were not shown previously. Further, on grade–sex category analyses, 5th-grade girls from divorced families were found to have a significant difficulty in only one behavioral measure even though multiple criteria were examined, suggesting that girls have very little divorce-related maladjustment by this age level. In contrast, 5th-grade divorced-family boys were the most adversely affected group, with a wider variety of significant deficiencies than those observed at earlier grade levels. Kurdek (1981) observed that sex differences may dissipate over time, since the studies not reporting greater divorce adjustment problems for boys included older children (Kurdek *et al.*, 1981; Reinhard, 1977). This study contradicts the Kurdek finding, in that the sexes differed most at the oldest age level considered. It further reflects the importance of age–sex interaction analyses as focal points for further study.

In contrast to pervasive sex differences among divorce subjects, analyses of current age of subjects, age at time of divorce, and length of time spent in a divorced household yield inconsistent findings. The results of the present study indicate that younger children display somewhat better adjustment to divorce than older children. This finding is in conflict with the work of Kurdek *et al.* (1981), who report that older children experience fewer adjustment problems. It also conflicts with other research findings which range from more detrimental effects of divorce being associated with younger age (Hetherington, 1972) to no relationship between age of the child and degree of maladjustment (Kalter & Rembar, 1981). This study supports Wallerstein and Kelly's (1974, 1976) contention that there are differential effects of divorce on children dependent upon their present developmental stage. It further shows inconsistent patterns for the effects of age at time of parental divorce. Substantially different relationships with criteria were observed depending on grade level and sex. This is in agreement with the work of Kalter and Rembar (1981), who state that the timing of parental separation or divorce was related to different constellations of emotional-behavioral difficulties according to sex of the child. The present findings relating sex and length of time in a single-parent family also yielded confusing results. Whereas Hetherington *et al.* (1982) conclude that time in a single-parent home accounts for equilibrium and adjustment with differing effects by sex, the present results suggest that other intervening variables may make adjustment more complex.

The type of the divorce-related behavioral adjustment for boys has been consistent in most studies employing this type of criteria and is of special concern. The present results indicate that boys, in comparison to both girls from divorced homes and boys from intact homes, have a behavioral profile indicating high frequencies of negative acting out including aggression, opposition, and impulsivity. This has been previously found for children of similar age (Hess & Camara, 1979) and for preschool children over a 2-year span (Hetherington *et al.*, 1982). Aggression for boys was also previously found for those from intact families where marital discord was present (Block, Block, & Morrison, 1981). Further, impaired social competencies in terms of peer status and task-oriented interaction with peers were found in this study, which is similar to Hetherington *et al.* but not to Hess and Camara. Present findings also indicate decreased attentive behavior and optimism for divorced-family boys. Although similar sex differences in aggressive or under-controlled behavior are well known (e.g., Flanders, 1968; Ross, 1980), the present study and the others cited concerning this issue indicated this to be especially true for boys of divorce since control groups of intact-family children were included. This supports the sex-role explanation presented by Emery (1982) stipulating that boys react to the stress of divorce with aggression and girls by compensation through prosocial behavior. This response in boys is considered to be more obvious since undercontrolled behavior in children has been found to be overrepresented in referrals to clinics (Ross, 1980).

Comprehensive explanations for sex differences in children's divorce adjustment have been provided (see summary in Emery, 1982). This includes hypotheses of sex-role adjustments from various theoretical perspectives including attachment, modeling, discipline, and taking on a symptom; but these have not been adequately investigated. Research studies of boys' adjustment problems due specifically to divorce have provided more direct explanations. Kelly and Wallerstein (1976) suggested that boys are developmentally more vulnerable to such stressors as divorce. A sex-role modeling explanation is provided by Warshak and Santrock (1983), who attributed differences to the opposite-sex child-custody relationship typical for boys. Hetherington (1979) suggested that there may be sex differences in parenting styles, with custodial parents providing less emotional support for boys. Some support for the latter conclusion was found in this study in the fact that divorced-family status was related to poorer overall parent–child relationship for boys but not for girls ($r = .22$, $p = .001$) and the fact that boys from divorced homes were less likely than those from intact homes to tell mother when something good happened to them at school ($r = .13$, $p = .017$) whereas, again, no marital-status difference was noted on this variable for girls. Furthermore, it is apparent from Child Interview responses that divorced-group boys who maintain contact with the father perform better on several measures than those who do not. For example, aforementioned differences between those who tell father when they do something "nice" at school and those who do not possibly reflect the significant contributions of the noncustodial same-sex parent. Similar findings on other child interview items reinforce this conclusion. Although the size of these statistically significant correlations is small, the size limitation is offset in this case by their consistency across five of the seven criteria analyzed.

8. Conclusion

The scarcity of well-designed studies on this topic is probably a function of the relative recency of divorce rate acceleration, as well as such serious impediments to data collection as the concern over invasion of privacy. In an area fraught with severe emotional upheaval and drastic legal implications, data-gatherers are not entirely welcome. Those dedicated researchers who have thus far contributed to the interdisciplinary knowledge base have sensitized practitioners to a variety of important factors that may substantially enhance children's adjustment to parental divorce. However, these initial leads need further clarification through more precise research designs. We hope that this study has advanced the search for meaningful interventions. Through the support of the William T. Grant Foundation, NASP, and Kent State University, this search will be a continuing project focus through the next two years.

The substantial research effort reported here has incorporated a number of methodological improvements relative to earlier studies and thus provides more definitive conclusions about several important issues. Similar to earlier research, this study was limited by a lack of well-established social and adaptive behavior assessments for the ages in question. To compensate for this deficit, a multi-input approach was used. A related limitation is that although psychologists were urged to conceal the purpose of the study from teachers until they had completed their child ratings, some teachers may have recognized the research focus. The potential rating bias resulting from this awareness was another reason for inclusion of inputs from children, parents, and standardized tests.

Many critical questions about divorce effects and adjustment enhancing factors remain unanswered. For example, larger samples of father-custody and joint-custody children are needed to determine whether departures from traditional mother-custody procedure would benefit children of particular ages or sex. Other focal points for future research include resolution of the confusing age effects issue; identifying more school and home environment factors that relate to better adjustment; and examination of the characteristics of surrogate parents, stepparents, and extended-family members who supplement custodial parents' socialization efforts. An obvious but unresolved need is to assist parents in answering the increasingly common question: In what circumstances is parental divorce a better arrangement for children than continuing a conflict-laden marriage?

The problem of escalating divorce rates and their unfortunate sequelae for children does not appear to be a temporary phenomenon in our society. If census projections are at all accurate, divorce-related single-parent child rearing will increasingly replace traditional family socialization practices. In this atmosphere of instability, it appears likely that children and their parents will require expanded, empirically validated services from mental health practitioners.

Acknowledgments

Special gratitude is extended to 144 NASP members who provided an extensive data base, to Drs. Thomas Kehle and Caven Mcloughlin who helped in preparation of previous reports, and to graduate assistants and secretaries, Ms. Bonnie Nastasi, Miss Roberta Decker, Miss Janet Carden, Miss Jeanine Lightel, Dr. Bonnie Adams, Mrs. Bonnie Heaton, and Mrs. Marjorie Buehrle, who have provided invaluable assistance on a daily basis throughout the past 2 years.

9. References

Achenbach, T. M. Psychopathology of childhood: Research problems and issues. *Journal of Consulting and Clinical Psychology,* 1978, 46, 759–776.

Achenbach, T. M., & Edelbrock, C. S. The classification of child psychopathology: A review and analysis of empirical efforts. *Psychological Bulletin,* 1978, 85, 1275–1301.

Achenbach, T. M., & Edelbrock, C. S. Behavioral problems and competencies reported by parents of normal and disturbed children aged 4 through 16. *Monographs of the Society for Research in Child Development,* 1981, 46 (Serial No. 188).

Atkeson, B. M., Forehand, R. L., & Richard, K. M. The Effects of Divorce on Children. In B. B. Lahey & A. E. Kazdin (Eds.), *Advances in Clinical Child Psychology* (Vol. 5). New York: Plenum Press, 1982.

Belle, D. (Ed.). Lives in stress: Women and depression. Beverly Hills: Sage Publications, 1982.

Berg, B., & Kelly, R. The measured self-esteem of children from broken, rejected, and accepted families. *Journal of Divorce,* 1979, 2, 363–369.

Bernard, J. M., & Nesbitt, S. Divorce: An unreliable predictor of children's emotional predispositions. *Journal of Divorce,* 1981, 4(4), 31–42.

Biller, H. B. The father and personality development: Paternal deprivation and sex-role development. In M. E. Lamb (Ed.), *The Role of the father in child development.* New York: Wiley, 1976.

Block, J. H., Block, J., & Morrison, A. Parental agreement–disagreement on child-rearing orientations and gender-related personality correlates in children. *Child Development,* 1981, 52, 965–974.

Bloom, B. S. *Human characteristics and school learning.* New York: McGraw-Hill, 1976.

Bronfenbrenner, U. *The ecology of human development.* Cambridge: Harvard University Press, 1979.

Brookover, W., & Lezotte, L. *Changes in school characteristics coincident with changes in student achievement.* East Lansing: Michigan State University, College of Urban Development, 1977.

Brown, B. F. A study of the school needs of children from one-parent families. *Phi Delta Kappan,* 1980, 62, 537–540.

Cleminshaw, H. K., & Guidubaldi, J. Assessing parent satisfaction. *Resources in Education.* ERIC: Ed 200 858, 1981, 16(9).

Clingempell, W. G., & Reppucci, N. D. Joint custody after divorce: Major issues and goals for research. *Psychological Bulletin,* 1982, 91, 102–127.

Coleman, J. S., *et al. Equality of educational opportunity.* Washington, D.C.: U.S. Government Printing Office, 1966.

Colletta, N. The impact of divorce: Father absence or poverty? *Journal of Divorce,* 1979, 3(1), 27–35.

Edmonds, R., & Frederikesen, J. *Search for effective schools: The identification and analysis of city schools that are instructionally effective for poor children.* Cambridge: Harvard University, Center for Urban Studies, 1978.

Emery, R. E. Interparental conflict and the children of discord and divorce. *Psychological Bulletin*, 1982, *92*, 310–330.

Flanders, J. P. A review of research on imitative behavior. *Psychological Bulletin*, 1968, *69*, 316–337.

Glick, P. C., & Norton, A. J. Marrying, divorcing and living together in the U.S. today. *Population Bulletin*, *5*, 32. Washington, D.C.: Population Reference Bureau, 1977 (updated February 1979).

Guidubaldi, J. Status report extended: Further elaborations on the American family. *School Psychology Review*, 1980, *9*(4), 374–379.

Guidubaldi, J. Divorce research clarifies issues: A report on NASP's nationwide study. *Communiqué*, July 1983.

Guidubaldi, J., Kehle, T. J., & Murray, J. W. Assessment strategies for the handicapped. *Personal and Guidance Journal*, 1979, *30*, 245–251.

Guidubaldi, J., Cleminshaw, H. K., Perry, J. D., & Mcloughlin, C. S. The impact of parental divorce on children: Report of the nationwide NASP study. *School Psychology Review*, 1983, *12* (3).

Hess, R. D., & Camara, K. A. Post-divorce family relationships as mediating factors in the consequences of divorce for children. *Journal of Social Issues*, 1979, *35*(4), 79–96.

Hetherington, E. M. *Children and divorce*. Presidential Address, Division 7, American Psychological Association convention, New York, 1979. (a)

Hetherington, E. M. Divorce: A child's perspective. *American Psychologist*, 1979, *34*, 851–858. (b)

Hetherington, E. M., Cox, M., & Cox, R. The aftermath of divorce. In J. H. Stevens & M. Mathews (Eds.), *Mother/child, father/child relationships*. Washington, D.C.: National Association for the Education of Young Children, 1978.

Hetherington, E. M., Cox, M., & Cox, R. Family interaction and the social-emotional and cognitive development of children following divorce. In V. Vaughn & T. Brazelton (Eds.), *The family setting priorities*. New York: Science and Medicine Publishing Company, 1979. (a)

Hetherington, E. M., Cox, M., & Cox, R. Play and social interaction in children following divorce. *Journal of Social Issues*, 1979, *35*, 26–49. (b)

Hetherington, E. M., Cox, M., & Cox, R. Effects of divorce on parents and children. In M. E. Lamb (Ed.), *Nontraditional families: Parenting and child development*. Hillsdale, N.J.: Erlbaum, 1982.

Jacobson, D. S. The impact of marital separation/divorce on children: I. Parent–child separation and child adjustment. *Journal of Divorce*, 1978, *1*(4), 341–360. (a)

Jacobson, D. S. The impact of marital separation/divorce on children: II. Interparent hostility and child adjustment. *Journal of Divorce*, 1978, *2*, 3–19. (b)

Jacobson, D. S. The impact of marital separation/divorce on children: III. Parent–child communication and child adjustment, and regression analysis of findings from overall study. *Journal of Divorce*, 1978, *2*, 175–194. (c)

Jastak, J. F., Jastak, S. R., & Bijou, S. W. *Wide Range Achievement Test*. Washington, Del.: Jastak Associates, 1978.

Jencks, C. *Inequality: A reassessment of the effect of family and schooling in America*. New York: Harper, 1972.

Kagan, J. The influences of the family. *School Psychology Review*, 1980, *9*, 298–311.

Kalter, N. Children of divorce in an outpatient psychiatric population. *American Journal of Orthopsychiatry*, 1977, *47*(1), 40–51.

Kalter, N., & Rembar, J. The significance of a child's age at the time of parental divorce. *American Journal of Orthopsychiatry*, 1981, *51*(1), 85–100.

Kelly, J. B., & Wallerstein, J. S. The effects of parental divorce: Experiences of the child in early latency. *American Journal of Orthopsychiatry*, 1976, *46*, 20–23.

Kurdek, L. A. An integrative perspective on children's divorce adjustment. *American Psychologist*, 1981, *36*, 856–866.

Kurdek, L. A. (Ed.). *Children and divorce*. San Francisco: Jossey-Bass, 1983.

Kurdek, L. A., & Berg, B. Correlates of children's adjustments to their parents' divorces. In L. A. Kurdek (Ed.), *Children and divorce*. San Francisco: Jossey-Bass, 1983.

Kurdek, L. A., & Siesky, A. E. Sex role self-concepts of single divorced parents and their children. *Journal of Divorce*, 1980, *3*(3), 249–261. (a)

Kurdek, L. A., & Siesky, A. E. Children's perceptions of their parents' divorce. *Journal of Divorce*, 1980, *3*(4), 339–378. (b)

Kurdek, L. A., Blisk, D., & Siesky, A. E. Correlates of children's long-term adjustment to their parents' divorce. *Developmental Psychology*, 1981, *17*, 565–579.

Lamb, M. E. (Ed.). *The role of the father in child development* (2nd ed.). New York: Wiley, 1981.

Lamb, M. E. (Ed.). *Nontraditional families: Parenting and child development*. Hillsdale, N.J.: Erlbaum, 1982.

Lazarus, M. One-parent families and their children. *Principal*, 1980, *60*, 31–37.

Levitin, T. E. Children of divorce. *Journal of Social Issues*, 1979, *35*, 1–25.

McDermott, J. F. Parental divorce in early childhood. *American Journal of Psychiatry*, 1968, *124*(10), 118–126.

McDermott, J. J. Divorce and its psychiatric sequelae in children. *Archives of General Psychiatry*, 1970, *23*, 421–427.

Morrison, J. R. Parental divorce as a factor in childhood psychiatric illness. *Comparative Psychiatry*, 1974, *15*(2), 95–102.

Nay, W. R. *Multimethod clinical assessment*. New York: Gardner Press, 1979.

Perry, J. D., Guidubaldi, J., & Kehle, T. J. Kindergarten competencies as predictors of third-grade classroom behavior and achievement. *Journal of Educational Psychology*, 1979, *71*, 443–450.

Reinhard, D. W. The reaction of adolescent boys and girls to the divorce of their parents. *Journal of Clinical and Child Psychology*, 1977, *6*, 21–23.

Roff, M., Sells, S., & Golden, M. *Social adjustment and personality development in children*. Minneapolis: University of Minnesota Press, 1972.

Rosen, R. Children of divorce: What they feel about access and other aspects of the divorce experience. *Journal of Clinical Child Psychology*, 1977, *6*, 24–27.

Ross, A. O. *Psychological disorders of children*. New York: McGraw-Hill, 1980.

Santrock, J. W., & Warshak, R. A. Father custody and social development in boys and girls. *Journal of Social Issues*, 1979, *35*(4), 112–125.

Schaefer, C., Baker, E., & Zawel, D. A factor analytic and reliability study of the Devereux Elementary School Behavior Rating Scale. *Psychology in the Schools*, 1975, *12*, 295–300.

Sells, S. B., & Roff, M. *Peer acceptance–rejection and personality development*. Washington, D.C.: U.S. Department of Health, Education and Welfare, 1967.

Shinn, M. Father absence and children's cognitive development. *Psychological Bulletin*, 1978, *85*, 295–324.

Sparrow, S., Balla, D. A., & Chicchetti, D. F. *Vineland Adaptive Behavior Scales: Classroom edition* (Research ed.). Circle Pines, Minn.: American Guidance Association, 1981.

Spivack, G., & Spotts, J. *Devereux Child Behavior Rating Scale: Manual*. Devon, Penn.: Devereux Foundation Press, 1966.

Spivack, G., & Swift, M. The Devereux Elementary School Behavior Rating Scale: A study of the nature and organization of disturbed classroom behavior. *Journal of Special Education*, 1966, *1*, 71–90.

Spivack, G., & Swift, M. *Devereux Elementary School Behavior Rating Scale*. Devon, Penn.: Devereux Foundation, 1967.

Spivack, G., & Swift, M. Classroom behavior of children: Critical review of teacher administered rating scales. *Journal of Special Education*, 1973, *7*, 55–73.

Spivack, G., & Swift, M. *Hahnemann Elementary School Behavior Rating Scale: Manual*. Philadelphia: Department of Mental Health Services, Hahnemann Medical College and Hospital, 1975.

Spivack, G., & Swift, M. The Hahnemann High School Behavior (HHSB) Rating Scale. *Journal of Abnormal Child Psychology*, 1977, *5*, 299–307.

Spivack, G., Swift, M., & Prewitt, J. Syndromes of disturbed classroom behaviors. *Journal of Special Education*, 1972, *5*, 269–242.

Stevenson, H. W., Parker, T., Wilkinson, A., Hegion, A., & Fish, E. Predictive value of teacher ratings of young children. *Journal of Educational Psychology*, 1976, *68*, 507–517.

Stipek, D., Lamb, M., & Zigler, E. OPTI: A measure of children's optimism. *Educational and Psychological Measurement*, 1981, *41*(1), 131–150.

Sugar, M. Children of divorce. *Pediatrics*, 1970, *46*, 558–595.

Svanum, S., Bringle, R. G., & Mclaughlin, J. E. Father absence and cognitive performance in a large sample of six- to 11-year-old children. *Child Development*, 1982, *53*, 136–143.

Swift, M., & Spivack, G. Achievement-related classroom behavior of secondary school normal and disturbed children. *Exceptional Children*, 1969, *35*, 677–684. (a)

Swift, M., & Spivack, G. Classifying the relationship between academic success and overt classroom behavior. *Exceptional Children*, 1969, *35*, 99–104. (b)

Swift, M., & Spivack, G. Academic success and classroom behaviors in secondary schools. *Expectional Children*, 1973, *39*, 392–399.

Swift, M., Spivack, G., & Back, L. Patterns of disturbed classroom behavior of nondelinquent and delinquent adolescent girls. *Journal of Research in Crime and Delinquency*, 1973, *10*, 59–72.

Task Force on Pediatric Education. *The future of pediatric education*. Denver: Hirschfield, 1978.

Tucker, J., & Regan, R. A. Intactness of the home and behavioral problems in children. *Journal of Child Psychology and Psychiatry*, 1966, *7*, 225–233.

U.S. Bureau of the Census. Current Population Reports, Series P-23, No. 84. *Divorce, child custody, and child support*. Washington, D.C.: U.S. Government Printing Office, 1979.

U.S. Bureau of the Census. Current Population Reports, Series P-20, No. 371. *Household and family characteristics: March 1981*. Washington, D.C.: U.S. Government Printing Office, 1982. (a)

U.S. Bureau of the Census. Current Population Reports, Series P-20, No. 372. *Marital status and living arrangements: March 1981*. Washington, D.C.: U.S. Government Printing Office, 1982. (b)

Vineland Teachers Questionnaire, Standardization Edition (A/B). Circle Pines, Minn.: American Guidance Service, 1981.

Wallerstein, J. S., & Kelly, J. B. The effects of parental divorce: The adolescent experience. In E. Anthony & C. Koupernik (Eds.), *The child and his family* (Vol. 3). New York: Wiley, 1974.

Wallerstein, J. S., & Kelly, J. B. The effects of parental divorce: Experiences of the preschool child. *Journal of the American Academy of Child Psychiatry*, 1975, *14*, 600–616.

Wallerstein, J. S., & Kelly, J. B. The effects of parental divorce experiences of the child in later latency. *American Journal of Orthopsychiatry*, 1976, *46*, 256–269.

Wallerstein, J. S., & Kelly, J. B. California's children of divorce. *Psychology Today*, 1980, *13*(8), 66–76. (a)

Wallerstein, J. S., & Kelly, J. B. *Surviving the breakup: How children and parents cope with divorce*. New York: Basic Books, 1980. (b)

Warshak, R. A., & Santrock, J. W. The impact of divorce in father-custody and mother-custody homes: The child's perspective. In L. A. Kurdek (Ed.), *Children and divorce*. New directions for child development, *19*. San Francisco: Jossey-Bass, 1983.

Wechsler, D. *Wechsler Intelligence for Children—Revised*. New York: Psychological Corporation, 1974.

Westman, J. Effect of divorce in a child's personality development. *Medical Aspects of Human Sexuality*, 1972, *6*, 38–55.

Westman, J., Cline, D., Swift, W., & Krammer, D. Role of child psychiatry in divorce. *Archives of General Psychiatry*, 1970, *23*, 416–420.

Willis, J., Smithy, D., & Holliday, S. Item level validity of the Devereux Elementary School Behavior Rating Scale. *Journal of Abnormal Child Psychology*, 1979, *7*, 327–335.

Zakariya, S. B. Another look at the children of divorce: Summary report of the study of school needs of one-parent children. *Principal*, 1982, *62*, 34–37.

5   Clinical Applications of Direct Behavioral Observation

A Look at the Past and the Future

Barbara Hanna Wasik

[Since] there are no "shortcuts" in clinical assessment, a useful understanding of the child's problem behavior can only be obtained by focusing on the child's behavior interactions with his various social environments. (Wahler, House, & Stambaugh, 1976, p. 1)

The direct observation of behavior—a method of data collection used in research and clinical practice—has a long tradition in the history of psychology. It has been used to study the child in the natural environment, mother–infant interactions, and teacher–student interactions. Its use in clinical work is most closely related with behavioral approaches to therapy. This close relationship could have been anticipated since methods of clinical assessment typically follow from one's theoretical approaches to therapy.

In a comparison of traditional and behavioral assessment, Goldfried and Kent (1972) described the traditional approach as being directed toward an understanding of an individual's underlying personality characteristics or traits as a means for predicting behavior (e.g., projective tests and personality inventories). Behavioral assessment, by contrast, is directed toward providing information essential to the selection and implementation of appropriate treatment procedures. Behavioral treatment approaches that gained momentum in the 1960s stimulated interest in clinical behavioral assessment (Goldfried & Kent, 1972) because the successful use of such procedures necessitated an adequate

Barbara Hanna Wasik • School of Education, University of North Carolina, Chapel Hill, North Carolina 27514. This research was funded in part by the U.S. Department of Education Grant GO 0830001 1.

assessment of the problem behaviors and the variables maintaining those behaviors.

The close conceptual relationship between the direct observation of behavior and behavioral treatment procedures can be seen by reviewing early guidelines to clinicians for the conduct of their practice. Two of the first individuals to describe a role for clinicians that called for the direct observation of behavior were Ullmann and Krasner (1965), who saw behavior therapists as asking three questions:

> (a) What behavior is maladaptive, that is, what subject behaviors should be increased or decreased; (b) what environmental contingencies *currently* support the subject's behavior (either to maintain his undesirable behavior or to reduce the likelihood of his performing a more adaptive response); and (c) what environmental changes, usually reinforcing stimuli, may be manipulated to alter the subject's behavior. (p. 1)

Goldfried and Pomeranz (1968) also presented a description of what a clinician should focus on in order to determine the appropriate target for modification: (a) the relevant environmental antecedents, (b) the significant mediational responses and cues, (c) the observable maladaptive behavior itself, and (d) the consequent environmental changes. In both these models the role for the clinician is seen as requiring information from the direct observation of behavior. The views of these writers are also consistent with the model described by Baer, Wolf, and Risley (1968) in their elaboration of the dimensions or criteria for applied behavior analysis. They called for a concern with the actual behaviors of an individual that were both socially important and objectively measured.

Within behavioral approaches to therapy, the direct assessment of behavior in the natural setting has, at times, been viewed as not only necessary but sufficient for therapeutic assessment. Support for such exclusionary use, however, does not exist. Many individuals are presently calling for additional assessment procedures. Although most continue to see the need for the direct observation of behavior, they have also called for data on dimensions beyond the immediate antecedent and consequence conditions (Evans & Nelson, 1977). Examples of models of assessment that include a range of behaviors are the BASIC-ID model of Lazarus (1973), which includes the variables of behavior, affect, sensations, imagery, conditions, interpersonal factors, and drugs, and the S-O-R-K-C model of Kanfer and Saslow (1969), which adds the variables of schedules or contingency-related conditions (K), and the biological condition of the organism (O) to the A-B-C model originally adapted by many others (A = antecedent conditions, B = behavior, C = consequences). Peterson (1968) also recommended a broad scope for a conceptual framework for clinical assessment. He indicated that although behavior should be accented, the internal psychological functioning of individuals should also be included as well as the behavior of the individual in relation to society. These broader models have been influenced by theory that recognizes the contribution of a range of social, psychological, and biological variables in influencing behavior.

Regardless of the recommendations for broader behavioral assessment models, throughout the 1960s and 1970s numerous studies were conducted primarily using the direct observation of behavior to identify target behaviors and assess treatment effects. In fact, the history of the clinical applications of direct behavioral observations is often viewed as beginning in the 1960s with two events: (1) the application of learning theory and principles to maladaptive behavior and (2) the use of single-subject research designs in the experimental analysis of behavior. Writers have devoted attention both to the review of the theories and events that led to the development of behavior modification, behavior theory, or applied behavior analysis (e.g., Kanfer & Phillips, 1970; Ross, 1981; Ullmann & Krasner, 1965) and to the development of single-subject research design (Hersen & Barlow, 1976; Kazdin, 1982; Kratochwill, 1978). Although many writers recognize the integral role the direct observation of behavior has played in both these developments, few have focused directly on the historical developments of behavioral observations or considered how this method of data collection has itself influenced other developments. The purpose of this chapter is to provide a closer scrutiny of the direct observation of behavior, to consider its role in the study of child behavior and in clinical intervention, and to suggest possible future directions in research and practice.

To begin a historical account with the 1960s, however, does not do justice to the work that was conducted previously by a number of scholars. Consequently, in this chapter, a brief historical view of the role of the direct observation of behavior will be considered. From this historical view of research over the past century, one can see four different trends or developments that have contributed to our current status on the use of direct observational data for clinical purposes. These four trends can be distinguished as follows: (1) the early child development movement that focused upon observing the child primarily to obtain information on the child's social development in the natural setting, (2) the use of observational procedures in the laboratory setting to study infant and child behavior and parent–child interactions, (3) the observation of teacher and student behavior to understand and ultimately to modify the teaching–learning process, and (4) the systematic application of the principles of behavior change to child behavior, a development that occurred simultaneously with the use of research designs appropriate for studying individual child behavior. In reviewing the contributions from these different developments, the early child study movement will be considered first, divided into work up to 1940 and that between 1940 and 1960. Then the other three developments, all beginning around 1960, will be discussed.

By the 1970s, as behavioral clinicians and researchers looked at alternative treatment approaches such as self-management and cognitive behavior modification, and at alternative assessment procedures such as rating scales, hypothetical tasks, and permanent products of behavior, serious questions were being raised on the continuing utility and productiveness of the direct observation of behavior. In the final section of this chapter the author will address the need to continue to collect direct observational data while integrating such data with alternative assessment procedures in research and practice.

1. Historical Developments

Gellert (1955) identified a number of the major methodological issues that pertain to the direct measurement of child behavior. On the issue of reliability, she identified 13 factors that could contribute to poor reliability: (1) inadequate sampling, (2) lack of precision in defining behavior, (3) complexity of method of recording, (4) rapid, complex interaction, (5) difference in perspective of observers, (6) individual differences in degree of decisiveness of activities of subjects observed, (7) constant errors due to observer bias (overweighting, timing, "halo" effects), (8) requiring higher order inferences in classifying behavior, (9) demanding the simultaneous observation of too many variables, (10) excessively long periods of observation without interspersed rest periods, (11) inadequate training of observers, (12) the effect of individual observers upon the behavior of the subjects, and (13) degree of acquaintance with the subjects.

That so many critical methodological issues could be identified by Gellert almost 30 years ago causes one to wonder about the extent of the use of direct observation of children prior to 1955. Who were the early researchers; what were they studying; what methods did they use; what did they find; and lastly, what contribution did this early work have for clinical work with children?

1.1. Early Roots of Child Observation

Wright (1960) regards diary description as the oldest method of studying child development. This method requires the common recording techniques of a diary, namely narrative descriptions, in order to draw a sequential account of growth changes and behavior episodes from the life history of the child. Wright imposes the following definition on this method:

> The notations and descriptions necessarily are selective in the face of innumerable events that pass in an endless procession. Yet, they are not capriciously selective in the sense that the observer sets down only what is arresting. The entries in diary records are ruled on the contrary by a stable and objective principle of limitation, namely, that of recording in sequence new behavioral events in the behavior continuum of one subject, usually an infant or a child of preschool age. A special feature of the method has always been close and essentially continuous contact between the subject and the observer, who have invariably lived together as child and parent or other guardian. (p. 80)

The first psychological diary of longitudinal development may well have been Tiedemann's (1787) observations on the mental development of the child (Cairns, 1983). Almost a century later, Darwin's *Expressions of the Emotions in Men and Animals* (1872) and Preyer's two-volume work, *The Mind of the Child* (1888–1889), both using the method of direct observations, stimulated interest in studying the development of the child. One of the most notable uses of diaries as a method of data collection was by Piaget (1931), whose detailed observations on his own three children served as the basis for many of his extremely influential theories of child development.

An advantage of the diary description is that it provides information on the continuity of behavior, information that can only be obtained by observing children on an individual basis over a period of time. This point, so basic to the philosophy of the experimental analysis of behavior, was emphasized very succinctly by Shinn (1900). In presenting the record she had kept on her niece during the first year of life, she wrote the following:

> The biographical method of child study has the inestimable advantage of showing the process of evolution going on, the actual unfolding of one stage out of another, and the steps by which the changes come about. No amount of comparative statistics could given this. If I should find out that a thousand babies learned to stand at an average age of forty-six weeks and two days, I should not know as much that is important about standing, as a stage in human progress, as I should after watching a single baby carefully through the whole process. (p. 11)

Shinn's philosophy of observation reads like the forerunner to single-subject research designs. Her observational methodology, like that of others at the time, however, was not very systematic. We have to turn to later writers to look for more systematic methods of observation.

Goodenough and Anderson (1931) describe two methods for the systematic observation of child behavior. The first they label *situational* analysis; the second method was the time sample or *method of short samples*. The situational method was appropriate for studying such variables as the differences in indoor versus outdoor play, or the differences in nursery school versus home behavior. The time sample method was viewed as being useful for the study of individual differences in behavior and a considerable amount of data on each subject was considered necessary.

According to Goodenough and Anderson (1931), Olson (1929) developed the use of the time sample method and employed it in a study of the "nervous habits" in school children. Because of the similarity of Olson's procedures to many that were independently developed for use in the 1960s, it is instructive to read Goodenough's and Anderson's description:

> Olson's procedure was devised particularly for use with large groups of children in a situation where the subjects are not moving about and are in close proximity to each other. . . . An ideal situation of this kind is provided by the ordinary school class-room. A plan of the seating arrangement can be prepared in advance, and the records of the individual subjects entered directly on this behavior, such as inserting the finger into the mouth (regardless of the length of time it was kept there) and to record the number of five minute periods out of a total of twenty in which this form of behavior was observed to occur. Since an entire group was being observed simultaneously, it was not found feasible to attempt to record every occurrence of the event in question, but only to indicate for each individual subject whether or not it was observed at least once during a given five minute period. The highest possible score for each child would thus be equal to the number of separate time units included within the total series of observations. . . . This method has the great advantage of being very economical of time, since an entire group of subjects can be observed simultaneously in little more than the time required to secure an equal amount of data for a single subject when the individual method is used. (p. 431–432)

Several problems were noted with Olson's method. Among these was its lack of suitability for the study of complex behavior. Second, since the observations were taken in immediate succession, temporary factors could influence the behavior. Goodenough and Anderson suggested that one avoid the latter problem by scattering the observations over a number of occasions.

The first monograph in the *Child Development Monograph* series, edited by Thomas (1929), described several time sampling techniques for studying social behavior. Among the variables studied was physical contact between children; behaviors such as hitting, pushing, pulling, and pointing were recorded as well as information on which child initiated the behavior and which child was the recipient. Another variable studied was the reaction of children to material objects and to people. Goodenough (1930) used a 1-min time sample procedure to study laughter, compliance, anger, and talkativeness, among other behaviors, in a study of the interrelationships in the behavior of young children.

One of the most noteworthy aspects of the early use of a time-sampling technique was the identification of a number of factors affecting the reliability of the data. Reliability issues were noted, both the variability in the behavior of the same subjects from day to day, and the variability due to observational errors. Using two simultaneous observers independently to record the behavior of the subjects was seen as a way to check for an error of the second type. Another methodological factor was the frequency with which a behavior occurred. In fact, behaviors with a very low frequency were not viewed as appropriate for study by the time sample method.

Parten's (1932) research on the social participation among preschool children has been widely referenced, and her findings on cooperative, parallel, and solitary play among young children have served as a stimulus for other studies. In many ways, Parten's study of the social play of preschoolers could be considered the forerunner of the work at the University of Washington 30 years later in which individuals were involved in not only recording but also modifying the social behavior of nursery school children. Less well recognized, however, was Parten's innovative work in the area of time-sampling techniques and her use of these techniques in the study of child behavior. She took care in defining her categories, giving detailed examples to distinguish one kind of play from another. She also provided checks on the accuracy of observers by having assistants record data while she was recording and comparing each observer's record with her own. Her study may also have been the first systematic comparison of teacher perception and observed child behavior. Although some concerns can be identified regarding her procedure, she recognized the importance of studying differences in teacher perception of child behavior and actual child behavior almost a half century before others began to do so.

These early accomplishments were not limited to the study of the child in the nursery school setting. Goodenough (1931), for example, had a group of parents who "kept records on every outburst of anger shown by their children over intervals lasting from one to four months."

1.2. Contributions

Clearly these early researchers were true pioneers in child psychology. They contributed both a methodology and a body of knowledge. They were the first group of researchers to use systematic time sampling to obtain knowledge on child development. They identified issues in reliability, generality, and validity. They also recognized the advantages of the objectivity in time sampling compared to diary records, the importance of setting variables, the necessity of trained observers, and the problems with complex codes, such as coding too many behaviors at a time and coding infrequently occurring behaviors.

In their work is the beginning of a conceptualization of a developmental perspective to child psychology, recognizing that some behaviors are more likely to occur at one age than at another. Not only did they study typical behaviors in nursery school settings, they also looked at behaviors that today would be considered problematic from an emotional or adjustment viewpoint. Among these are the study of anger, resistance, noncompliance, aggression, crying, isolated play, and the recording of nervous habits in children. Also, they conducted research on the relationship between the direct observations of child behavior and teacher perceptions of child behavior, an area of research still important today.

1.3. Developments between 1940 and 1960

The 1940s and 1950s were marked by a slowdown in the effort psychologists were devoting to observational studies of child behavior, a phenomenon consistent with the general depression of research in developmental psychology during this same time period (Cairns, 1983). Wright (1960), for example, shows that there were 53 empirical, observational studies of child behavior (in selected journals) between 1930 and 1939, compared to 20 between 1940 and 1949, and 19 between 1950 and 1959. When Peterson and Hartmann (1975) identified 12 classic or near-classic references from the literature on observational methodology to determine how often they were referenced, only three were listed between 1940 and 1960: Arrington, 1943; Heyns and Lippitt, 1954; and Wright, 1960.

Gellert (1955) also noted this decline in her observation that from the late 1930s on there was a decrease in the popularity of systematic observation as a research method. She accounted for this decline in part by the fact that observational data are time-consuming and cumbersome to collect. She speculated that another contributing factor was that observational techniques did not lend themselves at that time to the study of such phenomena of personality as social perception or guilt feelings. Such methods also seemed to lack the "clean, decisive flavor of an experiment." Parke (1979) also noted that the 1950s were characterized by nonobservational approaches while interview techniques took on more importance.

Another very plausible explanation for the decline in popularity during this time was the attention being devoted to the statistical analysis of data. R. A. Fisher's efforts in the development of sophisticated statistical procedures during the 1930s were beginning to dominate research design in psychological research. By the 1950s the accepted design for applied research was the group comparison design, in spite of the history in psychology of studying individuals over time (Hersen & Barlow, 1976).

Hersen and Barlow (1976) described two approaches that were pursued by applied researchers who were reacting to the difficulties of the group-comparison approach. In one of these approaches, components of the therapeutic process, such as relationship variables, were studied. A second approach was the naturalistic study. Both approaches are similar in that the correlation between dependent variables and therapist or patient variables are studied. Experimental manipulation of independent variables was not part of these methods.

The emphasis upon such naturalistic procedures was also characteristic of the research during the 1940s and 1950s for the study of child behavior emphasizing ecological procedures. The ecological perspective was directly influenced by the methods and the theories of Lewin (1931a, b). Lewin not only saw the person and the environment as interdependent, but also called for studying individual children in their own environments, as contrasted with the alternative methods being proposed by others. Research in this area is exemplified by the work of Barker and Wright (1949, 1955) who studied the behavior of such specific populations as children in a small town in the midwestern United States. Wright (1960) also studied the behavior of children in communities of different sizes to try to link child behavior with conditions in their natural surroundings. Ecological procedures in field settings were also being used during this time by Gump and Schoggen (e.g., Gump, Schoggen, & Redl, 1957).

The research of these investigators involved more than just obtaining direct observational data. They were refining a methodology that has been described by Wright (1960) as specimen description. Wright saw specimen description and diary description as the two open methods of observational child study. Specimen description differs from diary description in that it includes the "continuous observing and narrative recording of a behavior sequence under chosen conditions of time and life." The observer tries to record everything that is seen that pertains to the behavior and situation of the child. Although this method was used by earlier researchers, it seems to be most clearly associated with researchers such as Wright, Barker, Schoggen, and Gump, who were using, refining, and publicizing these procedures during the 1950s.

One of the strengths of the specimen record procedure is that it describes behavior in context by including a description of the situation in which the behavior occurs. The rationale for recording the situation is the belief that the actual occurrence of a behavior and its significance are dependent upon situational variables. By providing a continuous record of behavior and the situation in which it occurs, one can conduct sequential analysis of the behavior of the child. If, for example, a child is observed in an interaction with the mother, one can note what behaviors of each served as antecedents and consequences to the other.

Another advantage of specimen records is that they are relatively neutral from a theoretical standpoint compared to other methods that incorporate many *a priori* decisions on the behavior to be observed.

Obvious disadvantages also exist. Among the disadvantages are the difficulties in reducing specimen records to a manageable level for analysis. A second disadvantage is that this recording procedure does not lend itself to recording systematically the experimental manipulation of variables. Another disadvantage is that one cannot readily determine reliability estimates or agreement between observers, another characteristic making it less than suitable for use in the experimental analysis of behavior.

1.4. Contributions 1940–1960

The contributions of this period can be viewed as the following: (1) speciman recording, (2) emphasis upon situation or setting variables, (3) emphasis upon ecological procedures, and (4) sequential analysis of behavior. These contributions have served as a legacy that can be used in our present work. These researchers were proposing an ecological approach to assessment years before others began to propose an ecological approach to intervention. They stressed the importance of knowledge about situational variables as critical for understanding a person's behavior in a given situation. In addition, they stressed the sequential analysis of interactions. The methodology, however, did not lend itself easily to the resolution of measurement issues, and the knowledge that was obtained did not seem to be integrated with or based upon theoretical models of interaction and thus may have suffered from an absence of unifying interpretations.

2. Developments between 1960 and 1980

Earlier we referred to four trends that contributed to our current knowledge on observational data. Three began during the 1960s. First was the shift from field- to laboratory-based research within developmental and social psychology combined with a renewed interest in studying infancy. Second was the emphasis within educational psychology on the observation of teacher and student behavior and teacher–student interaction data for the purpose of teacher training. The third major development was the systematic application of behavior principles to problem child behavior within the area of applied behavior analysis and its overlap with activities in clinical and school psychology.

2.1. Laboratory Studies on Parent–Child Interactions

Parke (1979), in describing the historical events in social and developmental psychology, saw a major methodological shift in the 1960s to the laboratory experiment as the dominant procedure for studying social interaction. He described this shift as bringing developmental psychology into the mainstream of psychology and of advancing our knowledge of perception, learning, and social development. At the forefront of research on the infant in laboratory settings was the work of Rheingold (1969) and Ainsworth (1969, 1973). Among the measures that were developed for the direct observation of infants in such settings were ones for studying mother–infant interactions (Ainsworth, 1969; Brown & Bakeman, 1975; Ramey, Farran, & Campbell, 1979), children's reactions to unfamiliar adults (Ainsworth, 1973; Rheingold, 1969; Rheingold & Eckerman, 1973), sharing (Rheingold, Hay, & West, 1976), and the social play of children (Eckerman, Whatley, & Kutz, 1975). The early focus of this research was on the influence of the mother on the child's social development based in part upon the strong belief in the importance of these interactions for the later normal social development of the child. Much of this early work was dominated by psychoanalytic theory as evidenced, for example, by the attention to attachment behavior. Later more attention was focused on the mother's influence on the child in relation to the child's cognitive and language development. The measures developed for the study of mother–child interactions have included categories that make possible a microanalysis of the verbal and nonverbal interactions in the mother–child dyad.

Two concerns, however, began to impact the methodology of social and developmental psychology (Parke, 1979). One concern was with the early and almost exclusive reliance upon a unidirectional model of parent–child relationships. Within this model, the direction of influence was from the parent to the child, a view based upon psychoanalytic theory. Although a bidirectional or reciprocal interaction view had been advocated earlier by such individuals as Lewin (1931a, b), Piaget (1931), and Sears (1951), it was not until later that this view came to be more widely accepted. The second concern was with the dominance of laboratory-based research which might be creating an unrealistic data base for theory on child development, a concern expressed by many individuals, including Barker (1963), Bandura (1973), and Patterson (1974). On the basis of these concerns, investigators have called for bidirectional or reciprocal models in mother–infant research (e.g., Parke, 1979; Ramey, Farran, Campbell, & Finkelstein, 1978) and for a balance between laboratory and field-based research (Bronfenbrenner, 1974; Parke, 1976; 1979).

These later events in social and developmental psychology in which the importance of observing reciprocal interactions in natural settings were being recognized and pursued were similar to developments occurring in the other two trends in the direct observation of behavior.

2.2. Observation of Teacher–Student Interactions

The second trend occurred within educational psychology, in which research was being focused on the study of teacher–student interactions. The objective of such research was to gain information that would be relevant to the training of teachers in order to enhance the cognitive and academic behavior of children. Later, accountability of teaching effectiveness became a strong motivator for classroom observational research (Borich, 1977). One of the first and best-known systems is that of Flanders (1960, 1964), who developed a social-interaction model of teaching which suggested how various teaching and learning activities are related. His own work dated back to 1957 (Amidon & Hough, 1967) when he first constructed a matrix to study the interdependence of coded classroom events. The work of Anderson (1939) and Withall (1949) on classroom behavior actually predates Flanders and serves somewhat as a bridge with the early child development movements. Flanders's work, however, was one of the most influential in stimulating research in this area. Within his system, the teacher is viewed as expanding student participation when using an indirect approach, and as restricting the student's freedom of participation when exercising direct influence. His work is particularly noteworthy because of the recognition of the reciprocal nature of teacher–student behavior. Ober, Bentley, and Miller (1971) modified Flanders's interaction system from a 10-category system to a 20-category system so that additional categories of student talk could be recorded. This system, the Reciprocal Category System (RCS), made possible the observation of classroom interaction while also recording the socioemotional climate of the classroom.

The field moved forward so quickly in the 1960s that *Mirrors of*

Behavior, published in 17 volumes (Simon & Boyer, 1967, 1970a, 1970b), documented 92 observational systems, of which 73 were specific to the classroom. Rosenshine and Furst (1973) conducted a detailed analysis of these 73 classroom observation systems. In their review, they analyzed instruments with both explicit and implicit theoretical or empirical bases, those that were modifications of other systems, and those that had author-originated category systems. They also reviewed the use of these instruments to study teaching. They concluded that the research had not been highly productive and called for several redirections in future work. These suggestions included the need to use variables from the existing category systems (numbering over 200 at that time) and not to develop new codes. They also suggested the need to study setting variables such as the textbook and supplementary materials, the relevance of the materials to the ability of the class, the amount of time a teacher spends preparing a class to do future work, and the influence of the school environment.

Within this area, a very productive line of research was initiated in the 1970s as investigators studied the relationship between time-on-task and the achievement of children in classroom settings, work based in part upon Carroll's (1963) model of school learning that related time spent on task to learning rates and achievement (e.g., Bloom, 1974; McKinney, Mason, Perkerson, & Clifford, 1975; Walker & Hops, 1976; Wyne & Stuck, 1979). Positive findings between these variables leads one to ask how teachers can increase time on task, a question that gives an important focus to the study of the observation of teachers' classroom behavior. It should be noted that, although there may be a statistical relationship between time-on-task and achievement, the modification of an individual child's performance, particularly a child with learning disabilities, may not occur through an increase in attending behaviors.

Related to the time-on-task research is the emphasis upon the direct observation of teaching as part of procedures to evaluate teachers. Currently a growing number of states have mandated the observations of teachers as part of the evaluation process (Odden & Dougherty, 1982). Such political and educational factors have many implications for the direct observation of child behavior in school settings and should be noted by psychologists who study children in such settings.

2.3. *The Experimental Analysis of Behavior: Clinical Applications*

The third use of the direct observation of behavior in the 1960s was perhaps the most dramatic, since the direct observation of behavior was extended to the experimental analysis of behavior in which the intentional manipulation of variables was conducted both to validate a knowledge of behavior principles and to modify socially significant behavior in applied settings. Because this event has the most direct application to clinical child therapy, it will be addressed in more depth than the other two developments during this time.

One of the major contributions to the direct observation of child problem behavior was made by a group of researchers working at the University of Washington in the early 1960s. Several of these researchers were involved in a number of studies on normal nursery school children who were showing one or more problem behaviors. In all the studies frequency measures were collected on the problem behavior over time or else a time sampling procedure was used in which the percentage of time in a given behavior was calculated.

The general procedures in this set of nursery school studies were characterized by those developed in working with a 3-year-old girl who was showing an excessive amount of crawling (Harris, Johnston, Kelley, & Wolf, 1964). Direct observations were made of the time the child spent off her feet, and a modification program was developed in which she was reinforced with teacher attention for on-feet behavior such as standing and walking. Within a week of reinforcing on-feet behavior, the child's behavior approached a normal pattern. To confirm the effects of adult social reinforcement, the reinforcement procedures were reversed, then reinstated. When crawling was followed by attention, it increased again to problem levels, but decreased again when social attention was made contingent on on-feet behavior. The clear results of this study led to further work on the relationship between child behavior and teacher attention.

In one of the subsequent studies, the number of crying episodes of the nursery children were observed daily throughout both baseline and treatment phases (Hart, Allen, Buell, Harris, & Wolf, 1964). In another study, a child who was frequently engaged in solitary play was of concern. Observations were made on his interactions with adults and other children. An intervention program was developed based upon withholding adult attention for solitary play while providing it contingently for interactions with other children. As his social play increased, recording the time spent with adults also provided additional information on the child's behavior, even though it was not a specific focus of the intervention (Allen et al., 1964).

This series of studies is significant for several reasons. First, observational data were collected in a nursery school setting not simply to study a significant clinical behavior in an applied setting, but also to investigate the effectiveness of a planned intervention program to alter the target behavior in a socially desirable direction. This use of a field-based intervention procedure coupled with an experimental design while focusing on a problem behavior heralded new directions both in terms of therapeutic efforts and applied research.

Most of the work referenced above used a *specific observational code* for the measurement of behavior. An alternative method was also developed by the nursery school staff at the University of Washington and was referred to as a *general observational code* (Bijou, Peterson, & Ault, 1968). Use of a general code allows the study of many behaviors in a given situation. For example, the verbal and motor responses of a child can be coded while also recording physical and social behavior. In the general observation code referred to here, a three- to four-track data recording sheet is employed and the observer notes the occurrence of each designated behavior during a given time interval. This procedure also allows the recording of additional information on child behavior as, for example, noting whether the recorded physical or social behaviors are aggressive.

Several other investigators were concurrently attempting to bring about change by applying principles of behavior modification to problematic child behavior (Ullmann & Krasner, 1965). In the process of doing so, these individuals were also collecting observational data on the target behaviors. Among the clinical problems studied by these early investigators were tantrum behaviors (Williams, 1959), vomiting (Wolf, Birnbrauer, Williams, & Lawler, 1965), and a range of behaviors with children who were identified as autistic (Wolf, Risley, & Mees, 1964), retarded (Bijou & Orlando, 1961), and hyperactive (Patterson, 1965).

These studies laid the foundation for hundreds of intervention efforts in preschools, schools, homes, and other applied settings. The majority of studies followed in the vein of selecting a target behavior, usually the problem behavior, and plotting change in this dependent variable over time as a function of a planned intervention effort employing principles of behavior modification.

2.3.1. Multicategory Codes

Some investigators were beginning at this time to use multicategory codes for clinical research. Among the first published studies using a multicategory code for intervention purposes were those by O'Leary and Becker (1967), Madsen, Becker, and Thomas (1968) and those based on research conducted at the Education Improvement Program at Duke University (Sibley, Abbott, & Cooper, 1969; Wasik, Senn, Welch, & Cooper, 1969; Wasik, 1970). In these latter studies, Spaulding's Coping Analysis Schedule for Educational Settings (CASES) was used as the measure for child behavior (Simon & Boyer, 1967). The coding instrument was advantageous for use in intervention studies because its 13 categories covered a wide range of child behavior from aggression to withdrawal while also including prosocial behaviors: (1) aggressive behavior, (2) inappropriate attention-getting behavior, (3) manipulating and directing others, (4) resisting authority, (5) self-directed activity, (6) paying attention, (7) sharing and helping, (8) social interaction, (9) seeking support, assistance, and information, (10) following directions passively and submissively, (11) observing passively, (12) responding to internal stimuli, and (13) withdrawn behavior. These categories were both exhaustive and mutually exclusive. When used in classroom intervention studies, the subcategories were classified according to the appropriateness of the behavior for the classroom.

In an early study collecting both child and teacher behavior, behavior modification techniques were used with two second-grade girls to increase their appropriate behavior and to decrease their aggressive, resistive, and inappropriate attention-getting behavior (Wasik *et al.*, 1969). The girls' behavior was coded according to CASES. The teachers' behaviors were coded by a category code with the following categories: positive, neutral, structure, question, and negative. The treatment variable in this study was positive social reinforcement—attention and approval contingent upon desirable classroom behavior—which was presented, withheld, or withdrawn by use of a time-out procedure. Because the treatment depended upon changes in the behavior of the teacher, a major purpose of this study was an analysis of the behavior of the teachers who were carrying out the modification procedures. The collection of such interaction data was facilitated by the use of a standard Esterline Angus 20-pen event recorder that made possible the simultaneous and continuous recording of teacher and child behavior. By collecting both teacher and child behavior simultaneously, it was possible to study the relationship between teacher behavior and child behavior. Recording teacher behavior also made it possible to determine whether or not the treatment variables were implemented as designed.

Other researchers began to develop systems for coding different areas of problem child behavior in more depth. A major contribution to direct behavioral observation was made by Patterson and his colleagues at the Oregon Social Learning Center (Reid, 1978). They have focused primarily upon the study of aggression in children and adolescents and have concentrated their measurement upon the family. One of the basic assumptions of their approach is that intervention procedures must be continually evaluated and changed as necessary over the course of intervention. The role of the parents as change agents for their child's behavior is an essential component of the treatment program, and consequently the coding system requires a comprehensive analysis of parent–child interactions, not simply a report of child behavior.

At CORBEH, the Center at Oregon for Research in the Behavioral Education of the Handicapped, a social assessment system was developed for the early screening and identification of children who may be at risk for developing poor social interaction patterns. These are children whose current social behavior with their peers can be described as "withdrawn, non-verbal, and characteristically non-interactive" (Greenwood, Todd, Walker, & Hops, 1978). The assessment procedure has three steps that call for the teacher first to rank all children in the class on their estimated frequency of verbal interaction. Then the teacher is asked to rate each of the five lowest-ranking children on nine positive and assertive social behaviors found to be highly related to a child's behavior during free time. Using established normative data on all three measures, a ranked child is defined as withdrawn if he or she meets the criteria on each measure. Once a child is so identified, several directions can be taken for determining treatment directions.

Wahler, House, and Stambaugh (1976) developed an ecological assessment code for recording child problem behavior in home, school and other settings. The coding system itself is one of three parts of a behavioral assessment package. The first part is an interview that serves both to educate the adults and, at times, the child on such items as the contingency control of behavior and to obtain information on specific response deficits that characterize the child's deviance.

The second part of the package calls for the significant adults in the child's life, parents or teachers, to provide a record of problem behaviors. The adults are asked to keep track of relatively low-rate behaviors such as temper tantrums, stealing, fighting, and destroying property. The involvement of such adults is critical to this system, since the authors believe that adults in the problem child's natural environment should provide the majority of the observational data. The third part of the package, direct observation by a trained observer, provides the objective part of the assessment package that serves to validate the other two sources of information.

These three instruments described above have obtained a high level of visibility in the field and are often referenced as suggested measures for obtaining direct observational data (Atkeson & Forehand, 1981; Barkley, 1981; Evans & Nelson, 1977; Ollendick & Cerny, 1981). Other systems that have been used in research include those reported by O'Leary, Romanezyk, Kass, Dietz, and Santogrossi (1971) for school settings, Forehand, Peed, Roberts, McMahon, Griest, and Humphreys, (1978) for home settings, and Quilitch, Christopherson, and Risley (1977) for day-care environments.

2.3.2. Setting Variables

During the 1960s and 1970s most research within an applied behavior analysis was focused upon either the immediate consequences of behavior or upon specific antecedent or stimulus events. Setting variables—also referred to as environmental, ecological, or situation variables—were recognized as influencing behavior, but such recognition typically led to keeping settings constant rather than manipulating them. Although research on setting variables is relatively unexplored, compared to research on the specific and immediate antecedents and consequences of behavior, writers such as Kantor (1959) and Bijou and Baer (1961) saw setting events as an important conceptual dimension for applied behavior analysis and provided descriptions of such events. Kantor included setting factors as important circumstances influencing stimulus—response relationships. The examples he gave to illustrate setting events included such organism variables as hunger, age, or hygenic or toxic condition, or the presence or absence of certain environmental events. Setting factors both preceded and overlapped with specific stimulus–response functions and influenced occurrence of these functions.

Bijou and Baer (1961) also maintained a distinction between setting events and the more discrete stimulus events, describing setting events as more complicated than a stimulus event. They saw setting events as encompassing stimulus–response situations that in themselves can influence behavior at a later time. Their definition distinguishes two aspects of setting events. The first is that setting events are not simply durational in nature but can consist of environmental events and the person's response to the events. Second, these events can occur at an earlier point in time yet still influence the later occurrence of behavior (Wahler & Fox, 1981).

The related issue of generality of behavior from one setting to another was addressed by several investigators who were interested in determining whether changes in behavior as a function of treatment effects in one setting would carry over to other settings. Wahler (1969), for example, studied two children in both their home and school settings. Treatment procedures were implemented in the homes and the results showed that the behaviors changed in the predictable direction in the home but not in the schools.

Some recent studies exist in which child behavior under different setting conditions has been systematically assessed (e.g., Hamilton & Wasik, 1982; Wahler, 1980; Wasik, Day, & DiRenzo, 1982) or in which conditions have been modified (Fowler & Baer, 1981; Krantz & Risley, 1977; Weinstein, 1977). Hamilton and Wasik (1982) observed learning disabled (LD) and normal children in two different classroom settings. The results showed that when each group of children was observed in teacher-lead small reading groups, the attending behavior was very similar for each group. When the groups were observed during an independent work time, the LD children showed significantly less attending behavior than their normal normal peers, a result suggesting the situation specificity of attending behavior for LD children.

In another study the relationship between setting variables within the classroom and child behavior was studied (Wasik et al., 1982). The observation system that was used, (the Wasik–Day Open and Traditional Learning Environments and Children's Classroom Behavior Scale) has eight main categories of child behavior, with subcategories under each (Wasik & Day, 1977). The code includes setting variable codes and categories on academic behavior and appropriate and inappropriate classroom behavior. The eight categories are time, place, group leader, number in group, movement, academic behavior (e.g., reading, math), communication, and classroom behavior (e.g., appropriate attending). These categories were based in part upon setting variables considered important in arranging classroom environments for young children. The instrument has been used to collect data across kindergarten and first-grade children for a number of years.

An analysis of data collected over a period of three years showed a significant relationship between child behavior and whether an adult leader is identifiable. When a teacher was leading the group the attending behavior was higher than when there was no group leader. A relationship also was shown to exist between group size and attending behavior. In general, the percent of on-task or attending behavior was lowest when the children were working alone and highest in groups of 16–25 or more than 25. An increase in attending behavior occurred for children working alone to being with at least one other person. This finding seemed to be influenced by whether the teacher or another adult was directing the group. Such results have important implications for efforts aimed at increasing attending or on-task behavior for individual children or groups of children.

In one of the few studies modifying setting variables in classrooms, Weinstein (1977) observer children before and after a change in the physical layout of a self-contained open classroom of second- and third-grade children. With selected small-scale changes in the classroom, the children's behavior changed in predictable directions. Children used areas of the room they had specifically avoided, their range of behaviors increased, and the frequency of behavior in specific categories changed.

Wahler and Fox (1981) call for expanding methodological considerations in order to be able to address the issues of setting variables. These include the measurement unit, the temporal relationships among these units, and the mode of unit analysis. First, they see a need to measure more global entities. Then, when correlations are established between environmental variables and behavior, fine-grain analysis of setting variables could take place. Further, they call for a broadening of our considerations of temporal relationships as a guide to studying setting events. If we restrict outselves to studying only those events in close proximity to the target behavior, important controlling events may be left unexplored. In calling for considering more global units of behavior, they even suggest studying ones that it may not be possible to vary later. As an example from his own research, Wahler found that mothers' extra-family contacts appeared to be serving as a setting variable for problems within the family (Wahler, 1980). Consideration of such setting variables relates to the increasing concern with the social validation of behavior (Kazdin, 1977b; Wolf, 1978), for which data on such variables can potentially provide empirical support.

2.3.3. Contributions from Clinical Applications

Perhaps the biggest contribution of measurement procedures that focused on direct, observable behavior was that they made possible the study of environmental events that were important in changing behavior. The study of the consequences of behavior led to the confirmation of the importance of the behavior of socially significant others on the behavior of the child. Many other investigators began to demonstrate that the intentional or unintentional behavior of adults was influencing deviant child behavior. Parents (Becker, 1971; Forehand, Sturgis, McMahon, Aguar, Green, Wells, & Breiner, 1979; Herbert & Baer, 1972; Johnson & Katz, 1973; O'Dell, 1974; Patterson & Gullion, 1968; Wahler, Wenkel, Paterson, & Morrison, 1965) and teachers (Buckley & Walker, 1970; Hall, 1971; Madsen & Madsen, 1970, 1972) were being taught how to change their own behavior in order to bring about desired changes in a target child's behavior. Alternative contingency arrangements were being explored, including individual contingencies in a group setting, group contingencies, and token economy systems. Time out and other forms of withdrawing positive consequences were explored. The results of these efforts led to numerous publications written for teachers and parents describing for them how they could pinpoint, directly observe and record, and consequate targeted child behaviors in order to increase appropriate ones and decrease inappropriate ones. Parent training and teacher training became part of the culture of child behavior therapy, and teaching parents and teachers to become recorders of child behavior became a part of the therapeutic procedures.

The direct observation of behavior also made major contributions to knowledge on the various childhood disorders during this time, ranging from autism to hyperactivity and conduct disorders. Although in this chapter knowledge of childhood disorders cannot be covered in any depth, it should be noted that behavioral observation has played a larger role than simply providing a method for assessing problem behavior and evaluating treatment effects. It has also served both to validate existing theories or assumptions and to provide an empirical base for the development of other theories.

In the area of autism, direct observation of behavior provided the validation that such children would respond to behavior principles (Wolf *et al.*, 1964), could learn to decrease self-stimulatory behavior, and learn language skills, all of which had been questioned at earlier times (Lovaas, Koegel, Simmons, & Long, 1973). Observational data has also increased our knowledge in the areas of hyperactivity and learning disabilities (Lahey, Hobbs, Kupfer, & Delameter, 1979) and on socially isolated (Gottman, 1977) and conduct-disordered children (Patterson, 1979). Conduct-disordered children, for example, have been found to display high rates of aversive behavior, and parents in turn respond with high rates of aversive responses (Forehand, King, Peed, & Yoder, 1975).

2.4. Sources of Inaccuracy in Observational Data

In considering the clinical applications of the systematic observation of behavior, several sources of inaccuracy that may effect the interpretation of such data will be described. These categories, originally conceptualized by Cronbach and his colleagues (Cronbach, Gleser, Nanda, & Rajaratnam, 1972) and elaborated on by Wasik and Loven (1980), are the following: (1) inaccuracy that arises from characteristics of the recording procedure and the instrumentation used, (2) inaccuracy that arises from characteristics of the observer, and (3) inaccuracy that arises from characteristics unique to the physical setting itself. These sources of inaccuracy interact in any given situation, thus contributing varying amounts of variance to the data as a function of the specific situation.

Several sources described inaccuracy in more depth than will be done here and should be referred to by those who desire more information (e.g., Johnson & Bolstad, 1973; Kazdin, 1977a; Kent & Foster, 1977; Wasik & Loven, 1980; Wildman & Erickson, 1977). The detail covered in those articles makes it unnecessary to discuss all the issues in depth here. Rather, this section will delineate some considerations from the standpoint of the practitioner.

Inaccuracy that arises from characteristics of the recording procedure and instruments used can be addressed in part by the clinician. Code complexity is one area that can often be varied in order to reduce bias. Mash and McElwee (1974) showed that higher observer agreements were obtained for four-category code systems compared to eight-category code systems. The clinician may wish to limit target behaviors to one, two, or possibly three at the maximum. In fact, the clinician will most likely not employ a complex category system and may not even use a time-sampling procedure. A frequency count of relatively discrete behaviors within a given time period may be the preferred data collection method. Such frequency counts or event recording may be the method of choice for participant observers, whether teachers, parents, or others.

The sampling procedures to be used to collect data will also effect the accuracy of the data. Repp, Roberts, Slack, Repp, and Berkler (1976) concluded from their research that there is an interaction among the rate and pattern of responding, the data collection procedures, and the data reported. Clinicians may be faced with the possibility of infrequent observations, a procedure that may result in a very inaccurate estimate of behavior. Care must be taken to assure that if observation time is limited observations occur in different settings or across days. Generalization in the absence of such procedures may not be possible.

Methods used to calculate observer agreement can be a source of variance. In clinical applications, the biggest obstacle may be arranging for any opportunity to check on the accuracy of a given observer. All the problems that have been delineated with trained observers are very probably magnified with participant observers (Hay, Nelson, & Hay, 1980). An often-mentioned problem with participant observers is the fact that observation is imposed upon their ongoing activities (teaching, parenting) while nonparticipant observers are free to devote full time to observing.

The second major category of inaccuracy is that of observer characteristics, which can be influenced by a number of variables. Among these are expectations, reactitivy to reliability assessment, observer drift, amount of training and experience, fatigue, and boredom. Self-observation by children, parents, or teachers takes on its own set of variance, especially that of reactivity to coding data.

In clinical work, expectancy may be much more difficult to control. Unless trained naive observers are employed, individuals will normally be knowledgeable about the child and the target behaviors that are of concern. Studies on expectancy have not shown a clear effect on the accuracy of observational data. Such studies, however, have typically focused on nonparticipant observers who were provided information on specific children (Kent, O'Leary, Diament, & Dietz, 1974; Shuller & McNamara, 1976). In a study addressing the question of the effect of background knowledge of an individual on observational data, King, Erhmann, and Johnson (1952) found that when one or both observers had background knowledge, observer agreements decreased. The possibility of bias with observers with background knowledge should not rule out having such individuals code data, but it does call for additional care in training and regular checks for accuracy.

In attempting to control for observer bias, Kazdin (1977b) has suggested that feedback, if given, should relate to the accuracy of observations and not to any changes in observed behavior. With participant observers, feedback on the actual changes in behavior may not be preventable or desirable.

The third major category of bias to be discussed here is that contributed by setting characteristics. The two dominant variables in this category are the reactions of the person being observed and the ecological variables of the setting itself (Wasik & Loven, 1980). Arrington (1943) was one of the first to note the potential reaction of the person being observed to the observer. She stressed that people know when they are being observed and will adapt their behavior to the observer's presence. She enumerated three conditions that should result in less distraction by the observer: (1) observations that occur during informal activity when observer movement is not restricted, (2) situations in which visitors are common, and (3) shifting by the observer of attention from individual to individual, this not calling attention to any one individual.

Most individuals have assumed that there would be reactivity on the part of the person being observed. In research by Mercatoris and Craighead (1974), Nelson, Kapust, and Dorsey (1978), and Johnson and Bolstad (1975), the results have not provided empirical support for changes in child, teacher, or parent behavior as a function of being observed. One should not necessarily assume at this point, however, that there is no reactivity to observer presence. First, in the above studies care was taken for the observer to be nonintrusive. Second, an individual's reactivity to being observed may also be specific to certain behaviors. For example, child abuse or very negative punishment may be very unlikely to occur in the presence of an observer.

Ecological or setting variables can also influence the accuracy of behavioral observations. Wahler and Leske (1973), for example, have shown that observers are not as sensitive as they might be to recording changes of a target child when the behavior of peers remained constant. Cunningham and Tharp (1981) also demonstrated sources of variance that are present in the observational setting. In studying global and specific observation condition, they found that the systematic observation was more resistive to influences in the environment than global methods.

2.5. Contributions of the Period from 1960 to the Present

Three major developments concerned with the direct observation of behavior can be identified beginning around 1960. In each area researchers and clinicians have struggled with similar issues of methodology, technology, and theory. Numerous observation codes have been developed. Systematic research has been conducted on methodological issues. Each area has contributed knowledge on child behavior based upon empirical studies. Advances have been made in our knowledge of normal and abnormal child behavior and on ways of modifying problem child behavior.

Yet, there are concerns with this work. One is the failure of exchange of information across the areas. Second is the influence of theory that has sometimes restricted the range of variables under study and led to possibly narrow interpretations of the data. At other times there has been an accumulation of data without sufficient attention to ways of integrating the knowledge that has been obtained.

3. Future Directions

The review of historical and current trends in the direct observation of behavior in this chapter was presented in order to place the developments in perspective and to serve as a knowledge base for making suggestions for future directions. In a review of these trends, the admonition that those who ignore history are doomed to repeat it comes often to mind, for considerable evidence exists to suggest that much of the work of the early pioneers had been lost on contemporary researchers. Furthermore, there appears to be little exchange of ideas, data, and methodology across the three concurrent trends. On the basis of this observation, a suggestion for the future is that we attend more to concurrent developments so that we can learn from, rather than repeat, the work of our colleagues. Another observation concerns the references made by writers across time to the importance of sociological phenomena. Although data from sociology have not been covered here, a consideration of the research and theory within sociology and its relationship with psychological phenomena can enhance our understanding of the child.

Three major recommendations for future efforts emerged from a study of the past developments. First is that there is a need for models to help integrate and interpret the data that are collected across time—broad models that are not restricted in their ability to incorporate important phenomena that influence individual behavior. A model proposed here for integrating data is that of reciprocal interactions; this model has been proposed by many others but has not always influenced research and practice. Yet, it has surfaced in every area of psychology that has studied the child in interactions with others (e.g., Bandura, Flanders, Parke, Levin, Piaget, & Sears).

Within the reciprocal interaction model, the child is viewed as both influencing and being influenced by the environment. This view necessitates viewing the child as an active influence on others, capable of modifying his or her own environment. Viewed developmentally, as the child's intellectual, verbal, and physical capacities develop, the child should take on an increasing active role in the reciprocal process. In the same way that individuals within a child's environment can be influenced by the child, they can also be influenced by other variables, such as their own physiological state or other events or people in their own lives. These variables can then influence the adults' interactions with a given child, and their impact should not be ignored.

In addition to considering a reciprocal interaction model, we must consider both an expanded time frame within which we should focus attention and a broader range of variables in order to look for meaningful and significant relationships of the child and the environment. An expanded time frame means going beyond immediate antecedent and consequent events to a consideration of a range of past and present setting events. It also means consideration of what the subjects say they plan to do in the future, information that may be very valuable in interpreting or modifying present behavior.

A broader consideration of ecological, behavioral, and cognitive variables will influence methodology and measures. It leads us to a multidimensional model for data collection. Direct observation of behavior should be a part of this model, but so should information from a variety of other sources, including setting variables, the perceptions of significant others, the child's perceptions of his or her own behavior, and products of a child's behavior.

The need to look at integrating models as well as an expanded time scope and multidimensional data collection applies both to those primarily in research positions and those in clinical practice. In the remainder of this section, suggestions for future work will be viewed separately under research and clinical headings. Since research and practice are distinguished here, it is relevant to look for a moment at the practitioner–scientist model and to decide whether looking at future directions under these two different headings violates this tradition within clinical psychology. Within the practitioner–scientist model, an integration of research and practice was called for. This model was more workable when applied to those who were primarily in research settings. The situation has changed considerably in the past 15 years, with many more psychologists in private practice or working primarily in other service programs. Perhaps it is timely to recognize that within the practitioner–scientist model one might have two kinds of professionals, the primary researcher addressing clinical or socially significant issues and the primary clinician who may find opportunities to validate his or her work experimentally in the course of professional practice. This distinction suggests a recognition and acceptance of constraints within alternative professional settings and differences in agency or institutional goals for research and practice. This view would be consistent with a theme that has emerged in the literature–that some methodologies and procedures are appropriate for research purposes but are not possible at the same level within a clinical setting (Emmelkamp, 1981; Hayes & Nelson, 1981; Wilson, 1981). Acceptance of this view should make us aware that future assessment activities may be different for those who are primarily engaged in research versus those who are primarily engaged in practice. Among these differences in activities are the amount of data collected, the range of measures used, the unit of analysis, and the opportunity to control variables experimentally.

3.1. Research-Oriented Psychologists

For those primarily engaged in research, the following topics are suggested as ones that may be addressed in the future: (1) technology, (2) methodology, (3) development of assessment instruments, (4) comparison of alternative assessment instruments, (5) validation of new treatment approaches, (6) normative data on clinical and nonclinical populations, and (7) validation of theories of normal and abnormal child psychology.

3.1.1. Technology

Within the field of observational data, the paper, pencil, and stop watch or other timing device has been the mainstay of recording aids. For most clinical purposes, this procedure will probably continue into the future. From a research standpoint, many potential areas need to be explored. These areas range from inexpensive pocket or wristwatch calculators to the use of microcomputers.

The use of sophisticated mechanical devices is not new to the field. Lovaas (Lovaas, Freitag, Gold, & Kassorla, 1965), and Wasik (Wasik *et al.*, 1969), employed Esterline Angus event recorders during the 1960s, and in more recent studies data have been collected using a Datamyte system with computer interface (Brown & Bakeman, 1975; Ramey *et al.*, 1978). The use of such equipment, however, is almost prohibited for routine clinical work. Some newer devices may not be so restrictive. A digital wristwatch, for example, is inexpensive and quieter than a stop watch. It is readily accessible and transportable and can be used by teachers, parents, and paraprofessionals. The use of portable battery-powered microcomputers may have a major impact on the direct observation of behavior in some settings. These microcomputers make readily available the recording of sequential and simultaneous behaviors and allow the determination of both frequencies and durations (Wadham, 1979). Thus, detailed data on teacher–child or child–child interactions could become much more accessible. The use of such equipment might also enhance the establishment of normative data.

3.1.2. Methodology

Herbert and Attridge (1975) presented an excellent set of criteria which instrument developers could use as a guide in their work. These criteria include such items as specifying the individuals and situations in which the instrument should be used, using clear and unambiguously defined behaviors, making items representative of the dimension of behavior under study, using mutually exclusive items, keeping observer inference low, reducing and/or controlling for the nature and extent of observer inference, describing and substantiating the nature of inference from the data, and specifying the statistical and other methods of inferential treatment of data. Many other criteria are enumerated, including controls for observer effects and enhancements of reliability and validity procedures. It is uncommon, however, to find instruments that have addressed many of these criteria.

Other methodological issues must still be addressed. The progress of the 1970s focused attention on such variables as observer accuracy and ways to increase it. To cite just one area of inaccuracy, it is the rare professional who does not recognize that his or her presence in the home or classroom might alter parent, teacher, or child behavior. We must understand more about how and why the presence of such individuals influences behavior and what can be done to reduce reactivity.

A continuing methodological issue relates to the unit of analysis. The question is not simply one of molar versus molecular analysis, but consideration of the more meaningful unit within each area. The unit of analysis has been an issue within each of the trends discussed in this chapter and has major implications for future research directions.

3.1.3. Instrument Development

Many excellent coding systems exist for the purpose of recording child behavior for intervention purposes. Yet, although there are coding systems by individuals such as Bijou, Patterson, Wahler, Walker, and O'Leary there is no counterpart to the *Wechsler Intelligence Test for Children—Revised* for the direct observation of behavior. Perhaps the most obvious difficulty with the existing measures is the lack of standardization of code categories, consequently making it difficult, if not impossible, to compare data across codes.

Mash and Terdal (1981) have identified a number of prejudices implicit within available observation codes for children. One example is the relatively large number of codes that exist for recording child compliance and adult directiveness compared to affectional responses of children and adults as illustrated in Patterson's (1976) coercive–compliance sequence. Such characteristics of the coding system can lead toward one set of conclusions on child behavior rather than another. Mash and Terdal express a similar concern with the fact that most observational codes with children focus more on family interactions than on peer interactions, again leading to possibly biased conclusions of controlling variables.

In addition to standardization of codes and settings, some have also called for the development of distinct codes for specific problem areas (Mash & Terdal, 1981; Reid, 1978). Although well-developed specialized codes exist for some problems such as aggression and withdrawn children, highly developed codes are lacking for other areas of child psychopathology.

3.1.4. Comparison of Alternative Assessment Instruments

As the area of behavioral intervention broadened its scope and began to focus on such areas as cognitive behavior modification and interpersonal problem solving, there has been an increase in interest in self-report measures, behavior-rating forms, and assessments of what individuals might do if confronted with certain problem situations. There has also been an increased interest in interviewing. The arguments for the use of such instruments are compelling and attractive: for example, rating scales are easy to use, obtain information on low-frequency behavior, and provide important information on the perceptions of significant adults in the child's life.

Perhaps the most fruitful research that can be conducted at this time would be research directed toward a comparison of the type of information obtained from a number of alternative assessment procedures. An example of a needed area for research is the comparison of behavior ratings and behavior observations. Cairns and Green (1978) point out that although this is not a new problem (e.g., Allport & Allport, 1921), it is one that has not been fully resolved. In considering the literature over the past 70 years, Cairns and Green have provided a careful analysis of the contributions of these two methods, including considerations of the underlying assumptions, potential sources of variance, and the reliability of each method and suggest some new interpretations of the differences between ratings and observations. Believing that each method may be valuable for specific purposes, they suggest that rating scales can be useful for those who want to describe individual differences in behavioral style or to quantify judgments made about other people, especially in obtaining information on expectations about others. When, however, one wants to obtain information on how social patterns are maintained and changed and new patterns are developed, Cairns and Green see no substitute for the direct analysis of behavior, a conclusion consistent with that quoted from Wahler, House, and Stambaugh (1976) at the beginning of this chapter and consistent with the views of many of other investigators.

3.1.5. Validation of New Treatment Approaches

The direct observation of behavior must be employed in the assessment of newer therapeutic approaches. Among these approaches are those that fall under the heading of cognitive behavior modification and include self-control, self-management or self-instructional procedures, and problem-solving procedures.

In two current reviews conducted of available assessment instruments for evaluating procedures for teaching children interpersonal problem solving, very few references were made to studies that employed the direct observation of behavior (Butler & Meichenbaum, 1981; Kendall, Pellagrini, & Urbain, 1981). Most evaluations have included assessing the child's performance in a hypothetical situation or obtaining information on the perceptions of others. Yet these intervention procedures will not reach the credibility they need until supported by socially relevant changes in the natural environment.

3.1.6. Normative Data on Clinical and Nonclinical Populations

A need exists for normative data, regardless of theory, that can serve as an anchorpoint for interpreting observations on individual children. Data are needed on many kinds of behaviors and their frequencies in homes, schools, and other settings. Examples of some areas wherein normative data would be beneficial are sharing and cooperation, attending behavior, activity levels, social problem-solving skills, aggression, resistance or noncompliance, withdrawn behavior, and depression. In all these areas we must establish normative data that can provide a much needed developmental perspective.

The accomplishment of such goals will be expensive and time-consuming. Numerous methodological issues will have to be resolved: Which instrument to use? Whose definition of attending, helping, or social problem-solving should be used? How many setting variables will have to be measured? Yet, without such data we often make clinical decisions and draw conclusions in a vacuum.

3.1.7. Validation of Theories of Normal and Abnormal Child Development

Historically, information on child development has been based as much on theory as on fact. Although developmental norms exist for many physical characteristics of children and for intellectual development, we do not have a comparably strong set of data on the behavioral, social, or emotional development of the child. Hartup (1976), in summarizing the work on the social psychology of childhood, describes most of the literature on children's social behavior as nondevelopmental. He reports few age-related studies of aggression, altruism, or dependency and describes none of the cooperation and competition literature as developmental. Although advances have been made in investigating some areas developmentally, such as perspective-taking, much work must be done; otherwise we continue to accept unsubstantiated theories of child development and to use such theories as a basis for treatment approaches.

In the area of abnormal child psychology too many instances again exist in which theory, not data, have influenced both public opinion and professional practice. One early example of unsubstantiated theory affecting practice was the belief that the cause of autistic child behavior was the rejecting, cold, and unfeeling reactions of the parents. Many other assumptions of the behavior of children with handicappping conditions have not been supported by empirical data, and studies based upon empirical data have been contributing information on the range of behaviors that can be mastered by children with problems (e.g., autistic, retarded, or hyperactive children).

One of the more significant ways in which the use of the direct observation of behavior could influence child behavior therapy in the future is to provide data for a behaviorally based classification system of childhood disorders. The most current generally accepted diagnostic system for children is the *Diagnostic and Statistical Manual-III* (1980). The Manual, however, is based upon a theoretical interpretation of children behavior that is not grounded in data, and although it has been noted by many for its advantages over previous classification systems, it still falls short of the standards that should be demanded in this field.

3.2. Clinically Oriented Psychologists

The responsibilities that fall to the clinically oriented psychologists are different from those of the primary researcher because the expectations and resources differ. Nevertheless, to advance the field of clinical child psychology, there are activities in which the clinician should be engaged. The major recommendation for the clinician in the future is to engage in multidimensional assessment and to establish collaborative efforts with schools, families, and other pertinent individuals and settings so that helpful observational data can be collected.

During the infancy of behavioral assessment in applied settings, direct observation of behavior was typically the only measure that was consistently used. At present, our knowledge of the value of alternative assessment approaches indicates that we should not rely upon a single assessment option. One of the major needs now is to intensify the study of the different kinds of knowledge obtained from alternative assessment procedures and to analyze the complementary nature of data collected from different sources. Practitioners can potentially make a major contribution in this regard, especially those in settings in which records can be kept across time on children. Barlow (1981), for example, has suggested that if clinicians around the country collected accurate, realistic, and convenient measures on a given subject population, we could begin to make clearer statements on treatment effectiveness.

In a multidimensional approach practitioners should consider using (1) direct observation of child behavior, (2) interview with adults and the focal child, (3) rating scales from significant adults, (4) analogue measures, (5) hypothetical tasks, (6) psychometric measures, and (7) data on a range of setting variables. Although all these measures will not necessarily be called for in any given situation, nor will such always be possible, reliance upon one procedure to the exclusion of one or more of the other procedures at this time will preclude opportunities to make needed comparisons.

Regardless of the measures one uses, a carefully structured interview is essential to provide information on the nature of the child's problems, the settings in which the problems occur, information on frequency and duration, and information on the child's reactions to significant others (parents, siblings, peers, teachers) and their reactions to the child. Such information serves as a guide to develop preliminary hypotheses of the child's difficulties and helps to determine the specific kinds of assessment procedures that might need to be subsequently initiated.

With the interview one can, if appropriate, obtain information on additional related problems of the child and on adult expectancies, establish desired outcome goals, learn more about the child's difficulties with different people in different settings, determine in more depth the child's adherence to rule-governed behavior, and acquire data on successes and failures of other procedures that have been tried with the child.

Other advantages exist for a well-conducted interview. It helps to establish communication with important adults in the child's life, and it allows the practitioner to make judgments on that person's intellectual, motivational, and emotional status, knowledge which is often crucial in planning any treatment program that would involve the support and participation of the interviewee. Several good formats are available for structuring an interview, including ones by Hanf (1970), Patterson *et al.* (1975), and Holland (1970). The advantages of any of these adult interviews are a considerable advance over a briefer interview directed toward a specific presenting problem. The interview, however, has not been the target of extensive research efforts, and as its use increases in popularity, increased attention must be given to its value as an assessment procedure. Attention should also be given to interviewing the child, when appropriate, to obtain information on how the child views the concerns of the adults and to assess variables similar to that assessed with the parents or teachers (e.g., motivation, cooperation, expectancies, and goals).

Many clinicians only infrequently obtain information from direct observation of behavior. A number of factors can be viewed as contributing to the clinician's lack of active involvement in the collection of behavioral observation data. The collection of observational data does not appear to be as efficient or as cost-effective when compared to other procedures, such as the interview, rating forms, or standardized measures. All the objections of time, costs, intrusiveness, and representativeness referred to by many others are pertinent here.

There are also, however, serious costs associated with failure to collect behavior observational data. Among these costs are the differences in the perceptions of parents and teachers and actual child behavior, a factor that can lead to serious problems in assessment, in arranging intervention programs, and in evaluating intervention. Several authors have addressed the lack of congruence between parent report and child behavior. Other writers have described the tendency of parents to report positive change in child behavior over time, even when there is not a documented change. These concerns should force attention on the need to look at creative ways of facilitating the practitioner's ability to collect observational data.

Keller (1980) sees the use of observational assessment as a means of enhancing collaborative consultation with school personnel and with families. Such collaborative efforts can actually be mutually beneficial in that the practitioner who wishes to obtain observational data in these settings will find it easier to do so if the time has been taken to establish good ongoing professional relationships.

There are many others besides the psychologist engaged in data-collection procedures. These individuals include parents, teachers, aides, and other adults. When a teacher, parent, or teacher aide is actually involved, one is then using a participant observer, a procedure that has both advantages and disadvantages. As a participant observer, one has the advantage of being available when problem behaviors, especially low-frequency behaviors, occur. The process of attending to the problem behavior in itself, however, can change the behavior of the observer toward the child which could lead to changes in child behavior.

Some practitioners work directly in applied settings such as schools and residential centers. These individuals are in a particularly advantageous position for observing directly the behavior of the child—a position that is often not available to other professionals. For those practitioners who work in settings that do not make observations in natural settings possible, it can be advantageous to set up a procedure for analogue observation. An excellent example of the use of such procedures is the clinic analogue setting reported by Barkley (Barkley, 1981; Barkley & Cunningham, 1979).

4. Conclusion

Children—at home, in school, in clinics, in laboratories, on playgrounds—have often been the focus of observation. From the diary of Tiedemann to the work of Darwin and Preyer a century later to the child development movement beginning in the 1920s to our present work, countless studies have been conducted—to understand the child's social development, to explore learning, to establish normative information, and to serve as an assessment and evaluation procedure in clinical practice. From a review of this work, one must come to the inevitable conclusion that the direct observation of behavior transcends theory and theorists.

This method of data collection has a universality that has permeated, at one time or another, every branch of psychology that deals with children. It is essential to any clinical approach that wishes to obtain a comprehensive understanding of the child. In research, also, what children do—in contrast to what they say they do and how others perceive what they do—must never be neglected.

The methods developed more than half a century ago still serve us well, as does much of the data. Currently we have a more advanced technology for data collection and analysis and we have considerably more data. In the future we can refine our technology and increase our data base. But perhaps the more important tasks are expanding the time frame within which to consider the influence of past events and the potential influence of future goals, investigating a range of behavioral, ecological, and cognitive variables, and developing ways of integrating and interpreting present and future data to help advance research and practice.

ACKNOWLEDGMENTS

The author is deeply grateful to the following individuals who responded to drafts of this chapter: Dr. Robert Cairns, who gave generously of his time and his knowledge on the history of developmental psychology; Drs. Robert Wahler, Donald Meichenbaum, and Donna Bryant for their many thoughtful comments; and Drs. William Burke, Gary Stuck, and Marvin Wyne for sharing their knowledge of teacher education.

5. References

Ainsworth, M. D. S. Object relations, dependency, and attachment: A theoretical review of the infant–mother relationship. *Child Development,* 1969, *40,* 969–1025.

Ainsworth, M. D. S. The development of infant–mother attachment. In B. C. Caldwell & H. R. Ricciuti (Eds.), *Review of child development research.* Chicago: University of Chicago Press, 1973.

Allen, K. E., Hart, B. M., Buell, J. S., Harris, F. R., & Wolf, M. M. Effects of social reinforcement on isolate behavior of a nursery school child. *Child Development,* 1964, *35,* 511–518.

Allport, F. H., & Allport, G. W. Personality traits: Their classification and measurement. *Journal of Abnormal Psychology and Social Psychology,* 1921, *16,* 1–40.

American Psychiatric Association. *Diagnostic and statistical manual of disorders* (DSM III). Washington, D.C.: Author, 1980.

Amidon, E. J., & Hough, J. B. (Eds.). *Interaction analysis: Theory, research, and application.* Reading, Mass.: Addison-Wesley, 1967.

Anderson, H. H. The measurement of domination and of socially integrative behavior in teachers' contacts with children. *Child Development,* 1939, *10,* 73–89.

Arrington, R. E. Time sampling in studies of social behavior: A critical review of techniques and results with research suggestions. *Psychological Bulletin,* 1943, *40,* 81–124.

Atkeson, B. M., & Forehand, R. Conduct disorders. In E. J. Mash & L. G. Terdal (Eds.), *Behavioral assessment of childhood disorders*. New York: Guilford Press, 1981.

Barlow, D. H. A role for clinicans in the research process. *Behavioral Assessment*, 1981, *3*, 227–233.

Baer, D. M., Wolf, M. M., & Risley, T. R. Some current dimensions of applied behavior analysis. *Journal of Applied Behavior Analysis*, 1968, *1*, 91–97.

Bandura, A. *Aggression: A social learning analysis*. Englewood Cliffs, N.J.: Prentice-Hall, 1973.

Barker, R. G. *The stream of behavior*. New York: Appleton-Century-Crofts, 1963.

Barker, R. G., & Wright, H. T. Psychological ecology and the problem of psychosocial development. *Child Development*, 1949, *20*, 131–143.

Barker, R. G., & Wright, H. F. *Midwest and its children: The psychological ecology of an American town*. New York: Harper & Row, 1955.

Barkley, R. A. Hyperactivity. In E. J. Mash & L. G. Terdal (Eds.), *Behavioral assessment of childhood disorders*. New York: Guilford Press, 1981.

Barkley, R. A., & Cunningham, C. E. The effects of Ritalin on the mother–child interactions of hyperactive children. *Archives of General Psychiatry*, 1979, *36*, 201–208.

Becker, W. C. *Parents are teachers, a child management program*. Champaign, Ill.: Research Press, 1971.

Bijou, S. W., & Baer, D. M. *Child development I: A systematic and empirical theory*. Englewood Cliffs, N.J.: Prentice-Hall, 1961.

Bijou, S. W., & Orlando, R. Rapid development of multiple-schedule performances with retarded children. *Journal of the Experimental Analysis of Behavior*, 1961, *4*, 7–16.

Bijou, S. W., Peterson, R. F., & Ault, M. H. A method to integrate descriptive and experimental field studies at the level of data and empirical concepts. *Journal of Applied Behavior Analysis*, 1968, *1*, 175–191.

Bloom, B. S. Time and learning. *American Psychologist*. 1974, *29*, 682–688.

Borich, G. D. *The appraisal of teaching: Concepts and process*. Reading, Mass.: Addison-Wesley, 1977.

Bronfenbrenner, U. Developmental research, public policy, and the ecology of childhood. *Child Development*, 1974, *45*, 1–5.

Brown, J. V., & Bakeman, R. *Mother–infant behavior codes, birth through three months* (Tech. Rep. 3). Atlanta: Georgia State University, Infancy Laboratory, June, 1975.

Buckley, N. K., & Walker, H. M. *Modifying classroom behavior*. Champaign, Ill.: Research Press, 1970.

Butler, L., & Meichenbaum, D. The assessment of interpersonal problem-solving skills. In P. C. Kendall & S. D. Hollen (Eds.), *Assessment strategies for cognitive-behavioral intervention*. New York: Academic Press, 1981.

Cairns, R. B. The emergence of developmental psychology. In W. Kessen (Ed.), *Carmichael's manual of child psychology* (Vol. 1, 4th ed.) New York: Wiley, 1983.

Cairns, R. B., & Green, J. A. How to assess personality and social patterns: Observations or ratings? In R. B. Cairns (Ed.), *The analysis of social interactions: Methods, issues, and illustrations*. Hillsdale, N.J.: Erlbaum, 1979.

Carroll, J. B. A model of school learning. *Teacher's College Record*. 1963, *64*, 723–733.

Cronback, L. J., Gleser, G. C., Nanda, H., & Rajaratnam, N. *The dependability of behavioral measurements: Theory of generalizability for scores and profiles*. New York: Wiley, 1972.

Cunningham, T. R., & Tharp, R. G. The influence of setting on accuracy and reliability of behavioral observation. *Behavioral Assessment*, 1981, *3*, 67–78.

Darwin, C. R. *The expression of the emotions in man and animals*. London: John Murray, 1872.

Eckerman, C. O., Whatley, J. L., & Kutz, S. L. Growth of social play with peers during the second year of life. *Developmental Psychology*, 1975, *11*, 42–49.

Emmelkamp, P. M. G. The current and future status of clinical research. *Behavioral Assessment*, 1981, *3*, 249–253.

Evans, I. M., & Nelson, R. O. Assessment of child behavior problems. In A. R. Ciminero, K. S. Calhoun, & H. E. Adams (Eds.), *Handbook of behavioral assessment*. New York: Wiley, 1977.

Flanders, N. A. *Teacher influence, pupil attitudes, and achievement*. Minneapolis: University of Minnesota, 1960.

Flanders, N. A. Some relationships among teacher influence, pupil attitudes, and achievement. In B. J. Biddle & W. J. Ellena (Eds.), *Contemporary research on teacher effectiveness*. New York: Holt, Rinehart & Winston, 1964.

Forehand, R., King, H. E., Peed, S., & Yoder, P. Mother–child interactions: Comparison of a noncompliant clinic group and a nonclinic group. *Behavior Research and Therapy*, 1975, *13*, 79–84.

Forehand, R., Peed, S., Roberts, M., McMahon, R., Griest, D., & Humphreys, L. *Coding manual for scoring mother–child interaction* (3rd Ed.). Unpublished manuscript, University of Georgia, 1978.

Forehand, R., Sturgis, E., McMahon, R., Aguar, D., Green, K., Wells, K., & Breiner, J. Parent behavioral training to modify child noncompliance: Treatment generalization across time and from home to school. *Behavior Modification*, 1979, *3*, 3–25.

Fowler, S. A., & Baer, D. M. Do I have to be good all day? The timing of delayed reinforcement as a factor in generalization. *Journal of Applied Behavior Analysis*, 1981, *14*, 13–24.

Gellert, E. Systematic observation: A method in child study. *Harvard Educational Review*, 1955, *25*, 179–195.

Goldfried, M. R., & Kent, R. N. Traditional versus behavioral personality assessment: A comparison of methodological and theoretical assumptions. *Psychological Bulletin*, 1972, *77*, 409–420.

Goldfried, M. R., & Pomeranz, D. M. Role of assessment in behavior modification. *Psychological Reports*, 1968, *23*, 75–87.

Goodenough, F. L. Inter-relationships in the behavior of young children. *Child Development*, 1930, *1*, 29–47.

Goodenough, F. L. *Anger in young children*. Minneapolis: University of Minnesota Press, 1931.

Goodenough, F. L., & Anderson, J. E. *Experimental child study*. New York: Century, 1931.

Gottman, J. M. Toward a definition of social isolation. *Child Development*, 1977, *48*, 513–517.

Greenwood, C. R., Todd, N. M., Walker, H. M., & Hops, H. *Social assessment manual for preschool level: SAMPLE*. Eugene, Ore.: Center at Oregon for Research in the Behavioral Education of the Handicapped, 1978.

Gump, P. V., Schoggen, P., & Redl, F. The camp milieu and its immediate effets. *Journal of Social Issues*. 1957, *13*, No. 1.

Hall, R. V. Behavior management series. *Part 1: The measurement of behavior. Part 2: Basic principles. Part 3: Applications in school and home*. Lawrence, Kansas: H and H Enterprises, 1971.

Hamilton, M. H., & Wasik, B. H. *The relationship between attending behavior and classroom settings*. Paper presented at the American Psychological Association meeting, Washington, D.C., August 1982.

Hanf, C. *Shaping mothers to shape their children's behavior*. Unpublished manuscript, University of Oregon Medical School, 1970.

Harris, F. R., Johnston, M. K., Kelley, C. S., & Wolf, M. M. Effects of positive social reinforcement on regressed crawling of a nursery school child. *Journal of Educational Psychology*, 1964, *55*, 35–41.

Hart, B. M., Allen, K. E., Buell, J. S., Harris, F. R., & Wolf, M. M. Effects of social reinforcement on operant crying. *Journal of Experimental Child Psychology*, 1964, *1*, 145–153.

Hartup, W. W. *Toward a social psychology of childhood: From Patterns of Child Rearing to 1984.* Presidential address, Division on developmental psychology, American Psychological Association, Washington, D.C., September 1976.

Hay, L. R., Nelson, R. O., & Hay, W. M. Methodological problems in the use of participant observers. *Journal of Applied Behavior Analysis*, 1980, *13*, 501–504.

Hayes, S. C., & Nelson, R. O. Clinically relevant research: Requirements, problems, and solutions. *Behavioral Assessment*, 1981, *3*, 209–215.

Herbert, J., & Attridge, C. A guide for developers and users of observation systems and manuals. *American Educational Research Journal*, 1975, *12*, 1–20.

Herbert, E. W., & Baer, D. M. Training parents as behavior modifiers: Self-recording of contingent attention. *Journal of Applied Behavior Analysis*, 1972, *5*, 134–149.

Hersen, M., & Barlow, D. H. *Single case experimental designs.* New York: Pergamon Press, 1976.

Heyns, R. W., & Lippitt, R. Systematic observational technique. *Handbook of Social Psychology* (Vol. 1). Cambridge, Mass.: Addison-Wesley, 1954.

Holland, C. J. An interview guide for behavioral counseling with parents. *Behavior Therapy*, 1970, *1*, 70–79.

Johnson, S. M., & Bolstad, O. D. Methodological issues in naturalistic observations: Some problems and solutions for field research. In L. A. Hamerlynck, L. C. Handy, & E. J. Mash (Eds.), *Behavior change: Methodology, concepts, and practice.* Champaign, Ill.: Research Press, 1973.

Johnson, S. M., & Bolstad, O. D. Reactivity to home observation: A comparison of audio-recorded behaviors with observers present or absent. *Journal of Applied Behavior Analysis*, 1975, *8*, 181–185.

Johnson, C. A., & Katz, R. C. Using parents as change agents for their children: A review. *Journal of Child Psychology and Psychiatry.* 1973, *14*, 181–200.

Kanfer, F. H., & Phillips, J. S. *Learning foundations of behavior therapy.* New York: Wiley, 1970.

Kanfer, F. H., & Saslow, G. Behavioral diagnosis. In C. M. Franks (Ed.), *Behavior therapy: Appraisal and status.* New York: McGraw-Hill, 1969.

Kantor, J. R. *Interbehavioral psychology.* Granville, Ohio: Principia Press, 1959.

Kazdin, A. E. Artifact, bias, and complexity of assessment: The ABC's of reliability. *Journal of Applied Behavior Analysis*, 1977, *10*, 141–150. (a)

Kazdin, A. E. Assessing the clinical or applied significance of behavior change through social validation. *Behavior Modification*, 1977, *1*, 427–452. (b)

Kazdin, A. E. *Single-case research designs: Methods for clinical and applied settings.* New York: Oxford University Press, 1982.

Keller, H. R. Issues in the use of observational assessment. *School Psychology Review*, 1980, *9*, 21–30.

Kendall, P. C., Pellegrini, D. S., & Urbain, E. S. Approaches to assessment for cognitive-behavioral interventions with children. In P. C. Kendall & S. D. Hollen (Eds.), *Assessment strategies for cognitive-behavioral interventions.* New York: Academic Press, 1981.

Kent, R. N., & Foster, S. L. Direct observational procedures: Methodological issues in applied settings. In A. Ciminero, K. S. Calhoun, & H. E. Adams (Eds.), *Handbook of behavioral assessment.* New York: Wiley, 1977.

Kent, R. N., O'Leary, K. D., Diament, C., & Dietz, A. Expectation biases in observational evaluation of therapeutic change. *Journal of Consulting and Clinical Psychology*, 1974, *42*, 774–780.

King, G. F., Erhmann, J. C., & Johnson, D. M. Experimental analysis of the reliability of observations of social behavior. *Journal of Social Psychology*, 1952, *35*, 151–160.

Krantz, P. J., & Risley, T. R. Behavioral ecology in the classroom. In R. D. O'Leary & S. G. O'Leary (Eds.), *Classroom management: The successful use of behavior modification*. New York: Pergamon Press, 1977.

Kratochwill, T. R. (Ed.). *Single subject research: Strategies for evaluating change*. New York: Academic Press, 1978.

Lahey, B. B., Hobbs, S. A., Kupfer, D. L., & Delamater, A. Current perspectives on hyperactivity and learning disabilities. In B. B. Lahey (Ed.), *Behavior therapy with hyperactive and learning disabled children*. New York: Oxford University Press, 1979.

Lazarus, A. A. The elimination of children's phobias by deconditioning. In H. J. Eysenck (Ed.), Behavior therapy and the neuroses. New York: Pergamon Press, 1960.

Lazarus, A. A. Multimodal behavior therapy: Treating the "BASIC ID." *Journal of Nervous and Mental Disease*, 1973, *156*, 404–411.

Lewin, K. Conflict between Aristotelian and Galileian modes of thought in psychology. *Journal of General Psychology*, 1931, *5*, 141–177. (a)

Lewin, K. Environmental forces in child behavior and development. In C. Murchison (Ed.), *A manual of child psychology*. Worcester, Mass.: Clark University Press, 1931. (b)

Lovaas, O. I., Freitag, G., Gold, V. J., & Kassorla, I. C. Recording apparatus and procedure for observation of behaviors of children in free play settings. *Journal of Experimental Child Psychology*, 1965, *2*, 108–120.

Lovaas, O. I., Koegel, R., Simmons, J. Q., & Long, J. S. Some generalization and follow-up measures on autistic children in behavior therapy. *Journal of Applied Behavior Analysis*, 1973, *6*, 131–166.

Madsen, C. H., Becker, W. C., & Thomas, D. R. Rules, praise, and ignoring: Elements of elementary classroom control. *Journal of Applied Behavior Analysis*, 1968, *2*, 139–150.

Madsen, C. H., & Madsen, C. K. *Teaching/discipline, behavioral principles toward a positive approach*. Boston: Allyn & Bacon, 1970.

Madsen, C. K., & Madsen, C. H. *Parents, children, discipline: A positive approach*. Boston: Allyn & Bacon, 1972.

Mash, E. J., & Terdal, L. G. Behavioral assessment of childhood disturbance. In E. J. Mash & L. G. Terdal (Eds.), *Behavioral assessment of childhood disorders*. New York: Guilford Press, 1981.

Mash, E. J., & McElwee, J. D. Situational effects on observer accuracy: Behavioral predictability, prior experience, and complexity of coding categories. *Child Development*, 1974, *45*, 367–377.

McKinney, J. D., Mason, J., Perkerson, K., & Clifford, M. Relationship between classroom behavior and academic achievement. *Journal of Educational Psychology*, 1975, *67*, 198–203.

Mercatoris, M., & Craighead, W. E. Effects of nonparticipant observation on teacher and pupil classroom behavior. *Journal of Educational Psychology*, 1974, *66*, 512–519.

Murchison, C., & Langer, S. Tiedemann's observations on the development of the mental facilities of children. *Journal of Genetic Psychology*, 1927, *34*, 205–230.

Nelson, R. O., Kapust, J. A., & Dorsey, B. L. Minimal reactivity of overt classroom observations on student and teacher behaviors. *Behavior Therapy*, 1978, *9*, 695–702.

Ober, R. L., Bentley, E. L., & Miller, E. *Systematic observation of teaching: An interaction analysis–instructional strategy approach*. New Jersey: Prentice-Hall, 1971.

Odden, A., & Dougherty, V. *State programs of school improvement: A 50-state survey*, Report No. 182–3. Denver, Col.: Education Commission of the State, 1982.

O'Dell, S. Training parents in behavior modification: A review. *Psychological Bulletin*, 1974, *81*, 418–433.

O'Leary, K. D., & Becker, W. C. Behavior modification of an adjustment class: A token economy program. *Exceptional Children*, 1967, *33*, 637–642.

O'Leary, K. D., Romanczyk, R. G., Kass, R. E., Dietz, A., & Santogrossi, D. *Procedures for classroom observation of teachers and children*. Unpublished manuscript, State University of New York at Stony Brook. Revised, September 1971.

Ollendick, T. H., & Cerny, J. A. *Clinical behavior therapy with children*. New York: Plenum Press, 1981.

Olson, W. C. *The measurement of nervous habits in normal children*. University of Minnesota, Institute of Child Welfare Monograph Series No. 3. Minneapolis: University of Minnesota Press, 1929.

Parke, R. D. Social cues, social control and ecological validity. *Merrill Palmer Quarterly*, 1976, *22*, 111–118.

Parke, R. D. Parent–infant interaction: Progress, paradigms and problems. In G. P. Sackett (Ed.), *Observing behavior* (Vol. 1). *Theory and applications in mental retardation*. Baltimore, Md.: University Park Press, 1978.

Parke, R. D. Interactional designs. In R. B. Cairns (Ed.), *The analysis of social interactions: Methods, issues, and illustrations*. Hillsdale, N.J.: Erlbaum, 1979.

Parten, M. B. Social participation among pre-school children. *Journal of Abnormal and Social Psychology*, 1932, *27*, 243–269.

Patterson, G. R. An application of conditioning techniques to the control of a hyperactive child. In L. P. Ullmann & L. Krasner (Eds.), *Case studies in behavior modification*. New York: Holt, Rinehart & Winston, 1965.

Patterson, G. R. A basis for identifying stimuli which control behaviors in natural settings. *Child Development*, 1974, *45*, 900–911.

Patterson, G. R. The aggressive child: Victim and architect of a coercive system. In E. J. Mash, L. A. Hamerlynck, & L. C. Handy (Eds.), *Behavior modification and families*. New York: Brunner/Mazel, 1976.

Patterson, G. R. A performance theory for coercive family interaction. In R. B. Cairns (Ed.), *The analysis of social interactions: Methods, issues, and illustrations*. Hillsdale, N.J.: Erlbaum, 1979.

Patterson, G. R., & Gullion, M. E. *Living with children: New methods for parents and teachers*. Champaign, Ill.: Research Press, 1968.

Patterson, G. R., Reid, J. B., Jones, R. R., & Conger, R. E. *A social learning approach to family intervention: Families with aggressive children* (Vol. 1). Eugene, Ore.: Castalia Publishing, 1975.

Peterson, D. R. *The clinical study of social behavior*. New York: Appleton-Century-Crofts, 1968.

Peterson, L., & Hartmann, D. P. A neglected literature and an aphorism. *Journal of Applied Behavior Analysis*, 1975, *8*, 231–232.

Piaget, J. Children's philosophies. In C. Murchison (Ed.), *A handbook of child psychology*. Worcester, Mass.: Clark University Press, 1931.

Preyer, W. *Die Seele des Kindes*. Leipzig: Ferman, 1882. *The mind of the child* (2 vols.) New York: Appleton, 1888–1889.

Quilitch, H. R., Christophersen, E. R., & Risley, T. R. The evaluation of children's play materials. *Journal of Applied Behavior Analysis*, 1977, *10*, 501–502.

Ramey, C. T., Farran, D. C., Campbell, F. A., & Finkelstein, N. W. Observations of mother–infant interactions: Implications for development. In F. Minifie & L. Loyd (Eds.), *Communicative and cognitive abilities—Early behavioral assessment*. Baltimore: University Park Press, 1978.

Ramey, C. T., Farran, D. C., & Campbell, F. A. Predicting IQ from mother–infant interactions. *Child Development*, 1979, *50*, 804–814.

Reid, J. B. (Ed.). *A social learning approach to family intervention. Vol. 2: Observation in home settings*. Eugene, Ore.: Castalia Publishing, 1978.

Repp, A. C., Roberts, D. M., Slack, D. J., Repp, C. F., & Berkler, M. S. A comparison of frequency, interval, and time-sampling methods of data collection. *Journal of Applied Behavior Analysis*, 1976, *6*, 175–186.

Rheingold, H. L. The effect of a strange environment on the behavior of infants. In B. M. Foss (Ed.), *Determinants of infant behavior, IV*. New York: Wiley, 1969.

Rheingold, H. L., & Eckerman, C. O. Fear of the stranger: A critical examination. In H. W. Reese (Ed.), *Advances in child development and behavior* (Vol. 8). New York: Academic Press, 1973.

Rheingold, H. L., Hay, D. F., & West, M. I. Sharing in the second year of life. *Child Development*, 1976, *47*, 1148–1158.

Rosenshine, B., & Furst, N. The use of direct observation to study teaching. In R. M. W. Travers (Ed.), *Second handbook of research on teaching*. Chicago: Rand McNally, 1973.

Ross, A. O. *Child behavior therapy: Principles, procedures, and empirical basis*. New York: Wiley, 1981.

Sears, R. R. A theoretical framework for personality and social behavior. *American Psychologist*, 1951, *6*, 476–483.

Shinn, M. W. *The biography of a baby*. Boston: Houghton Mifflin, 1900.

Shuller, D., & McNamara, J. R. Expectancy factors in behavioral observation. *Behavior Therapy*, 1976, *7*, 519–527.

Sibley, S. A., Abbott, M. S., & Cooper, B. P. Modification of the classroom behavior of a disadvantaged kindergarten boy by social reinforcement and isolation. *Journal of Experimental Child Psychology*, 1969, *7*, 203–219.

Simon, A., & Boyer, E. G. (Eds.). *Mirrors for behavior: An anthology of classroom observation instruments* (Vols. 1–6). Philadelphia: Research for Better Schools, 1967, ED 029 833.

Simon, A., & Boyer, E. G. (Eds.). *Mirrors for behavior: An anthology of classroom observation instruments* (Vols. 7–14 and *Summary*). Philadelphia: Research for Better Schools, 1970, ED 031 613. (a)

Simon, A., & Boyer, E. G. (Eds.). *Mirrors for behavior: An anthology of classroom observation instruments* (Supplementary Vols. A and B). Philadelphia: Research for Better Schools, 1970, ED 042 937. (b)

Thomas, D. S. Some new techniques for studying social behavior. *Child development monographs* (No. 1). New York: Teachers College, Columbia University, 1929.

Tiedemann, D. Beobachtungen über die Entwicklung der seelen Fähigkeiten bei Kindern. (First published in 1787. Altenburg Bonde, 1897. See C. Murchison & S. Langer, 1927.)

Ullmann, L. P., & Krasner, L. (Eds.). *Case studies in behavior modification*. New York: Holt, Rinehart & Winston, 1965.

Wadham, R. A. *Microcomputer applications in interaction analysis*. Paper presented at the American Education Research Association meeting, San Francisco, April 1979.

Wahler, R. G. Setting generality: Some specific and general effects of child behavior therapy. *Journal of Applied Behavior Analysis*, 1969, *2*, 239–246.

Wahler, R. G. The insular mother: Her problems in parent–child treatment. *Journal of Applied Behavior Analysis*, 1980, *13*, 207–219.

Wahler, R. G., & Fox, J. J. Setting events in applied behavior analysis: Toward a conceptual and methodological expansion. *Journal of Applied Behavior Analysis*, 1981, *14*, 327–338.

Wahler, R. G., & Leske, G. Accurate and inaccurate observer summary reports. *Journal of Nervous and Mental Disease*, 1973, *156*, 386–394.

Wahler, R. G., & House, A. E., & Stambaugh, E. E. *Ecological assessment of child problem behavior: A clinical package for home, school, and institutional settings.* New York: Pergamon Press, 1976.

Wahler, R. G., Wenkel, G. H., Paterson, R. G., & Morrison, D. C. Mothers as behavior therapists for their own children. *Behavior Research and Therapy,* 1965, *3,* 113–124.

Walker, H., & Hops, H. Increasing academic achievement by reinforcing direct academic performance and/or facilitative nonacademic responses. *Journal of Educational Psychology,* 1976, *68,* 218–225.

Wasik, B. H. The application of Premack's generalization on reinforcement to the management of classroom behavior. *Journal of Experimental Child Psychology,* 1970, *10,* 33–43.

Wasik, B. H., & Day, B. Measuring open and traditional learning environments and children's classroom behavior. *Forum on Education,* 1977, *5,* 27–38.

Wasik, B. H., & Loven, M. D. Classroom observational data: Sources of inaccuracy and proposed solutions. *Behavioral Assessment,* 1980, *2,* 211–227.

Wasik, B. H., Senn, K., Welch, R. H., & Cooper, B. R. Behavior modification with culturally deprived school children: Two case studies. *Journal of Applied Behavior Analysis,* 1969, *2,* 181–194.

Wasik, B. H., Day, B. D., & DiRenzo, P. *The relationship between classroom behavior and group size.* Paper presented at the American Psychological Association meeting, Washington, D.C., August 1982.

Weinstein, C. S. Modifying student behavior in an open classroom through changes in the physical design. *American Education Research Journal,* 1977, *14,* 249–262.

Wildman, B. G., & Erickson, M. T. Methodological problems in behavioral observation. In J. D. Cone & R. P. Hawkins (Eds.), *Behavioral assessment: New directions in clinical psychology.* New York: Brunner/Mazel, 1977.

Williams, C. D. The elimination of tantrum behavior by extinction procedures. *Journal of Abnormal and Social Psychology,* 1959, *59,* 269.

Wilson, G. T. Some thoughts about clinical research. *Behavioral Assessment,* 1981, *3,* 217–225.

Withall, J. The development of a technique for the measurement of social-emotional climate in classrooms. *Journal of Experimental Education,* 1949, *17,* 347–361.

Wolf, M. M. Social validity: The case for subjective measurement or how applied behavior analysis is finding its heart. *Journal of Applied Behavior Analysis,* 1978, *11,* 203–214.

Wolf, M. M., Birnbrauer, J. S., Williams, T., & Lawler, J. A note on apparent extinction of the vomiting behavior of a retarded child. In L. P. Ullmann & L. Krasner (Eds.), *Case studies in behavior modification.* New York: Holt, Rinehart & Winston, 1965.

Wolf, M., Risley, T., & Mees, H. Application of operant conditioning procedures to the behaviour problems of an autistic child. *Behaviour Research and Therapy,* 1964, *1,* 305–312.

Wright, H. F. Observational child study. In P. Mussen (Ed.), *Handbook of research methods in child development.* New York: Wiley, 1960.

Wyne, M. D., & Stuck, G. B. Time-on-task and reading performance in underachieving children. *Journal of Reading Behavior,* 1979, *11,* 119–128.

6   *The Developmental Consequences of Childhood Exposure to Lead*

Recent Studies and Methodological Issues

HERBERT L. NEEDLEMAN AND DAVID BELLINGER

1. Introduction and Background

Among the recognized environmental pollutants, lead occupies a position unique in the fields of neurotoxicology and public health. It is the oldest and most thoroughly studied neurotoxin and probably the most ubiquitous. Recent studies by the National Center for Health Statistics (Annest, Mahaffey, Cox, & Roberts, 1982) indicate that 4% of American children of all races and social position have excess lead in their body. For those black children who live at the poverty level, the prevalence is startling: 18.6% have elevated blood lead levels. The absolute numbers which correspond to these percentages are formidable: about 678,000 American children under the age of 6 are lead-intoxicated.

At the same time, lead is easy to identify in the environment; its toxic mechanisms are relatively well understood; and the technical means for its removal from the proximity of humans are known and available. For these reasons, control of lead presents an important paradigm for the informed management of other more complex environmental dilemmas yet to be regulated. As a scientific problem, lead presents a

HERBERT L. NEEDLEMAN • Department of Psychiatry, School of Medicine, University of Pittsburgh, Pittsburgh, Pennsylvania 15260.   DAVID BELLINGER • Children's Hospital Medical Center, Boston, Massachusetts 02115.

number of challenging conceptual and pragmatic problems to the developmental specialist and neuropsychologist. It also challenges the epidemiologist and biostatistician whose task it is to tease out the causal threads that link lead and the manifold variables that affect child development.

The task confronting policy makers and regulators is no simpler. They are required to work with data bases that are of necessity less than complete and from these data bases to formulate defendable decisions about the state of risk. They then must set standards and regulations commensurate with the pronounced risk. These regulatory decisions are usually made in a context in which controversy is commonplace, and the stakes, economic, political, and hygienic, are extraordinarily large. For these reasons, careful and evenhanded explication of the issues, and research designs of the highest rigor are needed to achieve reasonable standards which must then withstand intense examination.

In this review, we attempt to summarize and examine critically those recent studies which bear on the question of what is a safe level of exposure to lead for children. We shall at the same time look at the common problems in design, execution, and interpretation which inhere in this issue. We hope, by these means, to enable the reader to be better able to evaluate future studies in this and related public health questions.

2. Historical Overview

Lead is mentioned in ancient Egyptian manuscripts dating from the time of the Hebrew exodus. It was used then as a cosmetic, in fishing weights, in figurines and ornaments. The Greeks were aware of the hazards attending its smelting. Dioscorides reported in the second century B.C. that "Lead makes the mind give way." Although the elder Pliny warned of the dangers of inhaling the fumes of molten lead, he curiously recommended its use in the making of wine. Because it is easy to work and resists corrosion, lead was widely used by the Romans in building homes and in conveying water. (The word *plumber* derives from the Latin *plumbum:* "lead.") The decreased birth rate and apparent increase in the incidence of madness in the Roman elite has been ascribed by some to excess lead exposure and indicted as a cause of the empire's decline (Gilfillan, 1965, Nriagu, 1983).

Lead colic occurred sporadically in the eighteenth century and prompted the passage of one of the first public health laws in the colonies. This law banned the use of lead in whiskey stills in the Commonwealth of Massachusetts, in order to prevent the "dry gripes" of lead colic in consumers of New England rum.

Childhood lead poisoning was first recognized at the turn of the twentieth century by an Austrailian opthalmologist, A. J. Gibson. Twelve years after he described the disease, Gibson was able to collect enough evidence to establish that lead on the railings and walls of the homes was the source for Australian children (Gibson, 1904). Gibson noted that lead found its way into the house dust and eventually into the children's gastrointestinal tracts by means of ordinary hand to mouth activity. The observation was ignored, only to be rediscovered in the past 10 years.

Childhood lead poisoning was first described in the United States in the second decade of the twentieth century (Thomas & Blackfan, 1914). The major cause was described as *pica*—the eating of foreign substances (*pica* = 'magpie' in Latin). It was believed to be exclusively a disease of poor inner-city dwellers, primarily black children. It was also widely held that if a child did not die of the disease, he would have no sequellae. This misconception was disproved by Byers and Lord (1943). They followed 20 children after recovery from lead poisoning, half of whom had no signs of encephalopathy during the acute phase of their disease. When followed up, almost all of the subjects were found to be behavior-disordered or to have sensorimotor deficits. The authors raised, for the first time, the possibility that some of the learning problems and conduct disorders found in schoolchildren were a product of undiagnosed lead intoxication.

In the middle 1960s, a blood lead level of 60 µg/dl (60 millionths of a gram per 100 ml of whole blood) was considered by clinicians to be at the toxic threshold. Screening studies of children who were considered normal showed that in some populations as many as 25% to 45% of children had blood lead levels in the range of 40–50 µg/dl. A few individuals, led by Jane Lin-Fu of DHEW (now the Department of Health and Social Security [DHSS]) began to question whether this was an adequate margin of safety and whether lead poisoning was an underdiagnosed disease (Lin-Fu, 1967).

At about the same time, Patterson, a geochemist (1965), was conducting studies of the geological flux of lead and its perturbation by human technological activity. Patterson's studies, conducted under the most meticulous conditions, showed that natural background levels of lead in soil, air, and foodstuffs had been raised as much as a thousand-fold by human activity. This convergence of findings from the fields of public health and geochemistry drew a substantial number of investigators to study the question of "subclinical lead intoxication." Because children were known to be more susceptible, most studies focused on younger age groups.

3. Biochemical Toxicology of Lead

Lead is a divalent, highly reactive cation. Because of its reactivity, it combines readily with proteins, particularly at sulfhydryl (SH) radicals. Since enzymes are proteins, many of the effects of lead can be understood as a result of altered enzyme activity. Among those enzymes known to be inhibited by lead are those in the heme synthetic pathway, the mixed-function oxidases, and adenylcyclase. Changes in these and other systems may account in part for the disordered central nervous system (CNS) function that accompanies lead intoxication. In the heme pathway, for example, inhibition of d-aminolevulinic acid hydroxylase results in an accumulation of its substrate, d-aminolevulinicacid. This compound, which is also increased in porphyria, has neuroactive properties. Adenylcyclase is a compound essential in neurotransmission. The mixed-function oxidases form part of the energy transfer system in the CNS. Lead recently has been shown to cleave the sugar-phosphate backbone of transfer DNA catalytically. This may represent a fundamental toxic mechanism (Brown, Hingerty, Dewan, & Klug, 1983).

At high dose, many organs are affected by lead, including the kidney, liver, gastrointestinal tract, myocardium, immune system, blood, and central and peripheral nervous systems. For children, the most significant target is the brain. At high dose, lead can produce edema and brain hemorrhage. These dire events usually occur at blood levels above 80 μg/dl, but encephalopathy has been reported at lower concentrations. Because the symptoms of mild encephalopathy (headache, irritability, drowsiness, etc.) are nonspecific and often misdiagnosed, many contemporary investigators have begun to wonder, as did Byers 40 years ago, whether these missed cases do not contribute to the pool of behavior-disordered and learning-disabled children of unknown etiology (see Needleman, 1980; Singhal & Thomas, 1980).

4. Fundamental Toxicologic Questions

The toxicity of a given dose of lead is influenced by many factors. These can be classified, according to Doull (1980), as (1) factors related to exposure, (2) factors inherent in the individual, and (3) environmental factors obtaining at the time of the exposure. Until the various com-

plex relationships among variables within these classes are well characterized, a full understanding of the toxicology of lead will remain an
unachieved goal. Because our knowledge of the human effects of lead
derives from natural experiments in which all pertinent variables cannot
be brought under perfect control, there will always be some degree of
uncertainty in the causal inferences drawn. Regulators cannot wait for
the delivery of data as well controlled as those collected in the physical
or chemical laboratory; standards must be set. How, then, should these
standards be achieved in the face of an incomplete and sometimes contradictory data base? This question will be addressed in the final portion
of this chapter. Here we identify some of the complexities involved by
reviewing factors known or suspected of influencing biologic responses
to the metal.

4.1. Factors Related to Exposure

The exposure-related factors include the dose and duration of exposure, the timing in relation to the developmental status of the child,
and the route or site of exposure. Almost all studies have focused on the
question of dose and compared developmental outcome of children who
varied in their lead burden. Most studies have limited themselves to
relating a one-time exposure assessment to a one-time outcome assessment. Differences among studies in other variables which may influence
the toxicity of lead account in part for the inconsistencies in results and
for different positions reviewers have taken on the amount of risk associated with low-level lead exposure (e.g., Bornschein, Pearson, & Reiter,
1980; Rutter, 1983).

A major methodologic problem inherent in cross-sectional studies is
the difficulty in determining the child's exposure history. Blood levels are
good markers of recent exposure only. Tooth lead levels, whether whole
tooth or dentine, are more useful indices of cumulative exposure, but
analytical methods for estimating time or duration of exposure are not
yet at hand.

There is little information about variations in toxicity in relation to
other variables. Although some longitudinal studies of lead exposure
and child developmental outcome are being conducted, only one group
has reported data examining the effects of intrauterine exposure to lead.
These data indicate that the human fetus is considerably more sensitive
to the effects of lead on both physical and cognitive development (Needleman, Bellinger, Leviton, Rabinowitz, & Nichols, 1983). The dose and
duration of exposure at various developmental epochs necessary to pro-

duce impairment are unknown. The relative contribution of ingested and respired lead to the child's burden is still a matter of controversy (DHSS, 1980; National Academy of Sciences, 1980). It is clear, however, that a greater proportion of a child's burden derives from hand-to-mouth activity than is true for adults (Charney, Sayre, & Coulter, 1980). Once lead enters the body, from whatever the route, the toxic potential is the same.

4.2. Factors Inherent in the Individual

Many host characteristics, either transitory or permanent, may affect an individual's vulnerability to lead. These include genetic variations in susceptibility, nutritional status, age, and behavior. These factors alter toxicity by altering the metabolism of lead. Nutritional factors, most notably iron, calcium, and zinc, are important in modifying the response to lead (Mahaffey & Michaelson, 1980). Some variability in vulnerability to lead may be due to genetic differences in the synthesis of a lead-binding protein (Rhagavan, Culver, & Gonick, 1980).

Age of the host affects vulnerability. Young children manifest impairment, for example, encephalopathy, anemia, increased FEP levels at lower internal doses than adults (United States Environmental Protection Agency, 1977). Among the suggested mechanisms responsible for this finding are increased permeability of the blood–brain barrier (Willes, Lok, Truelove, & Sandram, 1977), increased intestinal absorption (Ziegler, Edwards, Jensen, Mahaffey, & Fomon, 1978), increased cortical energy requirements (McCauley, Bull, & Lutkenhoff, 1979), and the differential effect of lead on the brain during the period of synaptogenesis (Averill & Needleman, 1980; McCauley et al., 1982).

Children differ in the amoung of their hand-to-mouth activity and in the predilection of some for eating nonfood substances (pica). Some studies attempt to relate the amount of lead in the child's body to the quality of mothering (Milar, Schroeder, Mushak, Dolcourt, & Grant, 1980). The designs of these studies do not permit the acceptance of these inferences with confidence.

4.3. Factors Relating to the Psychosocial Environment

Given the ubiquity of lead in the human environment, some exposure is inevitable. This is, however, not a random phenomenon. Although lead exposure is not a problem exclusively limited to the poor and minority citizens, it is an unpleasant fact that the lead exposure does vary inversely with social standing. Excess lead exposure accompanies a variety of demographic risk factors such as large family size, deteriorated housing stock, and low socioeconomic status (Stark, Quah, Meigs, & DeLouise, 1982), as well as other hazards to development, such as poor prenatal care and nutrition. Children exposed to lead appear to be exposed to cadmium as well (Petering, Yeager, & Witherup, 1973).

The sequelae of lead exposure are probably subject to the same effect modification that has been seen to operate with prematurity, malnutrition, and metabolic disease. In large part, studies of lead have not attempted to evaluate the degree to which other factors modify lead's effect. Instead, most have attempted to determine only whether lead is a marker for these other variables or whether it has an independent effect on child development. Because of the difficulty of adequately measuring the many potential confounders of lead, all studies are vulnerable, to greater or lesser extent, to the charge that efforts to neutralize confounding were not entirely successful.

When advances in the ability to conceptualize, measure, and evaluate the many inputs into the developmental trajectory are at hand, we should be in a better position to partition out and isolate the confounders, the effect modifiers, and lead's actions. This should allow investigators to answer with increased precision the following questions, of considerable importance to public health authorities and regulators:

1. Are there sensitive periods during either pregnancy or the preschool period in which children are particularly vulnerable? Is a small dose early more deleterious than a larger dose later?

2. How specific is the effect of lead? Are there primary functional areas of special vulnerability? Are there specific deficits related to different ages of exposure?

3. Are the toxic effects of lead expressed immediately, or are they delayed? Some deficits may reflect acute pharmacologic effects, while others may reflect changes in central nervous system connectivity, and still others may be due to cell death. Are effects which differ in onset time related to these or other different toxic actions or other targets? Do these carry different prognostic imports for the patient?

4. What effect do psychosocial environmental factors have on lead's cognitive actions?

5. Are early lead effects persistent? Does the manner of their expression change over time? It has been shown, for example, that rhesus monkeys exposed to PCBs prenatally appear hyperactive when tested as juveniles but hypoactive when tested as adolescents (Bowman, Hieronimus, & Allen, 1978, 1981).

6. What is the nature of the dose–response relationship in children? Is it linear? If not linear, what is the threshold for adverse health effect?

5. Epidemiologic Studies of Lead at Low Dose

Investigations of lead effects on neuropsychologal function can be classified into two basic designs: case-control and cohort. Our review will treat the significant studies under these two headings.

In case-control studies, subjects are classified as to the presence or absence of the trait or outcome under examination (i.e., intellectual, perceptual, or behavioral deficit) and the relative frequency of the risk factor (i.e., lead exposure) compared between groups. This design is most efficient when studying diseases of low incidence but is vulnerable to problems of retrospective analysis: biased selection of subjects, misclassification of exposure, and biased reconstruction of covariates.

In cohort studies, subjects are selected on the basis of the presence or absence of the risk factor and the relative frequency of the disease under consideration compared. In one special case of this design, the retrospective cohort study, subjects are classified according to a risk factor measured at the same time that outcome is evaluated. This design requires that a marker of exposure that is both long-lasting and valid be available.

Four methodological problems or flaws have been encountered in many of the investigations published in the past two decades (Needleman & Landrigan, 1981; Bellinger & Needleman, 1983). The degree to which a given study successfully deals with these design problems will determine to a large extent the validity of the conclusions drawn by the investigator.

The first design difficulty, mentioned earlier, is the selection of an accurate index of past exposure. The maximum period of vulnerability and of excess exposure to lead is in early childhood. Indeed, it may be that intrauterine exposure is the most important determinant of outcome. Most studies have identified, classified, and evaluated the neuropsychological status of children after they have entered school. Lead's residence time in the blood is relatively brief; the half-life is about 27 days (Rabinowitz, Whetherill, & Kopple, 1976). If their exposure has terminated or decreased in the interim, children could be readily misclassified if blood lead, the most common exposure marker, is employed. Surrogate exposure markers, such as urban density or distance from a point source contain other important sources of error.

The second design flaw is the use of insensitive or inappropriate measures of outcome. The search for effects of lead at doses heretofore thought to be innocuous requires the identification of subtle effects of the neurotoxin. The use of such outcome measures as screening tests or group tests is obviously an inadequate strategy to elicit subtle deficits, should they be present. This flaw will lead to Type II errors.

Inadequate control of covariates that could confound the effects of lead is the third flaw. Many other factors in the child's world affect development. Some of these are correllated with lead and may thus confound its effects. Measuring these covariates and controlling for them either by matching or biostatistical control in the analysis of the data is essential. Under this category of design flaws we include the building of improper causal models, which may lead to overcontrol of covariates. It may be possible to confuse an outcome variable such as school assignment for a control variable. Controlling for the effect of such variables may result in partialing out some of lead's effect.

Finally, a number of studies have not dealt adequately with the issues of ascertainment or selection bias. When less than the total population is sampled, it is possible that those who decline participation or who are screened out may differ systematically from those who enter the study. Mothers who are worried over their children's development may reject participation in a study of childhood development (or they may seek it out as a less painful way of having their fears addressed). A rigorous study should attempt to evaluate the direction and magnitude of potential bias.

This review of the literature on low-level lead exposure and children's neuropsychological development will deal in greater detail with those studies published since 1979, because a number of comprehensive reviews of the earlier studies have been published (Bellinger & Needleman, 1982; Needleman & Landrigan, 1981; Rutter, 1980). We briefly examine those studies of particular interest in the pre-1979 period.

5.1. Cohort Studies Prior to 1979

The first paper to assert that lead toxicity without full-blown encephalopathy (by which was implied cerebral edema and hemorrhage) was followed by psychological residua was published in 1943 (Byers & Lord). They followed 20 children who had recovered from lead poisoning. Only half had evidence of encephalopathy. When tested later while in public school, 19 were found to have intellectual, perceptual, or behavioral impairment. This was the first paper to raise the question of undiagnosed lead toxicity.

De la Burde and Choate (1975) followed a group of children enrolled in the NICHD Collaborative Perinatal Study who were found to have pica. They found a significant increase in the lead-exposed group in the proportion of children with inferior IQ scores, behavioral abnormality during testing, and perceptual dysfunction. When tested again at age 7, the lead-exposed children again achieved significantly lower IQ scores.

The incidence of abnormal neurological function and abnormal behavior was also significantly higher in the lead-exposed group.

Perino and Ernhart (1974) followed up a group of black preschoolers whose blood lead levels were elevated. Their scores on the McCarthy Scales were inferior to controls. Landrigan, Baloh, Whitworth, Staehling, and Rosenblum (1975) studied a group of children who lived in the vicinity of a lead smelter. Children with blood levels greater than 40 $\mu g/ml$ had lower scores on the WISC-R Scales, controlling for socioeconomic status, ethnicity, and duration of residence near the smelter. Another study of a sample of children from the same area failed to find a relationship between exposure and outcome (McNeil, Ptasnik, & Croft, 1975).

5.2. Case-Control Studies

David and colleagues (1976) classified 119 children attending a pediatric clinic into five groups: (1) a group of children with hyperactivity of unknown cause ("pure" hyperactive group) (2) a group with a "probable" cause (e.g., prematurity, hyperbilirubinemia), (3) a group with a "possible" cause, (4) a lead-poisoned group, and (5) a normal control group. Blood lead levels were were found to be elevated in Groups 1, 3, and 4. After provocative chelation with penicilamine, Group 1 excreted more lead in the urine than Groups 2 or 5. In a later paper, David *et al.* reported that chelation was associated with greater behavioral improvement in "pure" hyperactives than in those with "probable" cause. These studies are intriguing but merit cautious interpretation. The authors did not control for SES covariates but relied on the fact that their sample was drawn from a homogeneous population. The treatment study is suggestive; but the number of subjects was small, assignment to treatment category was nonrandom, and no treatment placebo group was employed.

5.3. Studies Published since 1979

Needleman and colleagues established that the shed deciduous tooth is a useful marker of earlier exposure to lead (Needleman, Tuncay, & Shapiro, 1972; Needleman, Davidson, Sewell, & Shapiro, 1974) and utilized this tissue in a large-scale retrospective cohort study (Needleman, Gunnoe, Leviton, Reed, Peresie, Maher, & Barrett, 1979). They collected teeth from 2,235 children attending 1st and 2nd grade in two towns near Boston. Children were classified according to the level of lead in the dentine of their shed deciduous teeth. Covariate data were obtained on 39 nonlead variables including SES, parent education, perinatal variables, and maternal IQ. Children included in the study were compared to those who were excluded on two dimensions: the distribution of dentine lead levels, and teachers ratings of classroom behavior. Children who were born at term and who had no history of clinical lead poisoning, head injury, or seizures, were eligible for the detailed neuropsychological evaluation. Concordant dentine lead levels were required for a child to be entered into the NP follow-up. If the values did not agree, the subject was designated as unclassified and not studied further.

High- and low-lead subjects differed at $p < 0.1$ on 5 of the 39 nonlead variables. These were entered as covariates into an analysis of covariance and thus controlled. High-lead children scored significantly lower on the Wechsler Intelligence Scale for Children (Revised), both verbal and full-scale. Significant differences were also found on three measures of auditory and speech processing, the Seashore Rhythm Test, the Token Test, and the Sentence Repetition Test. High-lead subjects were slower at longer intervals of delay on a reaction time task. Teachers blind to the children's tooth lead levels described them as more distractible, more disorganized, less independent at their work, less able to follow directions, and in general functioning at a lower level than their peers. When the entire sample was classified on the basis of their dentine lead levels and their classroom behavior evaluated, a dose-dependent increase of negative ratings associated with lead was observed (Figure 1). Additional analyses indicate that the amount by which a child's observed Full-Scale IQ falls short of the value expected based upon his socioeconomic characteristics increases with increasing dentine lead levels (Bellinger & Needleman, 1983).

Winneke and colleagues carried out two studies of children classified according to whole tooth (as opposed to dentine) lead level. The first study was undertaken in Duisberg (Winneke, Hrdina, & Brockhaus, 1982). From 1,238 children who gave teeth, those 458 who donated two incisors were selected. After analysis, those children with tooth levels below 3ppm and above 7ppm were identified. Twenty-six pairs matched on the basis of age, sex, and father's occupational status were selected. The instruments administered to the subjects were a German version of the WISC, three tests of visual-motor integration (adaptations of the Bender Gestalt, the Benton, and a subscale from the Hetzer Developmental Series).

High-lead subjects scored significantly lower than controls on all scales of the WISC, but the difference did not achieve significance at the level of .05. High-lead subjects commited significantly more errors on

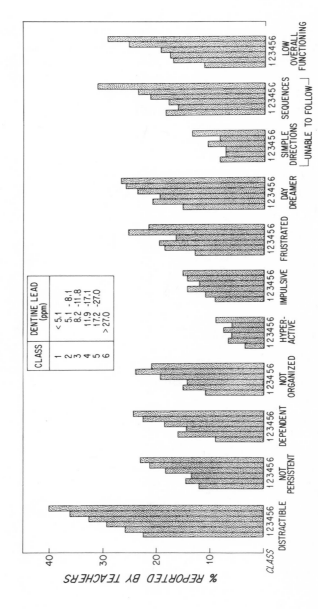

FIGURE 1. Distribution of negative teacher's ratings on an 11-item, forced-choice questionnaire in relation to dentine lead level. From "Deficits in Psychologic and Classroom Performance in Children with Elevated Dentine Lead Levels" by H. L. Needleman, C. Gunnoe, A. Leviton, R. R. Reed, H. Peresie, C. Maher, & P. Barret, *New England Journal of Medicine*, 1979, *300*, 689–695. Copyright 1975 by the New England Journal of Medicine. Reprinted by permission.

the adapted Bender Gestalt Test. Differences on the other visual-motor tests were not significant, although all scores favored the controls.

In the second study, Winneke and colleagues (Winneke, Kramer, Brockhaus, Ewers, Kujanek, Lechner, & Janke, 1983) collected deciduous teeth from 338 children from Stolberg, West Germany, and, after discarding carious or filled specimens, analyzed 317. These children were classified into three groups on the basis of their whole tooth lead levels: low (<4.2ppm), middle (5.8–7.2ppm), and high (>9.8ppm). Parents were interviewed, and a large number (50) of covariates were scaled. Four of these (occupational status of father and mother, school placement, and duration of labor) differed between exposure groups. These, with child's age and sex, were entered as covariates in a stepwise multiple regression analysis. The assessment protocol used in this study included, in addition to the measures used in the first study, a serial reaction time task (Weiner Reaction Device), two behavior questionaires, a finger–wrist tapping task, and a cancellation task. Before correction for covariates, the scores of the high-lead subjects were significantly lower than those of the controls. After correction, the difference in verbal IQ scores was reduced to 4.6 points, not significant at the .05 level. Differences on the perceptual-motor integration test, the reaction time test, and four items of the mothers' behavioral ratings remained significant after correction.

Although this study is well planned and executed, the sample size (115 for three groups) is small and the power of the analysis not sufficient to demonstrate a significant IQ difference. It should be noted that the IQ score difference after adjustment was about the same as that found by Needleman and Yule.

Ernhart, Landa, and Schell (1981) followed up 63 of 80 children originally studied in 1974. As in the earlier study, they administered the McCarthy Scales of Children's Abilities. In addition, the children's scores on standardized reading tests were culled from school records. Unfortunately, these scores were based on a total of 11 different tests, weakening the validity of their use in comparing children. Finally, teachers rated the children on the Conners Scale. Parental IQ was evaluated by the Quick Test of Intelligence, treated as a covariate in a multivariate regression. Because subjects' blood lead levels had dropped over the five-year period since the first study, new criteria for high- and low-lead classification were applied. Earlier blood lead levels were not related to General Cognitive Index scores five years later. Contemporary blood lead levels, however, were significantly associated with GCI scores after controlling for sex, parent IQ, and education. The authors discounted the importance of this difference largely on the grounds that the reading tests did not differ between groups.

The interpretations of the authors are open to question on a number of grounds: although they controlled for parent IQ and education, they overlooked socioeconomic status. They asserted that the families were of uniformly low SES, but their earlier paper stated that the parents were comprised of white and blue collar workers, managers, and welfare recipients. Furthermore, the reported relationship between school-age blood lead level and IQ, as measured by the investigators, an intriguing finding, should not be dismissed because an assorted group of tests, administered under differing circumstances, did not show a relationship. It appears, then, that this study warrants interpretation as evidence for a significant effect of lead at low levels.

Yule and colleagues (Yule, Lansdown, Millar, & Urbanowicz, 1981; Lansdown, Yule, Urbanowicz, & Millar, 1983) studied a group of children living in the proximity of a lead smelter in London. The sample was comprised of 166 children. Blood lead levels were used to classify the subjects. The mean blood lead level was 13.5 µg/ml; only two children of the entire sample had levels in excess of 30 µg/ml. Outcomes measured were the WISC-R and standardized tests of reading, spelling, and mathematics. Behavior was assessed by the same 11-item scale employed by Needleman *et al.*, the Connors Scale and the Rutter B2. After controlling for age, sex, and SES, significant differences were found between groups on IQ and on the reading and spelling scores. A remarkably similar relationship between lead burden and teachers' ratings to that reported by Needleman's group was found. An association was also found between lead and scores on the Connors and Rutter scales.

6. Design Issues and Review of Findings

In addition to the design problems noted above, there are several potential pitfalls in analyzing and interpreting the import of these studies. A different set of pitfalls are associated with "negative" studies—those which fail to find an effect of lead on children's cognitive function—and those which do find an effect.

6.1. Negative Studies

Negative studies must be evaluated from the standpoint of power, that is, the likelihood of correctly rejecting the null hypothesis of no association between lead and developmental dysfunction ($1 - \beta$, where β is the probability of committing a Type II error). The power of a study varies most notably with sample size, β (the level set by the investigator

TABLE 1
Power of T-Tests Mean Difference in IQ

N in each group	4	5	6	7	8
80	.46	.64	.79	.90	.96
70	.41	.58	.74	.86	.93
60	.36	.52	.67	.80	.89
50	.31	.45	.60	.73	.83

as the acceptable rate of Type II error), and the magnitude of association in the population between the independent and dependent variables, or effect size. Table 1 presents the power of *t*-tests to detect 2- to 10-point differences between the IQ scores of exposed and control subjects for sample sizes of 25–200 children per group (assuming $\alpha = .05$, two-tailed, $\delta = 15$, and equal group sizes). Under these assumptions it is clear that studies of 25, 50, or even 75 children in each group do not reach acceptable levels of power (generally considered to be .80) for effect sizes smaller than 8 IQ points. Many studies in the literature on lead had less than a 50% chance of detecting an IQ difference of even this magnitude. Calculations of the power of analysis of variance, assuming either a linear dose response or a threshold model for lead's effect, yield similar conclusions.

Some studies have employed correlational analysis, using continuously distributed measures of independent and dependent variables. Reference to power tables for correlational analysis (Cohen & Cohen, 1975) indicate that in order for a study to have a power of .80 to detect a population correlation of $-.2$ to $-.3$ (the range typically observed), the total sample size should be 150 or more (assuming $\alpha = .05$, two-tailed).

Few studies of low-level lead exposure, either negative or positive, have achieved adequate power.

Although statisticians counsel investigators to weigh carefully the relative costs of Type I and Type II errors in designing a study, most attention is usually paid to Type I errors. Even then, α is rarely set at any value other than .05. This is probably because this number has achieved special status in separating real from chance effects. Either Type II error rates are not considered at all, or a very large probability of error (i.e., low power) is tolerated. The literature on the developmental effects of low-level lead exposure contains a large number of studies with marginally significant trends ($.05 < p < .15$) favoring the unexposed groups. Given the consistency of the direction of effect, it appears likely that cross-study differences in power may contribute to the inconsistency in

the statistical significance of the findings. We concur with Rutter's conclusion (1980) that the consistency of direction should be weighted more
heavily than the failure of some trends to cross the threshold of $p = .05$.
This set of studies would be especially suitable for meta-analysis (Strube
& Hartmann, 1982) or other multisample analysis (Lazar & Darlington,
1982), which permits statistical integration of data produced by independent studies.

Frequently investigators use multiple regression analysis in an attempt to control covariates that confound any observed association between lead and developmental outcome. The requirement that all potential confounders be forced into the regression model before lead is
evaluated is often asserted. If the association remains significant after
this procedure is followed, the likelihood that a causal link exists is
enhanced, since this procedure most likely underestimates the magnitude of the relationship. The proper interpretation if the adjusted association fails to remain significant is not so straightforward. Some covariates may be markers for lead, either because they are highly correlated
with lead or because they are in the causal pathway between lead and
outcome. For example, SES and lead exposure are usually inversely
related to each other, and both are related to developmental outcome.
Much of the variance that each "explains" may be "explained" as well
by the other, because of the multicollinearity of the two variables. If SES
is considered before lead, it will, in effect "use up" the variance in the
outcome that is shared by SES and lead, leaving only the portion unique
to lead available to estimate lead's significance. If a study measures a
large number of indicator variables which may affect development, and
compares their distribution in high- and low-lead groups, some of these
will differ at the .05 level simply on the basis of chance, in the same way
that multiple tests of outcome will produce some spurious differences.
Entering all of these variables into the model will overcontrol, since the
variables are not orthogonal to each other.

One or more of the covariates may in fact be outcome variables, and
controlling for them may remove part of the variance due to lead's
action. For example, certain patterns of infant temperament may be
associated with less optimal development at 6 months of age. Control
for temperamental status may reduce the strength of the relationship
between lead and developmental outcome. This would be expected if
lead is responsible, at least in part, for variations in infants' temperament. In this case temperament would be a proxy variable, and would
accept some of the variance which should be assigned to lead, the prior
independent variable.

Dramatic changes in the magnitude or sign of the coefficient for lead should alert the investigator to the presence of some suppressor, moderator, or distorter variables in the model. Careful inspection of the correlations between lead and the covariates and the regression of lead on the other predictors may clarify the issues. Following the conventional, conservative approach to variable entry reduces the risk of a Type I error, but additional exploratory analysis may be necessary to be sure that this was not purchased at the cost of increased risk of a Type II error.

6.2. Positive Studies

Those studies which report an association between lead and developmental dysfunction must be examined from the viewpoint of Type I error. Most investigators have employed a wide array of outcome measures in order to insure that they would uncover any effect of the agent. This tactic increases the risk of finding spurious associations on the basis of chance. A variety of strategies to adjust in order to reduce the false positive rate are available (Games, 1971). Once the specific functions that are most vulnerable to lead are delineated, other investigators can reduce the number of outcomes in their studies and thereby avoid this design problem. In the final analysis, independent replication is the most convincing rebuttal to the criticism of multiplicity of outcomes.

Studies which have employed multiple outcomes can also reduce the outcome space by factor analysis or use omnibus statistical methods to evaluate the overall effect of multiple dependent or independent variables.

6.3. General Considerations

Most studies of lead and development are cross-sectional in design. These types of designs do not lend themselves to ready discernment of the direction of the causal relationships. Most refined determination of the causal pathways requires prospective studies that follow the developmental trends. In such studies, the temporal relationships between changes in exposure and in behavior, the interactions among dose, timing, duration of exposure, the social and familial context in which development occurs, and the course of development can be explored.

Given such a data set collected over time, many basic questions that have in the past been refractory to analysis can be explored. Among these are the following: Is there a critical period in which children are most sensitive to lead toxicity? Are toxic effects manifested immediately, or is there a time lag in their appearance? Which factors modulate the effect of a given dose of lead?

The use of prospective designs confronts the investigator with a series of experimental problems not encountered in cross-sectional work. We have found in our prospective study that children's blood levels fluctuate considerably over time. This is probably a result of varying exposure and changes in the child's physiological status. Although cross-sectional studies of changes only in the dependent variable over time must be modeled, here the investigator is required to model changes in both dependent and independent variables. The construction of structural equation models incorporating autoregressive terms to capture changes in blood levels appears to be a promising method (Jareskog, 1979). Different models can be constructed to reflect different *a priori* hypotheses about the causal relationships linking the variables of interest. Because a transactional approach to development underlies the modeling process, the distinction traditionally held between dependent and independent variables becomes blurred.

Three alternate causal models are presented in Figure 2. Although lead is known to produce aberrant behavior, it is possible that aberrant behavior, for example, pica, which could be a result of impaired development, causes increased exposure to lead. A third possibility is that both pica and lead exposure share a common risk factor.

Models can be enriched by the inclusion of other variables which

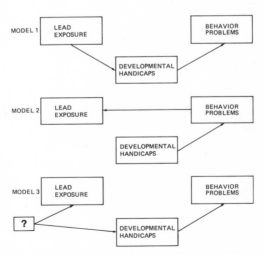

FIGURE 2. Possible causal models of the relationships between lead exposure, developmental handicap, and behavior disorder.

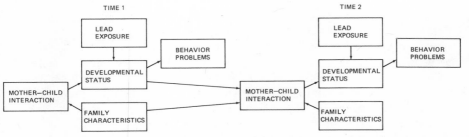

FIGURE 3. A transactional model of the effects, over time, of lead, family, behavior, and development.

can influence the course of cognitive development over time. This is illustrated in Figure 3. Here two influences, mother–child interaction and family characteristics (e.g., maternal IQ, familial stress), are added. Other causal paths could be added or eliminated to conform with the investigator's hypotheses about the real world situation. A path from lead exposure at time 1 to developmental status at time 2 (dotted arrow) could be inserted if the investigator believed that there was a lag between exposure and the expression of toxicity. A path between behavior and lead exposure could be added to form a positive feedback loop among exposure, behavior, and developmental problems. Assessing the effect of lead on children's development forces the investigator to formulate a coherent theory of both development and the way in which exposure alters the complex paths of influence specified by his theory.

Adequacy of the model and competing models can be evaluated by techniques such as maxmium likelihood estimation. Goodness of fit of the data for the models can be measured and the models ranked. It should be noted that, like the null hypothesis, the "truth" of any given model cannot be proven (Seifer & Sameroff, 1982).

7. Synthesis

Epidemiological investigations do not prove causal relationships. They can never hope to attain the degree of rigor that laboratory experimentation enjoys. Indeed, the concept of causality cannot, as David Hume has shown, be demonstrated empirically. What epidemiology can provide in the study of toxic substances is a series of models of the complexities of real world interactions among the environment, the genetic heritage of the host, and an apparently limitless set of other variates, some of which affect the outcomes of interest.

In such a circumstance, the investigator looks for patterns of the relationships of interest to emerge that describe a picture of the phenomenon under inquiry that is both coherent and aesthetically satisfactory—that is to say, sensible and parsimonious. If proof of a causal relationship cannot be obtained, we must then rely on substitutes to test whether the relationships we observe have causal properties and to evaluate the degree to which these relationships can be used to make such practical decisions as whether or not to ban the use of a certain chemical. The five criteria for judging causal inferences provided by the Advisory Committee to the Surgeon General (United States Department of Health, Education, and Welfare, 1964) have served well in this regard. The criteria they list are as follows:

1. *Time sequence of variables.* The causal agent must precede the effect. Establishing the true sequence of events in time may, however, prove quite difficult.

2. *Strength of association.* The stronger an association, the more readily one may accept it as causal.

3. *Specificity of the association.* By this is meant the precision with which one variable predicts another.

4. *Coherence of the explanation.* This refers to whether the observed relationship fits with known data about the biology of the phenomena under examination.

5. *Consistency and replication.* If the relationship is causal, it should display consistency. Given a similar set of conditions, a similar set of outcomes should occur. The single sternest test of a reported relationship is whether it can be replicated independently under similar conditions. In real-world epidemiology, no two studies can hope to achieve complete replication of variables. Similarity of conditions and findings are sufficient.

If one examines the three studies of school-age children conducted since 1979 according to these criteria, a broad pattern can be seen.

1. Although it is not possible to determine with complete certainty the time sequence of the variables in these studies, lead ingestion has been shown to precede intellectual deficit in many clinical case reports. It has been argued by some that the eating of foreign substances is a marker for impaired development, and this precedes and results in elevated body lead stores. The study of Needleman, Leviton, and Bellinger (1982) adjusted for the mothers' reports of pica and then found that the adjustment did not alter the relationship between lead exposure and IQ scores. Animal studies, in which exposure to lead unequivocally preceded altered behavior showed effects which resemble the human studies.

2. The strength of the association between lead and impaired devel-

opment is not strong. This is due in part to the many variables, some quite powerful, which alter development and modify lead's effect. Still the three contemporary studies show a difference between mean IQ scores in exposed and unexposed groups that ranges between 4 and 7 points on the IQ scales. Although this difference between means seem small, it predicts a three- to four-fold increase in the risk ratio for severe deficit: IQ scores below 80 (Needleman *et al.*, 1982).

3. The specificity of the deficits associated with lead is not high. Many other agents—malnutrition, infection, trauma, and environmental deprivation—can lead to clinical pictures that resemble those seen with lead.

4. The findings in studies of low-level lead exposure are congruent with the body of biological knowledge about the deposition of lead and its toxicology and are coherent with the findings seen in cases of clinical lead poisoning.

5. The final test of consistency and replication has been met. Although the three studies of Needleman, Yule, and Winneke are not identical replicates, they all dealt with samples of children enrolled in school who were thought not to have been lead-intoxicated; they employed an IQ measure and a teachers' rating; and they controlled for a number of markers of socioeconomic status. The Winneke and Needleman studies both used lead in dental tissue as the lead marker, whereas the Yule study used blood lead levels. Yule employed the same teacher rating scale that Needleman did, and both found results strikingly similar to each other.

All three studies found IQ deficits in the high-lead children of the magnitude of 4–6 points between the means.

This body of human data, in which complete control of all variates has not been achieved, and the massive collection of animal studies together paint a clear pattern. The most parsimonious explanation for this pattern is that that lesser levels of lead than those that produce recognizable symptoms are associated with deficits in neuropsychological function. The principal function which appears to be most sensitive to lead is psychometric intelligence; this was found by Ernhart *et al.* (1981), Needleman *et al.* (1979), Winnecke *et al.* (1982), and Yule *et al.* (1981). Classroom behavior, particularly those items which deal with the ability to attend, inhibit distracting stimuli, and follow directions, appear to be sensitive to lead's actions.

8. Public Health Considerations

The NHANES studies mentioned earlier indicate that over 600,000 American children have excess lead in their bodies. Cowan and Leviton

(1980) used the data of Needleman to calculate measures of attributable risk due to lead, calculating Attributable Risk (AR) as

$$AR = \frac{Ie - Io}{Io} = \frac{.26 - .08}{.08} = .69,$$

where Ie = incidence of the disease (low overall classroom functioning) in the exposed group (26%) and Io = incidence of the disease in the unexposed group (8%). The attributable risk for low overall classroom functioning in high lead children is 69%.

Using the same data base, Provenzano (1980) calculated the national costs for neuropsychologic deficit in children exposed to lead as ranging between $700 million and $1200 million per year. These estimates may be considered conservative, since they rely on prevalence figures that were available before the NHANES study and require recalculation in the light of the most recent data. Even these conservative estimates support the assertions, made by a few public health specialists, that the problem of lead exposure is one of the most serious risks for American children.

The sources of lead are manifold. The commonest high-dose source remains old paint. For the majority of children, however, the most important source is airborne lead, which enters the body directly through inhalation and through the ingestion of leaded dust. The major source of lead in the atmosphere is automobile emissions. Although the total amount of lead in the atmosphere has decreased with the reduction of leaded gasoline sales, over 50,000 tons of lead are still inserted into the air each year through auto exhausts. The decline in blood lead levels over the past five years has been clearly related to decreased gasoline lead additives in three studies (Annest et al., 1983; Fachetti & Geiss, 1982; Rabinowitz & Needleman, 1983).

The case for removal of lead from gasoline has received increased attention in the past few years and is under consideration in Australia, Great Britain, the United States, and the European Community of Nations.

Lead in old housing stock is still a serious hazard and, although abatement of this source is formidably expensive, could be a part of broader programs to renovate housing and energy conservation. At a time of severe underemployment, the renewal and making safe of urban housing could have powerful multiplying effects.

A final and substantial, if difficult to measure, benefit that could flow from the removal of lead from the human environment is that its control is a splendid paradigm for our ambivalent relationship to the technology we have created. At a time when people admit to pervasive pessimism about their ability to control such contemporary events as hunger, unemployment, weapons proliferation, and pollution, the reduction of the threat of lead could be one step in altering man's defeatist picture of himself in relation to the natural and technological world.

9. References

Annest, J. L., Mahaffey, K., Cox, D. H., & Roberts, M. S. Blood lead levels for persons 6 months–74 years of age: United States 1976–1980. *Department of Health and Social Services Publication*, (PHS) 82–1250, 1982.

Annest, J. L., Pirkle, J. L., Makuc, D., Neese, J. U., Bayse, D. D., & Kovar, M. G. Chronological trend in blood lead levels between 1976 and 1980. *New England Journal of Medicine*, 1983, *308*, 1373–1377.

Averill, D., & Needleman, H. L. Neonatal lead exposure retards cortical synaptogenesis in the rat. In H. Needleman (Ed.), *Low level lead exposure: The clinical implications of current research*. New York: Raven Press, 1980.

Bellinger, D., & Needleman, H. L. Low level lead exposure and psychological deficit in children. In M. Wolraich & D. K. Routh (Eds.), *Advances in developmental and behavioral pediatrics* (Vol. 3). Greenwich, Conn.: JAI Press, 1982.

Bellinger, D., & Needleman, H. L. Lead and the relationship between maternal and child intelligence. *Journal of Pediatrics*, 1983, *102*, 523–527.

Bornschein, R., Pearson, D., & Reiter, L. Behavioral effects of moderate lead exposure in children and animal models. *CRC Critical Reviews in Toxicology*, 1980, *8*, 43–99.

Bowman, R., & Hieronimus, M., & Allen, J. Hypoactivity in adolescent monkeys perinatally exposed to PCBs and hyperactive as juveniles. *Neurobehavioral Toxicology and Teratology*, 1981, *3*, 15–18.

Bowman, R., Hieronimus, M., & Allen, J. Correlation of PCB body burden with behavioral toxicology in monkeys. *Pharmocology, Biochemistry, and Behavior*, 1978, *9*, 49–56.

Brown, R. S., Hingerty, B. E., Dewan, J. C., & Klug, A. Pb(II)-catalyzed cleavage of the sugar-phosphate backbone of yeast RNA—Implications for lead toxicity and self-splicing RNA. *Nature*, 1983, *303*, 543–546.

Byers, R., & Lord, E. Late effects of lead poisoning on mental development. *American Journal of Diseases of Children*, 1943, *66*, 471–494.

Charney, E., Sayre, J., & Coulter, M. Increased lead absorption in inner-city children: Where does the lead come from? *Pediatrics*, 1980, *65*, 226–231.

Cohen, J., & Cohen, P. *Applied multiple regression/correlation analysis for the behavioral sciences*. Hillsdale, N.J.: Erlbaum, 1975.

Cowan, L., & Leviton, A. Epidemiologic considerations in the study of low level lead exposure. In H. Needleman (Ed.), *Low level lead exposure: The clinical implications of current research*. New York: Raven Press, 1980.

David, O., Hoffmen, S., Sverd, J., & Clark, J. Lead and hyperactivity: Behavioral response to chelation: A pilot study. *American Journal of Psychiatry*, 1976, *133*, 1155–1158.

de la Burde, B., & Choate, M. Early asymptomatic lead exposure and development at school age. *Journal of Pediatrics*, 1975, *87*, 1088–1091.

Department of Health and Social Security. *Lead and Health*. London: Her Majesty's Stationery Office, 1980.

Doull, J. Factors influencing toxicity. In J. Doull, C. Klaassem, & M. Amdur (Eds.), *Cassarett and Doull's toxicology: The basic science of poisons*. New York: Macmillan, 1980.

Ernhart, C., Landa, B., & Schell, N. Subclinical levels of lead and developmental deficit— A multivariate follow-up reassessment. *Pediatrics*, 1981, *67*, 911–919.

Fachetti, S., & Geiss, F. *Isotopic lead experiment: Status report*. Luxembourg: Commission of the European Countries, 1982.

Games, P. Multiple comparisons of means. *American Educational Research Journal*, 1971, *8*, 531–565.

Gibson, J. L. A plea for painted railings and painted walls of rooms as the source of lead poisoning among Queensland children. *Australian Medical Gazette*, 1904, *23*, 149–153.

Gilfillan, S. C. Lead poisoning and the fall of Rome. *Journal of Occupational Medicine*, 1965, *7*, 53–60.

Jareskog, K. Statistical estimation of structural models in longitudinal-developmental investigation. In J. Nesselroade & P. Baltes (Eds.), *Longitudinal research in the study of behavior and development*. New York: Academic Press, 1979.

Landrigan, P., Baloh, R., Whitworth, R., Staehling, N., & Rosenblum, B. F. Neuropsychological dysfunction in children with chronic low level lead absorbtion. *Lancet*, 1975, *1*, 708–712.

Lansdown, R., Yule, W., Urbanowicz, M., & Millar, I. B. Blood lead, intelligence, attainment and behavior in school children: Overview of a pilot study. In M. Rutter & R. R. Jones (Eds.), *Lead versus health*. New York: Wiley, 1983.

Lazar, I., & Darlington, R. Lasting effects of early education: A report from the consortium for longitudinal studies. *Monographs of the Society for Research in Child Development*. 1982, *47* (2–3, Serial No. 195).

Lin-Fu, J. S. *Lead poisoning in children*. DHEW Publication No. (HSA) 78–5142, 1967.

Mahaffey, K., & Michaelson, I. A. Interaction between lead and nutrition. In H. Needleman (Ed.), *Low level lead exposure: The clinical implications of current research*. New York: Raven Press, 1980.

McCauley, P., Bull, R., & Lutkenhoff, S. Association of alterations in energy metabolism with lead-induced delay in rat cerebral cortical development. *Neuropharmacology*, 1979, *18*, 93–101.

McCauley, P., Bull, R., Tonti, A., Lutkenhoff, S., Meister, M., Doerger, J., & Stober, J. The effect of prenatal and postnatal lead exposure on neonatal synaptogenesis in rat cerebral cortex. *Journal of Toxicology and Environmental Health*, 1982, *10*, 639–651.

McNeil, J., Ptasnik, J., & Croft, D. Evaluation of long-term effects of elevated blood lead concentrations in asymptomatic children. *Archives of Industrial Hygiene and Toxicology*, 1975, *14*, 97–118.

Milar, C. R., Schroeder, S. R., Mushak, P., Dolcourt, J. L., & Grant, L. D. Contribution of caregiving environment to increased lead burden of children. *American Journal of Mental Deficiency*, 1980, *84*, 339–344.

National Academy of Sciences. *Lead in the human environment*. Washington, D.C.: National Academy Press, 1980.

Needleman, H. L. *Low level lead exposure: The clinical implications of current research*. New York: Raven Press, 1980.

Needleman, H. L., & Landrigan, P. The health effects of low level exposure to lead. *Annual Review of Public Health*, 1981, *2*, 277–298.

Needleman, H. L., Tuncay, O., & Shapiro, I. M. Lead levels in deciduous teeth of urban and suburban American children. *Nature*, 1972, *235*, 111–112.

Needleman, H. L., Davidson, I., Sewell, E., & Shapiro, I. M. Subclinical lead exposure in Philadelphia schoolchildren: Identification by dentine lead analysis. *New England Journal of Medicine*, 1974, *290*, 245–248.

Needleman, H. L., Gunnoe, C., Leviton, A., Reed, R. R., Peresie, H., Maher, C., & Barrett, P. Deficits in psychologic and classroom performance in children with elevated dentine lead levels. *New England Journal of Medicine,* 1979, *300,* 689–695.

Needleman, H. L., Leviton, A., & Bellinger, D. Lead-associated intellectual deficit. *New England Journal of Medicine,* 1982, *306,* 367.

Needleman, H. L., Bellinger, D., Leviton, A., Rabinowitz, M. R., & Nichols, M. Umbilical cord blood lead levels and neuropsychological performance at 12 months of age. *Pediatric Research,* 1983, *17,* 179A.

Nriagu, J. Saturnine gout among Roman aristocrats. Did lead poison contribute to the fall of the empire? *New England Journal of Medicine,* 1983, *308,* 660–663.

Patterson, C. C. Contaminated and natural lead environments of man. *Archives of Environmental Health,* 1965, *11,* 344–360.

Perino, J., & Ernhart, C. The relation of subclinical lead level to sensorimotor and cognitive impairment in black preschoolers. *Journal of Learning Disabilities,* 1974, *7,* 26–30.

Petering, H., Yeager, D., & Witherup, S. Trace metal content in hair. II. Cadmium and lead content of human hair in relation to age and sex. *Archives of Environmental Health,* 1973, *27,* 327–330.

Provanzano, G. The social costs of low level lead exposure. In H. Needleman (Ed.), *Low level lead exposure: The clinical implications of current research.* New York: Raven Press, 1980.

Rabinowitz, M. R., & Needleman, H. L. Temporal trends in the lead concentration of umbilical cord blood. *Science,* 1982, *216,* 1429–1431.

Rabinowitz, M. R., & Needleman, H. L. Petrol lead sales and umbilical cord blood lead levels in Boston, Massachusetts. *Lancet,* 1983, *1,* 63.

Rabinowitz, M. R., Whetherill, G., & Kopple, J. Kinetic analysis of lead in healthy humans. *Journal of Clinical Investigation,* 1976, *58,* 260–270.

Rhagavan, S., Culver, B., & Gonick, H. Erythrocyte lead-binding protein after occupational exposure. I. Relationship to lead toxicity. *Environmental Research,* 1980, *22,* 264–270.

Rutter, M. Raised lead levels and impaired cognitive/behavioral functioning: A review of the evidence. *Developmental Medicine and Child Neurology,* Suppl. No. 42, 1980, *22,* 1–26.

Rutter, M. M. Low level lead exposure: Sources, effects and implications. In M. Rutter & R. R. Jones (Eds.), *Lead versus health: Sources and effects of low level lead exposure.* New York: Wiley, 1983.

Seifer, R., & Sameroff, A. A structural equation model analysis of competence in children at risk for mental disorder. *Prevention and Human Services,* 1982, *1,* 85–96.

Singhal, R. L., & Thomas, J. A. (Eds.). *Lead toxicity.* Baltimore: Urban & Scharzenberg, 1980.

Stark, A., Quah, R., Meigs, J., & DeLouise, E. Relationship of socioeconomic factors to blood lead concentrations in New Haven children. *Journal of Epidemiology and Community Health,* 1982, *36,* 133–139.

Strube, M., & Hartman, D. A critical appraisal of meta-analysis. *British Journal of Clinical Psychology,* 1982, *21,* 129–139.

Thomas, H. M., & Blackfan, K. Recurrent meningitis due to lead in a child of five years. *American Journal of Diseases of Children,* 1914, *8,* 377–380.

United States Department of Health, Education, and Welfare. *Smoking and health: Report of the Advisory Committee to the Surgeon General.* Washington, D.C.: Public Health Service, 1964.

United States Environmental Protection Agency. *Air quality criteria for lead.* Washington, D.C.: U.S. Government Printing Office, Publication No. EPA–68/8–77–017, 1977.

Willes, R., Lok, E., Truelove, J., & Sandaram, A. Retention and tissue lead distribution of 210-Pb(NO3)2 administered orally to infant and adult monkeys. *Journal of Toxicology and Environmental Health*, 1977, *3*, 395–406.

Winneke, G., Hrdina, K. G., & Brockhaus, A. Neuropsychological studies in children with elevated tooth lead concentrations. Part I: Pilot study using a matched pair approach. *International Archives of Occupational and Environmental Health*, 1982, *51*, 169–183.

Winneke, G., Kramer, G., Brockhaus, A., Ewers, U., Kujanek, G., Lechner, H., & Janke, W. Neuropsychological studies in children with elevated tooth lead concentration. *International Archives of Occupational and Environmental Health*, 1983, *51*, 231–252.

Yule, W., Lansdown, R., Millar, I., & Urbanowicz, M. The relationship between blood lead concentrations, intelligence, and attainment in a school population: A pilot study. *Developmental Medicine and Child Neurology*, 1981, *23*, 567–576.

Ziegler, E., Edwards, B., Jensen, R., Mahaffey, K., & Fomon, S. Absorption and retention of lead by infants. *Pediatric Research*, 1978, *12*, 29–34.

7 Food Additive Safety Evaluation

The Link to Behavioral Disorders in Children

BERNARD WEISS

1. Introduction

Deprived and disordered environments are such a compelling source of behavioral pathology that some of the intrinsic mediating links are eclipsed by their social and economic setting. Unremitting violence, inadequate health care, and decayed housing are such glaring faults that they easily can obscure these connections. But many of these mediating processes are destined to play an increasingly crucial role, both as explanatory concepts and as guides to intervention. The most provocative might be termed pathological molecular processes.

   This somatic ghost has been resurrected by the surge of new knowledge about the biological foundations of behavior. The contributions of chemotherapy to psychiatry, coupled with an avalanche of advances in neurobiology, provided key elements of this knowledge. But a spectrum of parallel developments in other disciplines is exerting an equally dramatic and significant impact. Nutritional science, for example, has documented unsuspected links between diet and brain chemistry. It has discovered that the combination of psychological and nutritional deprivation is vastly more damaging than either alone. Genetics is confronting us with the incredible polymorphism of the human population and stimulating speculation about the range of congenital defects, such as

BERNARD WEISS • Division of Toxicology and Environmental Health Sciences Center, University of Rochester School of Medicine and Dentistry, Rochester, New York 14642. Preparation of this chapter was supported in part by grants MH-11752 from NIMH and ES-01247 from NIEHS and by contract no. DE-AC02-76EV03490 with the U.S. Department of Energy at the University of Rochester Department of Radiation Biology and Biophysics with the assigned report number DOE/EV/03490-2326.

221

inborn errors of metabolism, that may underlie many inexplicable disturbances of behavior.

Developmental biology is generating a torrent of new information, new concepts, new strategies of intervention. Fetal alcohol and fetal hydantoin syndromes have emerged as potential sources of future problems for the immature organism that are not readily identified because they lack specificity. Behavioral teratology has developed in response to our recognition that a legacy of functional deficits could be even more disabling than morphological handicaps. Specialists in adolescent psychiatry are puzzling over the high incidence of unusual health problems, traumatic accidents, and prevalence of short stature among juvenile deliquents.

Perhaps the message of current biology is that we are all flawed, and all possess unique susceptibilities and sensitivities and patterns of defense. A benign environment traces a profile of our strengths. A malevolent environment amplifies our weaknesses. From this perspective, the central task of the environmental health sciences is to define how these special susceptibilities respond to particular environmental conditions. And the task of public health practitioners is to target interventions that arise out of the individual's unique attributes.

Behavioral science incurs special responsibilities in this enterprise because it reflects so faithfully the current dominant theme of the environmental health sciences—the subtle, often long-range consequences of environmental chemical exposures not severe enough to induce unmistakable clinical manifestations. The list of suspects linked to behavior is impressively long. It includes heavy metals, organic solvents, pesticides, halogenated hydrocarbons, food additives. More than half the substances on the current EPA priority list for research and standard setting exert some nervous system activity. The Toxic Substances Control Act explicitly recognizes that impaired behavioral function often may be rooted in chemical contamination of the environment. The burgeoning role of behavioral toxicology is consistent with the posture and strategy that the new biology implies for public health.

Children serve as sentinels of environmental contamination because of two special sources of vulnerability: immature mechanisms of metabolism and elimination, and organ systems still attaining structural and functional maturity. These factors conspire to face the developing organism with enhanced risks from toxic chemical exposures. The central nervous system is especially vulnerable. Its extended period of development, stretching long beyond the moment of birth, its heterogeneity of both structure and function and corresponding sensitivity to selective disruption, and, finally, its extraordinarily complex scheme of organization make it susceptible at many different developmental stages and in many different ways. Psychologists have to be especially sensitive to these implications because most of the time the manifestations of toxicity are not clear, direct, and overt. Instead, they most often tend to be subtle, nonspecific, and embedded within a setting from which few compelling correlations can be extracted.

Although behavioral toxicology is practiced in many different ways, the central issues remain the same: the detection of hazard and the assessment of risk. Determining that an agent is able to produce central nervous system impairment is a problem amenable to varied approaches. Psychology's long history provides an enormous array of tools and methods for making such a determination. The greater challenge is the assessment of risk, that is, the likelihood of damage to an organism given the source of exposure likely to prevail in settings beyond the laboratory. The fetal alcohol syndrome is a useful example. Ethyl alcohol is recognized as a neurotoxic agent. Alcohol represents a hazard to the fetus. If one assumes that the maternal consumption of four drinks daily, say, is likely to produce evidence of the syndrome, what is the risk of one drink daily, that is, the likelihood that any adverse effect will appear at this level? This is the kind of question that arises over and over in discussions of environmental contamination. It arises with fetal exposures to carbon monoxide from maternal smoking, from the consumption of maternal milk containing detectable amounts of polychlorinated biphenyls (PCBs), and from the incremental community burden of lead from gasoline. More recently, a new candidate has entered the arena—food additives.

2. The Feingold Hypothesis

What is known as the Feingold hypothesis alleges a link between hyperactivity or hyperkinesis and the ingestion of certain food constituents. Feingold (1975), a pediatric allergist and pioneer in allergy, asserted that a significant proportion of the children currently labeled as hyperactive and often treated with drugs such as methylphenidate and amphetamines are simply manifesting an elevated sensitivity to synthetic food colors, synthetic flavors, and certain natural constituents. He claimed that such sensitive children could be treated effectively by removing synthetic colors and flavors and foods containing salicylates from their diet. Most of these latter food items fall within the fruit group (oranges, apples, grapes, plums), and a few fall within the vegetable group (cucumbers, tomatoes). They are designated as *salicylate-containing* because of their historical link with aspirin sensitivity. Chemical analyses provide ambiguous support; salicylates are found in many foods in trace quantities.

Feingold's assertions were based upon clinical experience and parental testimony. Many parents reported that even children recalcitrant to counseling, psychotherapy, and drugs improved dramatically when the additives and specified fruits and vegetables were excised from the diet. Numerous parents, by constant experimentation, also claimed to have evolved a specific profile of intolerance for their child. Volunteer groups of parents, calling themselves Feingold Associations, were organized throughout the United States and even abroad to provide mutual guidance and support. It was a remarkable development to have occurred so spontaneously and widely. Although the Feingold hypothesis frequently is framed by others in terms of food allergies, Feingold himself was careful to speak only of elevated sensitivity. At best, he noted, the colors and flavors may act as haptens, or agents that attach to macromolecules which then provoke an immune-type reaction.

Feingold's claims, which were based on clinical observations, encountered rigid dismissal from most of the food industry and nutritionists and overwhelming scepticism from most physicians. The public, however, responded more favorably, eventually forcing both the industry and government agencies such as the Food and Drug Administration to consider the claims more seriously. Several controlled trials with children emerged from those programs and were accompanied later by both animal behavior and *in vitro* studies. The evidence is inadequate to yield any estimates of risk or prevalence, but clear enough to show that Feingold had observed a real effect. To me, however, the toxicologic implications of his hypothesis, and the policy issues they illuminate, transcend the possible therapeutic impact of his hypothesis. This chapter approaches the hypothesis from that viewpoint.

3. Food Additives

A food additive is a substance or blend of substances, deliberately added to basic foodstuffs during production, processing, storage, or packaging. An additive need not be synthetic to fall within this definition; some additives, such as spices, are natural products. Substances such as pesticides are not additives because they appear inadvertently.

Thousands of agents are approved as additives. Some are specifically designed by synthetic chemists. Others may be as commonplace as sugar and table salt. In the United States, all are governed by labeling regulations prescribed by the Food and Drug Administration. The dominant categories of food additives are listed in Table 1.

TABLE 1
Classification of Intentional Additives

1. Preservatives	33
2. Antioxidants	28
3. Sequestrants	45
4. Surface active agents	111
5. Stabilizers, thickeners	39
6. Bleaching and maturing agents	24
7. Buffers, acids, alkalies	60
8. Food colors	34
9. Nonnutritive and special dietary sweeteners	4
10. Nutritive supplement	117
11. Flavorings—synthetic	1610
12. Flavorings—natural	502
13. Miscellaneous: Yeast foods, texturizers, firming agents, binders, anticaking agents, enzymes	157
Total number of additives	2764

3.1. Flavors

The largest single group of additives consists of flavors, which number about 2,000. Of these, about 500 are extracted from natural sources. The rest are synthesized but many mimic structures found naturally in foods. Sucrose and sodium chloride are added in enormous quantities to processed foods to restore flavor lost in processing. Many flavors consist of mixtures. For example, there are 17 ingredients in artificial pineapple flavor. Mixtures are not tested for toxicity.

3.2. Colors

Although coloring agents from natural sources are readily available, synthetic dyestuffs are preferred because of their stability during processing and their strong coloring potency. Only a few synthetic colors are widely used in food. Each batch is certified by Food and Drug Administration chemists for adherence to prescribed standards of purity, typically 85%. Food dyes have undergone more testing for carcinogenesis than for any other adverse effect.

3.3. Preservatives

Food spoilage is a serious problem both for economic and health reasons. Chemical preservatives are now used in addition to the more traditional treatments such as smoking, drying, fermenting, souring, heating, and cooling. Antioxidants, such as butylated hydroxytoluene and butylated hydroxyanisole, help prevent rancidity in products containing fats (e.g., oil, lard, potato chips, crackers). Bread mold ("rope") is inhibited by calcium propionate and similar agents. Benzoic acid helps preserve margarine and fruit juices. Sulfur dioxide maintains wine and dried fruit, and antibiotics prevent spoilage of raw fish or other products. Nitrates and nitrites combat microbial toxins in products such as sausage and bacon but provoke anxiety about their carcinogenic potential since they may undergo transformation to nitrosamines. The FDA has limited the amounts of nitrites in bacon because of this concern.

3.4. Texture Agents

Emulsifiers, stabilizers, and thickening agents probably account for the greatest bulk among the additives. They find their way into baked goods, ice cream, pudding, toppings, soft drinks, and the new, textured vegetable proteins. Emulsifiers and stabilizers are exemplified by glycerol esters, carboxymethylcellulose, carrageenan, and propylene glycol, among others. Thickeners include modified starches and celluloses and natural products such as carob bean gum.

3.5. Miscellaneous Agents

Substances also are added to control acidity or alkalinity, to bleach and mature flour, to sequester trace metals, to retain moisture, to glaze surfaces, or to prevent wilting. The list is too extensive to be encompassed here.

4. Safety Evaluation

The original Food and Drug Act became law in 1906 as a consumer protection measure. In 1938, the Food, Drug, and Cosmetic Act provided an even more comprehensive regulatory framework, expanded since by the Food Additives Amendments of 1958. This last legislation called for prior approval by the Food and Drug Administration of new, commercially added food ingredients, on the basis of utility and safety. The procedures for safety (or toxicity) testing are now fairly standard (WHO, 1974), although they seldom extend to the immature animal.

4.1. Toxicity Tests

The earliest steps in toxicity testing are aimed at providing information about mode of action, species sensitivity, and other data useful in planning further studies. Such acute toxicity determinations generally use at least two test species, and often three. Long-term studies typically emphasize rodents, although dogs are sometimes used. The main purpose of such studies is to provide a model of human exposure, which may last a lifetime. The dominant concern is carcinogenesis, although many other observations also are made. Typical long-term studies last a minimum of 18 months in mice and 2 years in rats. Modern assessments of toxicity also include reproduction, embryotoxicity, and teratogenicity.

4.2. Extrapolation to Humans

To provide acceptable risks for humans on the basis of animal studies, a safety factor is introduced. The amount of a substance that can be included in the diet of a group of animals without producing detectable toxic effects is taken as the *no effect* level. Such a level is an arbitrary, statistical criterion, since the chances of finding an outcome, such as liver damage, depend upon the size of the subject sample. A safety factor, typically 100, then provides what is called the Acceptable Daily Intake (ADI) for humans. However, no additive is permitted at any level if it has been shown to induce cancer. This stipulation—the Delaney Clause—evokes constant debate because of its strict criteria.

4.3. Adequacy of Safety Evaluation

The foregoing procedures represent current toxicologic standards. Even if they are conducted according to recommended protocols, they still leave a residue of nagging questions.

4.3.1. GRAS

The 1958 food additives amendment exempted prior permits and substances in common use from the new regulatory requirements. Those substances became known as GRAS (for "Generally Regarded As Safe") substances. By 1969, enough skepticism has been voiced about the GRAS strategy to provoke a re-evaluation. The basis for that re-evaluation is now published and represents a landmark document in toxicology (FASEB, 1977). The theme of the report can be described as skepticism about permitting substances as food additives solely on the basis that proof of harm to humans is absent. To determine that an agent is indeed innocuous takes us beyond the limits of current toxicologic competence.

4.3.2. Laboratory Limitation

Even if current toxicologic protocols are carried out with unswerving dedication, they still fail to reflect certain features of the natural environment. They test only one agent at a time, whereas humans consume hundreds of different agents simultaneously. They rely on healthy animals fed a nutritious diet to evaluate substances consumed by people who may be malnourished, old, or sick. The basal diet is not irrelevant. Ershoff (1976, 1977) discovered that rats fed a low-fiber diet died after consuming food colors at levels that did not impair the health of rats fed the typical laboratory diet, which is high in fiber and minerals.

4.3.3. Epidemiology

Despite the most prolonged and thorough laboratory study, toxic substances are bound to slip through the screen. Allowable intake levels are certain, also, to be set occasionally at values that induce adverse effects in humans. If epidemiology is to act as a sentinel for such possible, even though unlikely, outcomes, patterns of consumption must be monitored. Such information is rarely available. Food processors need not file their formulations with the Food and Drug Administration. Without monitoring actual intake and industry practices, no one can be certain if the postulated limits are observed.

5. Adverse Effects of Additives

Carcinogenesis still dominates the toxicologic evaluation of additives and is the main reason for FDA categorical bans on any additives. Adverse effects may take many forms, however, most of which attract minimal regulatory attention but which pose troublesome problems for the public.

Some effects may be life-threatening. Within a period of one month, nine infants in a pediatric ward in Israel, ranging in age from 6 to 15 weeks, developed a significant methemoglobinemia (Nitzan, Volovitz, & Topper, 1979). The only suspicious finding was that all the affected infants, who had been recovering from acute gastroenteritis, had been fed a soybean hypoallergenic infant formula product. The outbreak eventually was traced to a manufacturer who had switched to a new fat preservative imported from the United States. This additive contained the antioxidants BHT, BHA, and propyl gallate. The authors suggested that the high physiological levels of hemoglobin characteristic of the fetus and neonate rendered them vulnerable to toxicity.

A food additive also has been implicated in the pathogenesis of ketosis-prone diabetes. An epidemiologic survey in Iceland (Helgason & Jonasson, 1981) indicated that males born in October showed a striking elevation in the incidence of this disease. After considering many alternative possibilities, such as viral infections, the authors settled on a food additive etiology. Vast amounts of smoke-cured mutton are consumed during the Christmas season. The meat is smoked and preserved with nitrates or nitrites, and the latter may react with nitrogen groups to form different N-nitroso compounds of which the diabetogenic agent streptozotocin is an example. The mechanism of this linkage remains under investigation.

Essential nutrients are also sometimes added, but in questionable roles and quantities. Between 1964 and 1967, heavy beer drinkers in certain parts of the United States and Canada fell victim to fulminating heart failure marked by pericardial effusion and raised hemoglobin levels (Berglund, 1978). The epidemic began to appear about 6 months after cobalt chloride was introduced as a beer additive to stabilize the foam. This cobalt-beer cardiomyopathy is in part a mystery because patients with the syndrome were estimated to have consumed 5–10 mg per day, a moderate dose compared to the daily dose of 18–37 mg sometimes given to patients with anemia. Perhaps alcohol enhanced cobalt toxicity, but the incident remains a lesson in unpredictability and the merits of caution.

In one study conducted with 122 patients suffering from a variety of what were diagnosed as allergic disorders, oral administration of 50 mg of the food dye tartrazine (FD & C Yellow No. 5) evoked reactions such as weakness, heat sensation, palpitations, blurred vision, rhinorrhoea, feelings of suffocation, pruritus, and urticaria (Neuman et al., 1978). Although a substantial dose, such as quantity of tartrazine would be consumed by a patient drinking only a few bottles of soft drinks during the day.

Reactions to various emulsifying and texturizing agents may also mimic allergies. Plant gums, such as gum acacia and tragacanth, often appear as stabilizers and thickening agents in both foods and drugs. LaDu (1979) observed that "a hyersensitive person might appear to be allergic to a drug but really be reacting to the plant gum in the pharmaceutic preparation."

One of the more serious manifestations of toxicity presenting as allergy took place in 1960 in the Netherlands (Mali & Kalten, 1966). A margarine producer had introduced a new emulsifying agent into a brand occupying about 14% of the market. Shortly afterward, an epidemic of generalized exanthema broke out, marked by sudden onset, that spread in 2–24 hr and was accompanied by severe itching. Some patients experienced high fevers, conjunctivitis, sore throat, and swollen lips. The first clues to the source of this epidemic, which involved about 50,000 of the approximately 600,000 persons estimated to have eaten the margarine, were provided by an observant young boy and a dermatologist who took seriously the boy's observation that he may have remained free of signs, unlike most of the rest of his family, because he ate butter rather than margarine.

Monosodium glutamate (MSG), the "flavor enhancer," probably deserves a chapter to itself because of the many ramifications generated by the debate about its safety for very young children and its capacity, like the sweetener aspartame, to damage the brains of young rodents. That association provoked its removal from prepared baby foods and restrained approval of aspartame. In adults, MSG is associated with the "Chinese restaurant syndrome," a tribute to the enthusiasm of Chinese chefs for MSG. The Chinese restaurant syndrome describes a conjunction of symptoms such as burning sensations, chest pressure, and facial pressure. It leads some victims to believe that they are experiencing a heart attack. Although at first it was thought that only a small subpopulation was sensitive to MSG, later studies showed sensitivity to be widely distributed and dose-related. In some individuals, the syndrome might be provoked by the 2–3 g of MSG often added to soups. Insensitive individuals might require as much as 20 g to experience the syndrome. In children, MSG has led pediatric specialists to deceptive diagnoses of epilepsy because it brings on "shudder" attacks in susceptible children (Reif-Lehrer, 1976). Such a broad distribution of sensitivity makes it particularly difficult to offer a diagnosis, because the details of individual exposure and consistency of response must be documented with great care if any reliable pattern is to be discerned.

Food allergies are remarkably prevalent in young children. Procedures for predicting the allergic potential of additives do not exist (Amos & Drake, 1976). At least part of this lack is attributable to the difficulty in determining that a specific substance is allergenic for a particular person. The classic skin patch tests may not work. The patient most typically employs a trial-and-error strategy aimed at eliminating from the diet those substances or foods that induce reactions. Moreover, the immune system is probably not involved in many reactions to foods, so that a pharmacologic hypersensitivity or intolerance may underlie responses such as asthma and urticaria.

Such reactions seem more often to occur in patients also sensitive to aspirin. A widely quoted paper (Juhlin, Michaelson, & Zetterstrom,

TABLE 2
Reactions to Tartrazine (FD & C Yellow No. 5)[a]

Patient	Dose (mg)	Reaction
1	1	Severe urticaria
2	2	Facial erythema, urticaria
3	1.5	Severe asthma, 4 days
4	1	Slight asthma
	5	Severe asthma
5	1	Flushing, itching, urticaria
6	1.5	Swelling of pharnyx, urticaria, malaise
7	1	Rhinitis, dyspnea
	5	Severe urticaria

[a]From Juhlin *et al.*, 1972.

1972) reports that the food color tartrazine (FD & C Yellow No. 5) and certain benzoic acid derivatives employed as preservatives can both precipitate symptoms (Table 2). Noid, Schulze, and Winkelmann (1974) found salicylate intolerance common in patients suffering from chronic urticaria and noted that tartrazine can also evoke the complaint in such individuals. Tartrazine appears in many different products. Table 3 is a

TABLE 3
Examples of Foods with Tartrazine (FD & C Yellow No. 5)[a]

Cereals:
Cheerios, Lucky Charms, Trix, Raisin Bran, Froot
Loops, Product 19
Baked goods:
Pancake mixes, Hungry Jack Hot Rolls, Tenderburst
Biscuits, Coffetime Pastries
Desserts:
Brownies (including chocolate), cake mixes, pudding
cakes, frostings (e.g., coconut pecan, sour cream, chocolate fudge), puddings (e.g., mocha nut, toasted coconut)
Candies:
Black Licorice Sandwich, Candy Corn, Sour Green
Apples, Pirate Chews, Spearmint Leaves, Banana
Chewees
Beverages:
Fresca, Fanta Banana, Santiba Island Mixer, grape, red
cherry, Funny Face mixes, black cherry, Tiki

[a]In most of these, tartrazine is one component of a blend of colors.

partial list taken from Noid *et al.* These and many other papers suggest that overt manifestations of intolerance, such as urticaria, may represent only a fraction of the total spectrum of adverse reactions, which may include behavioral aberrations.

6. Testing the Feingold Hypothesis

This discussion of food additives bears directly on the issue provoked by Feingold's assertions, which, as noted above, were not made in a medical or toxicologic vacuum. In fact, they were preceded by a substantial literature, especially that pertaining to allergy. Like any other body of clinical literature, of course, much of it consisted of clinical impressions, anecdotal reports, and testimonials. Still, Feingold's claims did not emerge as a total novelty, a feature of his hypothesis about which many of his critics remain ignorant.

The toxicologic implications of the Feingold hypothesis led me and colleagues from the University of California and the Kaiser-Permanente health maintenance system to undertake a test of those claims (Weiss *et al.*, 1980). The original published report was too terse to permit discussion of important issues related not only to the investigation itself, but to toxicology in general and behavioral toxicology in particular. I will discuss these in detail.

6.1. Estimates of Intake

Dose is the critical independent variable in pharmacology and toxicology. Dose–response functions provide information about toxic endpoints and mechanisms and validate the chosen measure of effect. How does an investigation of a phenomenon such as Feingold proposed deal with dose? Our experiment chose to study food dyes because they had been implicated by Feingold and because, as shown in Figure 1, they were limited enough in number to make a blend possible. Other investigators who adopted the same approach relied upon experimental cookies supplied by the Nutrition Foundation. The color blend in those cookies was based on a paper (Certified Color Industry Committee, 1968) that estimated intake by dividing total dye production by total population. The flaws in such an approach are easily recognized.

We adopted the tactic of conducting a dietary survey of parents in pediatric clinic waiting rooms in the Kaiser System. Parents were asked about the frequency and amount of consumption of specific products, by brand name, so that our project nutritionists could analyze the labels. Although dietary recollections suffer from problems of unreliability, a

TABLE 4
Color Content Estimates of Processed Food[a]

	Color in ppm	
Food category	Range	Mean
Confections	10–400	100
Beverages	5–200	75
Dessert powders	5–600	140
Cereals	200–500	350
Pet foods	100–400	200
Bakery goods	10–500	50
Ice cream	10–200	30
Sausage	40–250	125
Snack foods	25–500	200

[a]From the Certified Color Industry Committee, 1968.

prospective study was beyond our resources. With those data recorded, and confined to children 1–6 years of age, we estimated food color consumption by incorporating data about food processing practices (Table 4). Our estimates of food color consumption in Kaiser children of that age group are given in Table 5. We recorded an immense range of intakes. Some children consumed trace amounts; others consumed about 5 times the mean amount of 35 mg.

6.2. Composition of Drink

The colors were given in sweetened carbonated water and bottled by a local soft drink manufacturer. The blend was lypholized first, pro-

TABLE 5
*Food Dye Consumption Estimates in Children
1–6 Years of Age*

Color		mg/day	ADI[a]
Yellow	5	9.07	300
Yellow	6	10.70	300
Red	40	13.80	420
Red	3	0.57	150
Blue	1	0.80	300
Blue	2	0.15	37.3
Green	3	0.11	150

[a]Acceptable Daily Intake is based on conventional toxicity testing (see text).

ducing a reddish-brown powder that, in solution, resembled a cola drink. For the control drink, a solution of caramel coloring yielded an equivalent appearance. The experimental drink, however, left a reddish stain color on white paper and fabric that might enable parents to break the code. To avert this problem, cranberry coloring was added to both drinks in two different concentrations. Even the project staff was unable to make reliable discriminations on the basis of stain after this maneuver.

6.3. Behavioral Measures

The choice of measures occupied much of our attention as well. The available resources did not permit daily observation of the children by trained observers. Parents would have to serve in that role. Ancillary measures, such as the usual repertoire of psychological test procedures used in hyperkinesis research, also were rejected because they were not suitable for the children in the age group selected for study, would strain our resources, and, finally, seemed rather remote from the reasons for which parents adopted the Feingold diet in the first place. Even many psychologists (who should know better) allude to measures such as finger tapping as "objective" tests, and to behavioral observations and ratings as "subjective." We decided to rely on parents as the sources of our data because we believed that they would provide the information most pertinent to the question we asked. Given that decision, the next step was to decide on the structure of those observations. A standardized inventory might have provided certain advantages but did not suit our design because the children displayed the usual heterogeneity in a sample of humans and because the complaints that had prodded the parents to adopt the Feingold elimination diet in the first place varied so widely. Our solution was to provide each parent with a deck of punched cards containing items from several inventories of child behavior, requesting each parent to select, through a process of successive refinements, ten items that fit the child. Seven of these were to represent aversive behaviors, and three were to represent positive behaviors. We reasoned that a response to food dye challenge might take the form of a reduction in positive behaviors rather than a surge in aversive behaviors. Items for two children appear in Table 6.

Although Feingold centered his claims on the rather amorphous clinical entity of hyperkinesis, our inspection of the medical records of children in the Kaiser system who allegedly had benefitted from the elimination diet showed no such pattern. Some of the children manifested some of the behaviors associated with the syndrome, but others

TABLE 6
Parent-Selected Target Behaviors That Characterize Diet Infractions

Subject 55[a]	Subject 68
1. Bites, kicks, hits.	1. Bothers mother with toys.
2. Throws things inappropriately.	2. Twists mouth.
3. Goes aimlessly from one object or activity to another.	3. Cries easily.
4. Demands must be met immediately, easily frustrated.	4. Pinches the baby.
5. Mood changes quickly and drastically.	5. Fails to finish what he starts.
6. Inability for quiet play.	6. Unable to stop a repetitive activity.
7. No eye contact when spoken to.	7. Talks constantly.
8. Shows you his delight with toys and objects	8. Does his chores well.
9. Responds and socializes by talking, touching, etc.	9. Plays well by himself.
10. Aggreeable and accepting of activities that are suggested.	10. Plays with the baby well.

[a] For Subject 55, items 1 and 2 rose significantly after color blend challenge (Weiss *et al.*, 1980).

did not. The toxicologic implications of Feingold's assertions also extended beyond such a limited population. For these reasons, we recruited and screened children without attempting to set diagnostic boundaries. During the course of the investigation, we completed observations on 22 children, 15 boys and 7 girls, between the ages of 34 months and nearly 7 years. All were enrolled in the Kaiser system by the time their participation in the study began, and all, according to the parents, had benefitted from the diet. None had been maintained on the diet for less than three months by the start of their participation. Each child was subjected to a thorough pediatric examination, and all were free of clinically significant medical or psychiatric problems.

A study that relies on observations by untrained persons, particularly family members who might be eager for validation of certain hypotheses, must take other steps beyond the elimination of cues to the delivery of specific pharmacologic or toxicologic challenges. Our first concern was that parent observers might tend to an excessive sensitivity to the normal frequency of aversive behaviors expressed by young children. No such bias appeared. Table 7 shows the ratings of positive behaviors on control days. The scores indicate that these children, for the most part, were well behaved. What we could not control was the

TABLE 7
Target Behavior Ratings by Parents on Control Days[a]

Subject	Mean aversive	Mean positive
52	1.81	3.99
53	2.21	7.88
54	1.08	5.57
55	1.34	3.55
56(1)	1.94	2.21
56(2)	1.80	1.57
57	1.94	7.94
58	1.40	7.13
59	2.34	4.46
60	1.50	3.24
61	0.55	2.74
62	1.51	5.41
63	0.23	6.45
64	0.40	4.51
65	1.70	5.58
66	2.94	3.53
67	1.35	3.54
68	1.76	4.61
70	1.22	1.20
71	1.84	2.98
73	1.38	3.00
74	1.20	6.59

[a]1 = very little, 9 = a great deal.

influence of careful observation by the parents; it very likely enhanced their relationships with the children and by itself may have exerted beneficial effects on behavior. These observations embraced the categories listed in Table 8. Ratings of the ten behaviors selected from the combined item list were entered as a mark on a 9 cm line that later was translated by staff members as a score ranging from 0 (not at all) to 9 (a great deal). The observation periods during which parents counted the frequency of the ten behaviors consisted of two 15-min segments alloted to times during the day that the parents reported as especially critical for eruptions of aversive actions. Sleep disturbances also were monitored; some parents and clinicians earlier had reported that such disturbances were features of adverse responses following ingestion of ingredients eliminated by Feingold regimen. A standard scale also was included for comparison (Conners, Eisenberg, & Barchai, 1967). To help promote adherence to this schedule, which obviously required sustained effort by the parents, and to forestall incipient problems, staff members main-

TABLE 8
Parent Responsibilities during the 11-Week Study Period

1. Record sleep data.
2. Note infractions, medications, illness, etc.
3. Telephone report to staff.
4. Give soda pop at specified time.
5. Transfer pop labels to forms.
6. Reset and put on wrist counter.
7. Perform two 15-min behavior counts.
8. Rate target behaviors for total day.
9. Complete Conners form.
10. Record wrist counter score and times.
11. Complete diet inventory.

tained telephone contact with the parents each weekday. In addition, on the basis of that conversation, they also entered a score reflecting their estimate of parental response to the previous day's events.

6.4. Diet

Nutritional information is important in any toxicologic experiment, even though too many toxicologists ignore it. It was especially important for this study, of course. Our sensitivity to these issues grew as we began to realize, during our diet survey, that adoption of the Feingold regimen itself, although it usually improved nutritional values, was no guarantee that basic nutritional principles were being followed. The nutritionist on the staff therefore maintained weekly contact with the families even after she had familiarized them with what are considered desirable nutritional practices. On the basis of the intake records maintained by the parents, the children received at least adequate nutrition. One marker was the intake of vitamin C. Some of Feingold's critics had asserted that proscriptions in the diet meant to eliminate salicylates so restricted the consumption of certain kinds of fruits that vitamin C consumption might be lowered to unacceptable levels. Table 9 shows that most of the children in the experiment consumed vitamin C far in excess of the Recommended Daily Allowance, which itself is a rather conservative figure.

6.5. Experimental Design

Tests of the Feingold hypothesis make little sense as they typically have been conducted and analyzed. Although Feingold's claims about

TABLE 9
Vitamin C Intake of Study Sample

Subject	Mean per day (mg)	Percentage of RDA (6- to 9-years old)
52	120.4	301
53	53.8	135
54	70.2	176
55	66.4	166
56	55.7	139
57	75.3	188
58	135.1	338
59	38.4	96
60	51.7	129
61	183.2	458
62	91.1	228
63	150.0	375
64	387.3	968
65	57.9	145
66	144.9	363
67	159.5	399
68	55.0	138
70	41.6	104
72	37.9	95
73	81.4	204
74	76.9	192

the prevalence of responsiveness to the diet varied from about 30% to 60%, he never asserted that all supposedly hyperactive children benefitted from the regimen. Yet, except for our investigation, all the studies conducted before and since assumed implicitly that they were drawing subjects from a homogeneous population. We adopted another approach, one fostered by the emphasis of operant research and its applied technology on the individual organism. Each child in the study was treated as a separate experiment, so that the investigation comprised 22 single-subject trials. The individualized list of criterion behaviors also made such an approach reasonable. The study occupied 11 weeks for each child. The first two weeks, which followed a trial week, provided an opportunity for the routine to stabilize and to uncover any problems or misunderstandings still remaining. During the next eight weeks, each child consumed the challenge drink eight times, according to an algorithm that randomly assigned challenge days with the restriction that successive challenges be separated by at least two days. The last week of the study served as a postexperimental baseline. The sequence of challenges was maintained by the project statistician, who assigned the appropriate soft-drink bottles. Each week, when one of our behavior analysts visited the home, she brought the next seven-day supply.

Earlier unpublished reports had suggested that the main effects of colors emerged as acute pharmacologic responses, with a latency of perhaps 30 min to 3 hr. To ensure that such responses would be recorded, the drink was given to the child at a prescribed time each day, and the two 15-min behavioral observation periods conducted at specified times following ingestion. The first always was conducted within 3 hr of drink consumption with a latency determined individually for each child.

6.6. Statistical Analysis

Originally, we had planned to subject each child's data to time series analysis, a procedure especially suitable for single-subject designs. Our design followed the paradigm labeled as an interrupted time series by Glass, Willson, and Gottman (1975). These are powerful techniques, but they also make assumptions about the structure of the data that may be violated rather seriously in experiments such as this one (Weiss et al., 1979). They are parametric procedures and presume that the time series to be analyzed is stationary, that is, that its statistical properties are not time-dependent. To make such assumptions about our data would have aroused scepticism without convincing documentation, but such documentation was not feasible without a longer period of observation. For this reason, we turned to another powerful technique that required no such assumptions, namely, Randomization Tests (Edgington, 1980). Randomization Tests are direct applications of probability theory, assuming only that treatments are assigned at random. They are conducted by calculating, say, a mean for each possible permutation of treatment scores and comparing the differences to the actual mean differences obtained in the experiment. If the actual mean difference between experimental and control treatments, given 10,000 permutations, exceeds the permuted differences 9,900 times, then $p = .01$. Although the procedure is conceptually simple, it could not be carried out until the introduction of modern digital computer technology because of the vast number of calculations required, even with modifications that reduce that burden by sampling only a proportion of all possible permutations.

6.7. Results

Given the many opportunities for disaster in an experiment as susceptible to them as this one, we suffered remarkably few problems.

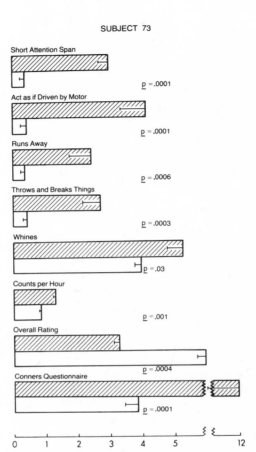

FIGURE 1. Responses of Subject 73 to challenge by food dye blend. Hatched bars represent challenge days; open bars, control days. The first five items were scored on a form translated into values between 1 and 9, as was overall rating. For the latter, a lower rating indicated a poorer day. *Counts per hour* denotes frequencies of aversive behavior recorded by the parent on a wrist counter. The *p*-values are based on randomization tests (Edgington, 1980). Reprinted with permission from Weiss *et al.* (1980).

Only one of the children contributed more than a few scattered violations of the diet. The parents, largely because we had involved them as joint experimenters rather than as subjects, carried out the demanding routine of the study with remarkably few complaints, although all were relieved when the regimen ended. (Some, in fact, had become interested enough in the behavioral procedures that they planned to explore further education in psychology.) At the same time, however, no child's series was totally free of the natural environment's perturbing influ-

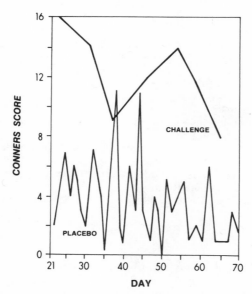

FIGURE 2. Conners Scale scores for subject 73 during the eight experimental weeks, comparing color challenge versus control comparison for subject 73. The upper tracing connects challenge days; the lower tracing connects control (placebo) days. Note high rating for control day 38 after challenge on day 37 and note comments in Figure 12.

ences, such as visits by relatives, vacation trips, respiratory infections, weather extremes, irritable siblings, and all the rest. Despite these sources of variability, two children showed cogent evidence of sensitivity to food dyes.

One of these children, a boy 3 years of age, showed significant rises in his mother's ratings on the two behaviors she had indicated earlier were most characteristic of episodes associated with the consumption of food items proscribed by the Feingold diet. The other, a girl aged 34 months, emerged as the most striking responder in the literature. As shown in Figure 1, the food-dye challenge elicited marked elevations in five of the seven aversive behaviors selected by her mother as characteristic of dietary infractions. Conners Scale ratings paralleled these results. Note especially, in Figure 2, the peaks that correspond to the challenge days. Also note the elevated score on Day 38, a placebo day that followed a challenge day. The mother commented that the effects of the challenge seemed to persist. In fact, the mother's comments turned out to be quite revealing. Table 10 contains her comments on days that she guessed correctly were challenge days. Table 11 contains sample comments on days that she guessed correctly were placebo days. One of her most dependable cues, apparently, was the response of her daugh-

TABLE 10
Mother's Comments on Correctly Guessed Challenge Days

Day	Comments
23	Morning very good. In afternoon more and more wound up. Activity to activity.
31	Good morning. Acting "hyper" 1 hr after drink. 1½ hr to fall asleep. Carryover to Day 32.
37	After lunch (drink) was monster. Would not do anything I asked. Day 38: Woke up like motor.
54	Fine morning. Monster in afternoon. 20 min after drink, smeared toothpaste. Constant motion.
58	Super morning. About 12:30 (drink at 11:20) turned into monster. Like a motor.

ter to orders to stop misbehaving. On the basis of these and other cues, she guessed that the challenge had been administered on 6 days. It actually had been administered on eight occasions, but one challenge was invalidated because a dietary violation had occurred on that day. She was correct on five of the those occasions, a pattern that could have occurred by chance with a probability of 1.6×10^{-5}.

7. The Feingold Literature

I regard the Kaiser study as a definitive demonstration that, in principle, Feingold was right. That is, some children respond with aberrant behaviors to food dyes delivered at levels encountered in the diet. I do not regard this as a surprising outcome given the many reports of other kinds of adverse responses induced by food dyes. I do not, however, regard the study as a test of Feingold's claims about the efficacy of

TABLE 11
Mother's Comments on Correctly Guessed Control Days

Day	Comments
56	While friend at cabin, was monster. When friend left, she was nice again.
73	Wild at school in morning. Best friend poor influence. I told her to shape up and she did. If she had had (an infraction), my telling her to behave herself wouldn't have had any effect.

the diet in treating the cluster of behaviors denoted by the term *hyperactivity*. Nor can I offer it as a cogent estimate of population sensitivity. It does support the conclusions, of a panel of toxicologists and pharmacologists appointed to study the procedures by which food additives are tested for toxicity, that *psychotoxicity* should be a necessary component of those procedures (FASEB, 1977).

Although several reviews of the Feingold literature claim that it fails to support Feingold, the reviewers (Conners, 1980; Kavale & Forness, 1983; Lipton, Nemeroff, & Mailman, 1979; Mattes, 1983; Stare, Whelan, & Sheridan, 1980) ignored several critical pieces of information. First, several of the papers claiming negative results were flawed either in design or interpretation. Since I have reviewed these in detail elsewhere (Weiss, 1982), I will single out only some examples. Harley *et al.* (1978) published the most extensive study of total diet. They investigated two groups of boys diagnosed as hyperactive, and provided what they claimed was the total family diet. Their crossover design, during an 8-week experimental period, embodied one segment devoted to the control (typical) diet and one devoted to the Feingold elimination diet. Although they found a high incidence of improved behavior, as measured by Conners Scale ratings, they disavowed its significance because most of the subjects showing improvement belonged to the group that underwent the Control diet–Feingold diet sequence. They failed, however, to note the sharp fall from the 2-week period that preceded the formal crossover sequence to the scores in the Feingold diet–Control diet group. The 36 subjects in this phase of the study ranged from 9–13 years of age. Another phase of the study focused on preschool boys. All ten of these subjects, independent of sequence, improved on the Feingold diet according to mothers' ratings. Harley *et al.* dismissed these findings with the comment that the boys were too young to undergo objective testing, so that the rating scale results could not be confirmed—by what later proved to be rather dubious objective criteria (Weiss, 1982).

Another study the interpretation of which puzzled me was published by Williams, Cram, Tausig, and Webster (1978). These investigators recruited 24 allegedly hyperkinetic subjects, all of whom were being treated with either amphetamine or methylphenidate. They induced the parents to adopt the Feingold regimen (although they appear to have provided little guidance as to what the regimen consisted of or which dietary items, by brand name, could be consumed). Each child, in a different order determined by a counterbalanced design, then underwent four experimental phases, each lasting one week: medication plus color challenge, medication plus placebo, placebo medication plus color challenge, and placebo medication plus placebo challenge. The color

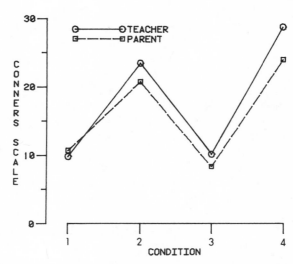

FIGURE 3. Subject 23 from Williams *et al.* (1978). Four conditions were studied, each lasting one week. (1) Medication plus control cookies; (2) medication plus challenge cookies (two, each containing 13.5 mg of total color), (3) placebo medication plus control cookies; (4) placebo medication plus challenge cookies. Note parallel responses of teacher and parent.

challenge was given in the form of cookies, prepared under the auspices of the Nutrition Foundation, that each contained 13.5 mg of a color blend. Each child consumed two cookies daily. Control cookies contained no synthetic colors; the color blend was masked by chocolate. Williams *et al.* reported that teacher ratings on a modified Conners Scale reflected an adverse impact of the food dye blend but that parent ratings did not. I performed a more extensive analysis of individual responses when I was given a copy of the raw data. By randomization test, I found that parent ratings under medication also showed a significant worsening of behavior during the challenge week, an effect largely attributable to a cluster of about one-quarter of the subjects (Weiss, 1982). I also detected one subject (Figure 3) who showed no response to medication but a rather marked response to the color challenge. Williams *et al.* also had noted that some of their subjects gave no evidence of hyperkinesis despite their having been placed on medication. When I analyzed the data further, I found that the subjects with the lowest Conners Scale scores tended to show no response either to medication or to the color challenge. That is a provocative finding, because it suggests that my original aim in the Kaiser study, to investigate the response to synthetic colors in children without clinical features of hyperkinesis, may have reduced the incidence of sensitive subjects.

The studies above are not the only ones, besides my own, to support the notion that some children may benefit from the elimination diet and that some children respond adversely to certain food dyes (for example, see Conners' review, 1980). Even Feingold's most tenacious critics, such as Stare et al. (1980), acknowledge that the prevalence of sensitivity is not zero. Prevalence, not principle, is the source of the disagreement. Feingold's claims ranged from 30% to 60% of hyperactive children, but these claims derived from clinical observations and parental testimony, which would be natural sources of inflated estimates. Suppose those claims are inflated, and the true incidence lies say, between 1% and 10%—a reasonably cautious figure.

The implications of that estimate are worth discussing in detail. First, that range of sensitivity is toxicologically significant. The rapidly emerging discipline of risk assessment (National Research Council, 1983) deals with adverse effects of environmental chemicals in the range of one case in one million persons. Carcinogenic potency usually is the issue, and risk typically is estimated from a combination of epidemiologic data and laboratory research. The evidence for food dye toxicity is much stronger than for most environmental chemicals. Second, with a prevalence in that range, adverse responses in the typical group design would be detectable only by using quite large samples. Consider a population consisting of 30% responders and 70% nonresponders. If the responders were to be shifted, by an experimental treatment, an average of one standard deviation, it would take about 260 subjects to produce a statistically reliable finding ($p = .01$) nine times out of ten. The largest study, so far, incorporated 36 subjects (Harley et al., 1978). Perhaps most important for future studies, group designs are simply irrelevant. They lead to the kinds of errors in logic that befell Mattes and Gittleman-Klein (1981) who set out to study a group of 13 children maintained on the Feingold regimen. They planned to administer a food dye blend in the form of cookies, incrementing the dose by one cookie (13 mg of the blend) daily to a maximum of six on the last 2 days of the experimental week. Three of the children failed to ingest the maximum of six per day, and two children were withdrawn before the actual study began. The results of this study were based, then, on eight children and treated by a two-way analysis of variance. Given what already was known about the lack of universal sensitivity to food dyes, it is perplexing that these authors should have designed such an experiment. It is equally perplexing that, in a study focused on diet, investigators should ignore critical factors such as diet practices and baselines and the high caloric load from the consumption of six cookies contributing 150 calories each. It surely makes sense that some of the children could not consume enough of the cookies to meet the intake criterion.

It simply is not possible at this time to meld the published studies into a reasonable estimate of prevalence, as Kavale and Forness (1983) tried to do by the approach of meta-analysis. No amount of statistical legerdemain can compensate for inherent methodologic flaws, for violations of the assumptions made by parametric statistical models (such as normality), and for the absence of critical dose–response information, the basic relationship on which toxicology and pharmacology depend. All we can evaluate at this time is whether the phenomenon exists, and it clearly does. If our interest lies in its mechanisms, then two alternatives are available. Human subject investigations should adopt the strategy that guided the Kaiser study, that is, single-subject designs that attempt to identify responders who then are studied further by varying dose and other key parameters. Laboratory animal and biochemical experiments, however, are more likely to point us to mechanisms and, in fact, already suggest productive research directions.

Among the most promising of these directions is the response of the neonate. Young organisms, and the immature central nervous system especially, often serve as the sentries of toxicity. The developing nervous system possesses heightened sensitivity to toxic metals, for example (Weiss, 1983), showing a vulnerability to methylmercury damage many times greater than the mature nervous system. The fetal alcohol syndrome also testifies to its greatly enhanced vulnerability. Even the Feingold literature suggests a developmental difference in sensitivity. The two responders in the Kaiser study were the youngest children in the group. Earlier, Goyette, Conners, Petti, and Curtis (1978) identified their color challenge responders as the youngest. And Stare et al. (1980), whose review was highly critical of Feingold's claims, acknowledged that the "sensitive group [of children] appears to be concentrated among younger participants" (p. 525).

Several experiments by Shaywitz and his collaborators, based on rats, support the human evidence. In their first study (Shaywitz, Goldenring, & Wool, 1979), they treated rat neonates, beginning at 5 days of age, with a blend of food colors at dose levels close to the values estimated for human intake and continued the treatment until 30 days of age. Half the rats also received intracisternal injections of 6-hydroxydopamine, an agent that produces selective brain dopamine depletion and that has been used by Shaywitz and others to model the often presumed neurochemical lesion underlying the hyperactivity syndrome. Rats receiving the color blend gave higher scores on an activity measure and lower scores on some measures of learning. A second study (Goldenring et al., 1980) tried to by-pass the problems of oral administration to neonates and reared the subjects by a system of continuous gastric infusion. With a dose of 1 mg/kg, well within the range of child consumption, the pups were significantly more active than controls and in addition showed marked impairment in avoidance performance at 28 days of age. A third study (Goldenring, Batter, & Shaywitz, 1982) was directed to the question of the pharmacologic basis of the findings. The authors noted that the three major components of the dye blend, Red no. 40, Yellow no. 5, and Yellow no. 6, are all azo dyes and that a direct metabolite of the two yellow dyes is sulfanilic acid, which has a long half-life in the body. Sulfanilic acid doses of 1 mg/kg daily, begining at 5 days of age, produced behavioral effects resembling those produced by the dye blend in early studies by this group.

There is also a somewhat narrow literature aimed at biochemical mechanisms, but its bearing on the Feingold controversy is unclear because it is dominated by Red no. 3, or erythrosine, which contributes a tiny portion of total food color intake. Unfortunately, investigators singled it out for more intensive study after Lafferman and Silbergeld (1980) claimed neurochemical effects on the basis of *in vitro* experiments. Mailman *et al.* (1980) demonstrated that such effects might not have been interpreted properly. Far more important from the standpoint of toxicology are aspects of food dye actions that often are ignored by toxicologists, nutritionists, and regulatory agencies. One such aspect is phototoxicity, pointed out by Valenzeno and Pooler (1979) to be "the neglected factor" in assessing the safety of dyes used in medical diagnosis and in foods. Some of these dyes, they noted, can produce lethal effects in cells and whole organisms on light exposure but not in the dark. Another even more crucial factor is diet. Ershoff (1976, 1977), as noted earlier, showed that coloring agents and other food additives could be toxic, even lethal, to weanling rats if administered with a diet low in fiber. If administered together with the typical, high-fiber commercial chow, they were not clinically toxic. Adding fiber to the basal low-fiber diet eliminated the toxic manifestations at the levels tested. The protective mechanism may be the inhibition of bioavailability by fiber, but fiber also modifies the enzymatic actions of gut flora which act to metabolize certain doses of dyes. Consider the typical diet of young children from this standpoint; how often is it high in fiber?

8. Conclusions and Implications

If Feingold can be credited with nothing else, he surely deserves recognition for being keen enough to detect a phenomenon that the rest of us simply ignored because it did not occur to us that common food additives could be so pharmacologically active. The biomedical community was so unprepared for it that even consistent evidence failed to shake its doubts. The prevailing misinterpretations of the evidence indicate that key publications were read and reviewed rather carelessly and superficially. The negative evaluation by the *Medical Letter* (1978), that dour critic of needless medication, is a cogent example. Of course, it must have seemed rather improbable, given the pervasive presence in our food supply of synthetic flavors and colors, that a phenomenon such as behavioral toxicity should be discovered by a retired allergist. Yet, the Food and Drug Administration neither requires behavioral toxicity data nor monitors additive consumption. Only after our survey in California did the agency undertake some calculations of its own, and even those were based on industry production figures.

Another reason for the rejection surely stemmed from entrenched concepts of disease: one agent, one illness. But whatever hyperactivity is, it is not like measles. It is not the expression of a unitary mechanism, but the complex, ambiguous outcome of divergent circumstances. Feingold's assertions also aroused doubt in the medical community because of a primordial loyalty to drugs. Dietary intervention is tedious and time-consuming, nutrition is not a standard part of the medical curriculum, and the practice of diet therapy is contaminated by a disagreeable circus of quacks, faddists, and fanatics.

The current evidence carries two major implications for public policy. One is the continuing debate over whether diet should be recommended as one of the therapies for hyperkinesis. A recent NIH Consensus Conference (1982) devoted to this issue acknowledged that some children with behavioral problems might benefit but cautioned that the Feingold diet might not be free of adverse effects. It failed to describe what nutritional disasters might follow from eliminating highly processed foods—actually, the main tenet of the diet. A more reasonable position would have been that no single tactic, neither drugs, behavior modification, nor diet, will serve all children equally and that diet, even if the chances of success are not high, is worth trying. Even if whatever improvement occurs can be attributed to a placebo effect, who is logically prepared to distinguish it from the effects of psychotherapy?

Even deeper issues have now surfaced, however, because of our past neglect of behavioral criteria in the evaluation of food additive safety. The usual approach to food additive toxicity testing since the 1958 amendments to the food and drug laws is to rely mostly on a 2-year feeding study, in rodents. As described earlier in this chapter, on the basis of such a study dietary levels are calculated from the dose–response function to correspond to a threshold; these so-called no-effect levels are determined on the basis of histopathology and gross clinical effects such as retarded weight gain. No behavioral variables are measured. The no-effect level (almost always based on incorporating the additive into a nutritious, high-fiber diet) is then divided by a factor, usually 100, to provide a level deemed safe for human consumption and denoted as the Acceptable Daily Intake (ADI). Table 5 compares the ADIs determined in this fashion with the amounts of food colors that the Kaiser study, and studies based on similar amounts in Nutrition Foundation cookies, found to evoke behavioral disturbances in some children. The ratios are startling. The community must make a choice between permitting demonstrably toxic materials in foods for cosmetic purposes and protecting the welfare of a small but significant subpopulation of children (and perhaps even adults).

9. References

Amos, H. E., & Drake, J. J. P. Problems posed by food additives. *Journal of Human Nutrition*, 1976, *30*, 165–179.

Berglund, F. Food additives. *Archives of Toxicology*, 1978, *1*(Suppl.), 33–46.

Certified Color Industry Committee. Guidelines for food manufacturing practices. Use of certified FD&C colors in food. *Food Technology*, 1968, *22*, 946–949.

Conners, C. K., Eisenberg, L., & Barchai, I. Effect of dextroamphetamine on children. *Archives of General Psychiatry*, 1967, *17*, 478–485.

Conners, C. K. *Food additives and hyperactive children.* New York: Plenum Press, 1980.

Edgington, E. S. *Randomization tests.* New York: Dekker, 1980.

Ershoff, B. H. Synergistic toxicity of food additives in rats fed a diet low in dietary fiber. *Journal of Food Science*, 1976, *41*, 949–951.

Ershoff, B. H. Effects of diet on growth and survival of rats fed toxic levels of tartrazine (FD & C Yellow No. 5) and Sunset Yellow FCF (FD & C Yellow No. 6). *Journal of Nutrition*, 1977, *107*, 822–828.

FASEB Select Committee on GRAS Substances. Evaluation of health aspects of GRAS food ingredients: Lessons learned and questions unanswered. *Federation Proceedings*, 1977, *36*, 2525–2562.

Feingold, B. F. *Why your child is hyperactive.* New York: Random House, 1975.

Glass, G. V., Willson, V. L., & Gottman, J. M. *Design and analysis of time-series experiments.* Boulder: Colorado Associated University Press, 1975.

Goldenring, J. R., Wool, R. S., Shaywitz, B. A., Batter, D. K., Cohen, D. J., Young, J. G., & Teicher, M. A. Effects of continuous gastric infusion of food dyes on developing rat pups. *Life Sciences*, 1980, *27*, 1897–1904.

Goldenring, J. R., Batter, D. K., & Shaywitz, B. A. Sulfanilic acid: Behavior changes related to azo food dyes in developing rats. *Neurobehavioral Toxicology and Teratology*, 1982, *4*, 43–49.

Goyette, C. H., Conners, C. K., Petti, T. A., & Curtis, L. E. Effects of artificial colors on hyperkinetic children: A double-blind challenge study. *Psychopharmacology Bulletin*, 1978, *14*, 39–40.

Harley, J. P., Ray, R. S., Tomasi, L., Eichman, P. L., Matthews, C. G., Chun, R., Cleeland, C. S., & Traisman, E. Hyperkinesis and food additives: Testing the Feingold hypothesis. *Pediatrics*, 1978, *61*, 818–828.

Helgason, T., & Jonasson, M. R. Evidence for a food additive as a cause of ketosis-prone diabetes. *Lancet*, 1981, *2*, 716–720.

Juhlin, L., Michaëlson, G., & Zetterström, O. Urticaria and asthma induced by food-and-drug additives in patients with aspirin hypersensitivity. *Journal of Allergy and Clinical Immunology*, 1972, *50*, 92–98.

Kavale, K. A., & Forness, S. R. Hyperactivity and diet treatment: A meta-analysis of the Feingold hypothesis. *Journal of Learning Disabilities*, 1983, *16*, 324–330.

LaDu, B. N. Effects of GRAS substances on pharmacologic effects of drugs. *Clinical Pharmacology and Therapeutics*, 1979, *22*, 743–748.

Lafferman, J. A., & Silbergeld, E. K. Erythrosin B inhibits dopamine transport in rat caudate synaptosomes. *Science*, 1979, *205*, 410–412.

Lipton, M. A., Nemeroff, C. B., & Mailman, R. B. Hyperkinesis and food additives. In R. J. Wurtman & J. J. Wurtman (Eds.), *Nutrition and the brain*. New York: Raven Press, 1979.

Mailman, R. A., Ferris, R. M., Tang, F. L. M., Vogel, R. A., Ketis, C. D., Lipton, M. A., Smith, D. A., Mueller, R. A., & Breese, G. R. Erythrosine (Red No. 3) and its non-specific biochemical actions: What relation to behavior changes? *Science*, 1980, *207*, 535–537.

Mali, J. W. H., & Kalten, K. E. The epidemic of polymorph toxic erythema in the Netherlands in 1960. *Acta Dermato-Venereologica*, 1966, *46*, 123–135.

Mattes, J. A. The Feingold diet: A current reappraisal. *Journal of Learning Disabilities*, 1983, *16*, 319–323.

Mattes, J. A., & Gittelman-Klein, R. Effects of artifical food colorings in children with hyperactive symptoms. *Archives of General Psychiatry*, 1981, *38*, 714–718.

Medical Letter. The Feingold diet for hyperactive children. *The Medical Letter on Drugs and Therapeutics*, 1978, *20*, 55–56.

National Institutes of Health. Defined diets and childhood hyperactivity. National Institutes of Health Consensus Development Conference Summary, 1982, *4*(3).

National Research Council. *Risk assessment in the federal government: Managing the process*. Washington, D.C.: National Academy of Sciences, 1983.

Neuman, I., Elian, R., Nahum, H., Shaked, P., & Creter, D. The danger of 'yellow dyes' (tartrazine) to allergic subjects. *Clinical Allergy*, 1978, *8*, 65–68.

Nitzan, M., Volovitz, B., & Topper, E. Infantile methemoglobinemia caused by food additives. *Clinical Toxicology*, 1979, *15*, 273–280.

Noid, H. E., Schulze, T. W., & Winkelmann, R. K. Diet plan for patients with salicylate-induced urticaria. *Archives of Dermatology*, 1974, *109*, 866–869.

Reif-Lehrer, L. Possible significance of adverse reactions to glutamate in humans. *Federation Proceedings*, 1976, *35*, 2205–2211.

Shaywitz, B. A., Goldenring, J. R., & Wool, R. S. Effects of chronic administration of food colorings on activity levels and cognitive performance in developing rat pups treated with 6-hydroxydopamine. *Neurobehavioral Toxicology*, 1979, *1*, 41–47.

Stare, F. J., Whelan, E. M., & Sheridan, M. Diet and hyperactivity: Is there a relationship? *Pediatrics*, 1980, *66*, 521–525.

Valenzeno, D. P., & Pooler, J. P. Phototoxicity: The neglected factor. *Journal of the American Medical Association*, 1979, *242*, 453–454.

Weiss, B. Food additives and environmental chemicals as sources of childhood behavior disorders. *Journal of the American Academy of Child Psychiatry*, 1982, *21*, 144–1152.

Weiss, B. Behavioral toxicology of heavy metals. In I. E. Dreosti & R. M. Smith (Eds.), *Neurobiology of the trace elements* (Vol. 2). Clifton, N.J.: Humana Press, 1983.

Weiss, B., Cox, C., Young, M., Margen, S., & Williams, J. H. Behavioral epidemiology of food additives. *Neurobehavioral Toxicology*, 1979, *1*(Suppl. 1), 149–155.

Weiss, B., Williams, J. H., Margen, S., Abrams, B., Caan, B., Citron, L. J., Cox, C., McKibben, J., Ogar, D., & Schultz, S. Behavioral responses to artifical food colors. *Science*, 1980, *207*, 1487–1489.

Williams, J. I., Cram, D. M., Tausig, F. T., & Webster, E. Relative effects of drugs and diet on hyperactive behaviors: An experimental study. *Pediatrics*, 1978, *61*, 811–817.

World Health Organization. *Toxicological evaluation of certain food additives with a review of general principles and of specifications.* World Health Organization Technical Report Series, No. 539. Geneva, 1974.

8 *Behavioral Methods in Pediatric Chronic Illness*

Christine A. Hovanitz, Edwin L. Gerwell, and Dennis C. Russo

1. Introduction

This chapter will focus on the behavioral assessment, treatment, and limitations of such treatment with chronically ill children. This area has received increasing attention as the number of children who suffer from chronic illness continues to climb steadily. Although medicine has made dramatic progress in the elimination of most infectious diseases, many physical disorders of both known and unknown etiology fail to respond, on a permanent basis, to any form of medical intervention. Approximately 10% of the children in the United States suffer from some type of chronic illness (Mattsson, 1977); for many of these children a behavioral intervention may help alleviate physical suffering and prevent maladaptive behavioral patterns associated with the disease process from generalizing and continuing into adulthood.

The field of behavioral pediatrics has expanded to the point at which a comprehensive review of developments in assessment and treatment is not possible within the present chapter. Thus, the focus of this chapter will be on the applications of behavioral assessment and treatment to the hospitalized, chronically ill child. The first section of this chapter will deal with general issues and definitions; the second will cover assessment of the chronically ill child, initially from a general perspective and then from the perspective of specific techniques intended to obtain quantitative data. The third section will discuss several current applications of behavioral intervention with the chronically ill child. Finally, a summary of the process of dealing with pediatric inpatients will be provided, followed by a discussion of the current implica-

CHRISTINE A. HOVANITZ, EDWIN L. GERWELL, AND DENNIS C. RUSSO • Harvard Medical School, Children's Hospital Medical Center, Boston, Massachusetts 02115.

tions and limitations of behavioral medicine treatment in the medical environment.

1.1. Chronic Illness and Developmental Issues

For a disorder to qualify for the label *chronic illness,* the presence of an existing diagnosed and documented pathological condition, such as asthma, functional heart disorder, or heart disease, must be made. An identifiable medical disorder serves to differentiate chronic medical disorders from conversion reactions and other psychiatric conditions that may produce similar symptomology. Such a distinction typically results in divergent methodologies for treatment as well as in differential control over the course of the disorder (Cataldo, Russo, Bird, & Varni, 1980). Chronic disease is further defined as that subset of disorders for which, at the present time, there is no established medical treatment that reliably and permanently eliminates underlying pathophysiology or the occurrence of symptomology.

Treatment of the child or adolescent with chronic disease can be viewed as a complex task involving the simultaneous consideration of numerous variables. A number of skill areas are often affected by the illness; deficits in certain areas and the inability to develop normally in others may be a typical situation for the more severely ill child. The interactions of these variables may be complex; less than optimal intellectual and social development may combine in an additive fashion with such immediate effects or demands of chronic disorder as limitations on physical activity and the necessity of adherence to a medical regime. In addition, the occurrence of physical symptomology in many diseases is exacerbated by environmental stressors. Unfortunately, the child's ability to cope with stress can be compromised by limitations in the development of skills.

The normal developmental achievements of children with chronic illness are made much more difficult by the failure of their abnormal environment to provide appropriate learning conditions. There are often hospitalizations which extend for a year or more; in these cases the child may or may not make a transition into another developmental stage. Extended isolation from familiar peer groups and the alterations of normal family interaction patterns may place the child at increased risk for numerous problems, but little empirical work has been conducted in this significant area that would allow the prediction of specific problem behavior.

The effects of chronic illness on the development of the child comprise one area of major interest; another involves the ramifications of developmental processes on the choice of treatment intervention technique. The methods of behavioral medicine have been largely developed for adult patients. Whether the direct applications of techniques derived from adult populations is appropriate remains an empirical question; differences between the responses of adults and children to various interventions have been suggested (Harris & Ferrari, 1983). However, the issue does not resolve itself into the simple question of the applicability of adult techniques to a population of children. With what is presently known about children in terms of cognitive and physical factors, it is reasonable to assume that pediatric behavioral medicine is not just dealing with a single group separate from adults but rather with many unique subgroups which share a homogeneity of developmental stages. The field has, to date, largely neglected to integrate into its data base the research available in developmental psychology (Harris & Ferrari, 1983). One hopes that the strong concern behavioral therapists have for the empirical and accountable nature of their techniques will result in the rapid assimilation of relevant data.

1.2. Empiricism and Accountability

The emphasis on empiricism and accountability in behavioral pediatrics differentiates this field from other areas of psychological medicine that focus on children. A uniting thread throughout all previous health psychology or psychosomatic treatment techniques has been the pattern of few scientifically verifiable successes. Although all approaches have claimed to be superior to their predecessors, it is hoped that a methodological difference in behavioral pediatrics may make that claim a reality. This difference is most salient in three ways: (1) the availability and rigorous application of empirical assessment, (2) a basis in process and outcome data analysis rather than in theoretical speculation (Russo & Varni, 1982), and (3) an emphasis on observable, measurable behaviors as criterion even when treatment is cognitively mediated.

Clear specification of the goals of treatment is required if a meaningful determination of success following intervention is to be made. In the behavioral treatment of chronic illness, success can be defined in two ways (Cataldo et al., 1980). In some cases a behavioral intervention can produce remediation of the disease itself. However, in most cases that target physical symptomatology, a realistic goal of treatment is the reduction of the frequency, intensity, or duration of the patient's discomfort. Typically the latter goal is reached by minimizing the exacerbations of the disorder or by maximizing the patient's ability to compensate for the difficulties the disorder imposes. These goals are usually determined in the assessment phase and should be communicated to all involved individuals so that expectations for success will be realistic (Pelcovits, Silver, & Russo, in press).

To meet these goals, a number of empirically derived and empirically validated behavioral techniques have been developed. The interventions in frequent use for research and practice in behavioral pediatrics can be placed in the following three areas of inquiry: (1) operant and social learning procedures, (2) cognitive and behavioral self-regulation procedures, and (3) biofeedback and physiological self-regulation procedures (Russo & Varni, 1982). In reality the distinctions among the areas tend to become blurred and some techniques clearly cross the boundaries, but in all cases the success or failure of these procedures can be evaluated in both experimental and clinical settings.

1.3. Behavioral Techniques in a Medical Context

The behavioral approach to chronic disorders starts with the assumption that treatment of the disorder will take place in the appropriate medical service and that behavioral intervention will occur only in conjunction with ongoing medical treatment (Cataldo et al., 1980). Here lies a major difference between traditional therapies and behavioral programs for medical patients; not only is the role of the behavior therapist generally one of a consultant, but the major responsibility of the patient's care remains that of the physician. The implications of this role in the treatment of patients are multiple but they can be summarized in the statement that many important variables relevant to the treatment of any given case are not within the knowledge base, or under the direct control, of the behavior therapist. The same statement can, of course, be made of the attending physician, although for obvious reasons the physician must retain ultimate control over the patient's course of treatment.

Despite the behavioral therapist's ultimate reliance upon the physician for the details of the course of a patient's illness, an independent knowledge of the general pattern of illness is very important both to the treatment and to the outcome evaluation of any behavioral pediatric intervention. The natural progression of a chronic disease is likely to be predictable, and advance knowledge of expected developments may greatly improve the capacity of behavioral methods to deal effectively with symptomatology. Complex interactions among such variables as response to treatment and severity of symptoms, environmental factors, family and peer relationships, health habits, and motivation for medical improvement are the norm rather than the exception. A focus on a few variables to the exclusion of others will limit the patient's potential to benefit from treatment and may in the long run be actually detrimental.

As with nearly any medical treatment, effective behavioral interventions begin with careful assessment. In many cases the assessment phase will be the only point of direct interaction made with medical personnel; the ease of these interactions appears to depend upon the compatibility of the psychological assessment model and techniques with the existing medical models. In this regard the behavioral approach may have certain advantages, as well as disadvantages, when compared with the traditional psychological approach. The next section will discuss these differences between traditional and behavioral assessment from a general perspective; this will be followed by an overview of specific techniques of behavioral assessment and special considerations for their use in hospitalized children.

2. Traditional and Behavioral Assessment

As noted by Mash and Terdal (1981), traditional assessment techniques have achieved popularity because they have provided information about children which is not otherwise apparent. Because behavioral assessment has intentionally maintained a minimum of inference, it provides information that may be seen as quite obvious to the consumers of assessment information. Validity, reliability, or even implications for treatment are not necessarily valuable considerations to the nonpsychologist. Consequently, the consumers of behavioral assessments may not perceive the work as skilled acts or as relevant. Greater respect and acceptance of behavioral methods seem to occur only after successive, dramatic treatment predictions and/or successes. Despite such virtues as accountability and empirical foundations, behavioral methods are often dismissed by the medical personnel, or by a patient and family, because the appeal of the behavioral methods does not equal their expectations as may more traditional methods (Mash & Terdal, 1981).

2.1. Differences in Assessment Model and Technique

This difference in assumptions is clearly reflected in the techniques used to assess the important variables. Traditional measurement with children is typically inferential and is made by the use of such personality tests as the Rorschach, Thematic Apperception Test, or the Draw-A-Person Test, whereas behavioral assessment is typically associated with such techniques as observation, physiological measurement, and self-report of patient's behavior in specific situations. Differences between individuals during behavioral assessment tend to reflect differences in the frequency, duration, or intensity of various specified behaviors rather than qualitative differences of less clearly defined attitudes, feeling states, and tendencies toward certain traits as occurs during traditional assessment. The traditional approach thus makes the assumption that an individual's underlying dispositions have the capacity for manifesting themselves in a variety of situations, and overt behaviors are interpreted as reflective of the underlying dynamics. The behavior approach, however, views overt behavior only within the context of a given stimulus situation; very few interpretations are made of the behavior outside of a quantitative analysis of the direct manifestation of a response.

Although the methods of traditional and behavioral assessment differ, the real distinction lies in the basic assumption and not with the methods *per se*. Although an important source of motivation for the development of behavioral observation techniques originated from a desire to create assessment strategies independent of traditional self report methods (Lick & Katkin, 1976), the revolutionary zeal that once motivated behavioral therapists to cast aside the empirical aspects of traditional psychology is now being replaced by more practical considerations. Traditional techniques are now frequently used by behavioral therapists out of necessity, for convenience, and because of their documented functional utility as a source of some types of valid information.

2.2. Normal Child—Abnormal Situation

Another basic difference between the traditional model and the behavioral model proposed here is the assumption that the child with chronic disease is typically best viewed as a normal individual who is functioning in an abnormal situation (Russo & Varni, 1982). The model makes the assumption that many children who had been able to cope at least reasonably well with daily events find themselves with recurring symptoms of a disease that require hospitalizations and intrusive, disruptive medical treatments. In this abnormal environment not only is an unusually large number of stressors present, but the learning characteristics of the hospital environment provide numerous opportunities for the learning of aberrant behavior (Varni, Bessman, Russo, & Cataldo, 1980). The source of the maladaptive behaviors is attributed to a difficult situation in this model rather than to a constitutional and idiopathic defect in the child as the more traditional model typically assumes.

Many aspects of chronic illness are likely to disrupt the normal pattern of everyday life. In addition to often painful medical procedures that must be endured, growing up with a chronic disease may necessitate lengthy hospitalizations, frequent separations from family members, parental overprotectiveness, and frequent absence from school. Other difficulties specific to the particular disease may cause more problems; these children may experience self-imposed (or peer-imposed) social isolation, symptoms which cause embarrassment, limitations to their ability to engage fully in sports and other strenuous activities, and courses of treatment which single out the child as different (Agle, 1977; Agle & Mattsson, 1976; Pelcovits *et al.*, in press).

Within such a difficult environment, some sort of maladaptive learning processes would seem to be inevitable. Two major forms of difficulties appear to occur: both an exacerbation of physical symptomology and an increase in the frequency of behavioral problems are often observed. Merskey (1970) and Oster (1972) have cited evidence that patterns of pain behavior are often learned in social situations. The child is likely to learn coping strategies that provide immediate relief or that obtain sympathy from others which may be counter to long-term recovery (Cataldo *et al.*, 1980; Fordyce, 1976). Such a pattern may be expected in many chronic disorders even though the disease may have a physiological basis for acute excerbations; the symptom that was originally produced by a pthological event may be maintained by a different set of external stimuli. Behavioral interventions are thus likely to profit from a focus on the immediate antecedents and consequences of each symptom complex.

Evidence for the presence of maladaptive behaviors and psychopathology in children with chronic illness is mixed. Many studies have reported an absence of psychological deviancy in most children with life-threatening or chronic diseases (Bedell, Giordani, Amour, Tavormina, & Boll, 1977; Kellerman, Zeltzer, Ellenberg, Dash, & Rigler, 1980; Tavormina, Kastner, Slater, & Watt, 1976; Zeltzer, Kellerman, Ellenberg, Dash, & Rigler, 1980), but others have reported some form of deviance (Agle & Mattsson, 1976; Creek & Christian, 1976; Holdsworth & Whitmore, 1974; Klove & Matthews, 1966; Molnar & Taft, 1975; Rose, Penry, Makush, Radloff, & Putman, 1973; Samilson, 1975; Varni, 1980). Given the nature of the environments in which many of these children develop, the scarcity of empirical studies reporting significant differences between chronically ill children and normal controls is surprising.

More difficulties may be noted as the chronically ill child matures. Clearly an individual's social learning history largely determines the adequacy with which the adult interprets and behaves in his or her present environment. The deficits in functioning observed in the chronically ill child are likely to generalize and to contribute heavily in future adaption to life. The behavior therapist who intervenes in response to some maladaptive behavior other than physical symtomatology can therefore be interpreted as providing preventive treatment for potential psychopathology (Yule, 1977). In this sense the normal child–abnormal situation model would predict an eventually maladapted adult–abnormal situation as an endpoint when appropriate preventive intervention is not forthcoming.

Given the chronically ill individual's abnormal situation, some have suggested that a normal ability to cope is not sufficient to deal comfortably with the situation. By teaching skills in areas other than those that are compromised, chronically ill individuals may be taught to be competent beyond their age expectation or to excel (Cataldo *et al.*, 1980; Wright & Nicholson, 1973) in areas that result in adequate or high levels of reinforcement in the natural environment.

The advantages of this model are many. Not only does the model allow positive change to occur once a maladaptive behavior becomes targeted, but also the model adds logic and predictability to the problems of children with chronic illness. The model is not necessarily applicable for every case. Clearly many children with chronic illness will have had a social learning history that has resulted in generalized maladaptive behavior patterns that are preexisting, and possibly prepotent, to the physical symptomology. Even in these cases, however, appropriate behavioral intervention may serve to prevent the likelihood of further difficulties.

3. Components of the Assessment Battery

Beyond conceptual differences between the traditional and behavioral approaches, however, a number of techniques specific to the behavioral method do appear. Initially the behavior model follows a procedure that parallels the traditional model. An interview, typically with the referring physician and with the patient (and/or family), is almost without exception the first step. Interviewing in the sense of ongoing discussions of problems and progress is also a frequent component of the behavioral assessment procedure. The context and quality of the initial interview, however, is generally unique in its subsequent impact on the intervention. Surprisingly little empirical work on factors related to effective behavioral interviewing is available. Most of the information that can be communicated on the topic is of a clinical nature.

The second major phase of the behavioral assessment, the functional assessment, is more amenable to quantitative techniques. For ease of discussion the assessment has been broken down into two phases; in actuality, the assessment process is ongoing throughout treatment and a major component occurs at the termination of treatment for the evaluation of outcome. In this section an overview of the interview and the functional analysis components of the behavioral assessment will be made as it occurs in the speical case of the chronically ill, hospitalized child. The subsequent section will focus on the specific techniques frequently utilized to obtain quantitative measurements of behavior during both functional analysis and evaluation.

3.1. The Initial Interview

The purpose of the initial interview, be it conducted with hospital staff, teachers, parents, or the child, is to define accurately and completely the problem and obtain hypotheses as to the maintaining conditions of the problem so that further assessment can take place and effective treatment may be instituted (Karoly, 1981; Morganstern, 1976). The interview itself is typically only part of the full assessment process, although on some less than optimal occasions it may be the only source of information. A great deal of care is warranted at this stage of intervention; inadequate or faulty assessments are generally identified as the primary cause of treatment failures (Kazdin, 1973; Lazarus, 1973).

When the interview process is the major source of data and direct observation is not possible, a degree of uncertainty as to how accurately the verbal report will reflect reality must be entertained. The source of the information may omit certain details that are believed irrelevant, important data may be forgotten, or the style of presentation by the informant (particularly if the source is a parent or the patient) may conceal certain details through embarrassment or guilt (Goldfried & Davison, 1976). Thus, collaboration of all possible data sources is always desirable.

Little specific information has been obtained on the optimal manner by which a behavioral interview should be conducted (Iwata, Wong, Riordan, Dorsey, & Low, 1982; Linehan, 1977; Peterson, 1968; Storrow, 1967). As with a traditional approach, the behavioral therapist must be sensitive to all indications given by the informant, and many behavioral therapists (Goldfried & Davison, 1976; Morganstern, 1976) have recommended utilizing traditional interviewing procedures at some point in the process (Sullivan, 1954). The emphasis in traditional work has been placed on a variety of therapist attitudes such as openness, empathy, and sincerity, which are believed to result in the collection of more accurate and thorough data (Goldstein, 1975; Kanfer, 1968; Marsden,

1971; Truax & Carkhuff, 1971). It is unclear to what extent particular therapist characteristics affect the acquisition of specific assessment information, continuation in therapy, compliance, and outcome measures in behavior therapy (Morganstern, 1976), particularly when much of the information is gathered from sources such as allied medical services where the subtle communication of efficacy, expertise, and competence may have more bearing.

The content of the interview with the patient, or the patient's parents, has been well described by other individuals (Karoly, 1981; Morganstern, 1976; Pelcovits et al., in press). Special issues of concern for the chronically ill child involve the developmental aspects of the child's behavior and the ramifications that his or her illness and treatment have for all critical aspects of life. The extent to which a detrimental effect has generalized across skill areas will determine the degree of intensity and intrusiveness to which the treatment intervention will be carried out. Observations of parent–child interactions can be obtained at the time of the interview, and this data, in conjunction with the parent's verbal report of their consistency and their distress over the current problem, will help determine their ability and willingness to carry out an intervention.

Once the target behavior has been identified, assessment for the purpose of documenting the maintaining conditions of the problem behavior and determining the optimal treatment intervention is appropriate. At the present time, behavioral treatment programs for pediatric chronic illness appear best dictated by the results of a functional analysis of the presenting problem (Pelcovits et al., in press) and by an accurate estimate of the cognitive abilities and capacity of the child or adolescent to carry out a self-control program. Clearly age, as it relates to developmental level (Harris & Ferrari, 1983), intelligence, and something like motivation (Bellack & Schwartz, 1976; Kanfer & Karoly, 1972) play a role in this determination. Other variables of importance include the parent's stability, consistency, concern over the targeted problem, and quality of their relationship with their child in terms of available reinforcers or punishers.

3.2. The Functional Analysis

Following the identification of the problem behavior, an attempt is made to determine the maintaining conditions. The functional analysis of the targeted behavior occupies one of the most important positions in behavioral assessment, and many authors have proposed guidelines by which to undertake the analysis (Goldfried & Pomeranz, 1968; Kanfer &

Saslow, 1969; Karoly, 1981; Mischel, 1973; Stuart, 1970; Wolpe, 1969). For the pediatric patient with chronic illness, the model suggested by Goldfried and Pomeranz is especially helpful because of its emphasis on environmental variables rather than complex cognitive factors. Before entering the model in some detail, however, it is helpful to draw a distinction between (1) those variables involved in a functional analysis of the targeted behavior and (2) those variables which have direct implications for the choice of the intervention techniques (Goldfried & Davison, 1976). The first set of variables identifies what contingencies must be altered so as to effect a behavior change, and the second set derives information that will determine which intervention strategy will function best. The distinction is of particular importance with children in a medical environment because frequently the variables identified as contributory in a problem behavior (1) will not be available for change by the behavior therapists and/or (2) will not be as directly relevant to the choice of therapy as the developmental level of the child.

Regardless of the purpose of a functional analysis, the variables studied by the therapist may fall into one or more of the following categories: (a) antecedent stimulus variables which may elicit or set the stage for the maladaptive behavior; (b) organismic variables such as the direct effects and side effects of medications, general energy or tension level, states of fatigue, and other similar physiological and constitutional factors; (c) response variables in the form of respondents, where consequences play a relatively minimal role in maintaining the response and the behavior is typically emotional such as fear or anxiety; and (d) response variables in the form of operants, where consequences play a relatively major role in maintaining the behavior (Goldfried & Davison, 1976). Most frequently a problem behavior is found, following a detailed functional analysis, to have components of more than one of the variables listed above. To determine which of the above functions a particular variable appears predominately to serve, an analysis of the ordering of events through time is necessary. As stated by Baer, Wolf, & Risley (1968), the therapist typically must manipulate the occurrence of events that are responsible for the occurrence or nonoccurrence of that behavior so that a determination of cause-and-effect relationship between behavior, setting, and reinforcing stimuli can be made. Ideally some quantifiable method of assessing these relationships is utilized.

Figure 1 illustrates a model of the process taken by the behavior therapist during the identification of a targeted behavior's maintaining conditions. During the functional analysis, variables serving a variety of functions are observed to interact in a way that creates the maintaining conditions for a behavior; for example, an antecedent variable in the form of a syringe may combine with a response variable such as fear and

TOPOGRAPHY OF TARGETED BEHAVIOR   POSSIBLE MAINTAINING CONDITION

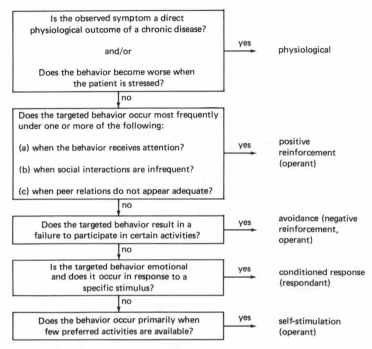

FIGURE 1. Model for determining the maintaining conditions of a targeted behavior.

result in a conditioned emotional response such as a needle phobia. Similarly, the maintaining conditions of a behavior may be physiological when organismic variables such as chronic tension are present. Figure 1 demonstrates a process capable of correctly identifying the maintaining conditions of most simple targeted behaviors, but the model is a greatly abbreviated illustration of the typical process undertaken by a behavioral therapist.

Most discussions of the functional analysis of behavior assume that only one behavioral manifestation (self-report or physiological response) is under investigation. Some individuals, however, have proposed that the measurement of multiple assessment channels and multiple treatment applications is superior to the measurement of simple motoric responses (Blanchard & Hersen, 1976; Hersen, Turner, Edelstein, & Pinkston, 1975; Russo, Bird, & Masek, 1980). Typically the self-report, motoric, and physiological response channels, when evaluated with regard to the same stimuli, are considered optimal. In such a case, the maintaining conditions of each form of response requires separate analyses; the variables maintaining a self-report of pain, high arousal levels in physiological response, and excessive pain behaviors, for example, are likely to differ. The hospital is, in fact, an ideal setting in which to engage in this form of assessment; the dependent child who is an inpatient and whose problem behavior is manifested within the hospital creates a situation wherein naturalistic observation, physiological response, and self-report data are all obtainable. Surprisingly little research has been conducted with this population in this fashion, although suggestions for its institution have been made (Russo *et al.*, 1980). Fortunately, although the conceptualization is applicable in many cases of pediatric chronic illness, the process is not necessary for the majority of cases. As noted by Stuart (1970), multifaceted behavioral assessment must be guided by the principle of parsimony.

4. Specific Techniques

The quantitative analysis component of a behavioral assessment may be carried out with the use of specific techniques that have varying and possibly documented strengths and weaknesses of reliability, validity, and ease of administration. The choice of technique is generally dictated by (1) the form of problem behavior (self-report, physiological, motoric), (2) hypotheses concerning the maintaining conditions of the behavior, and (3) such pragmatic considerations such as time, space, and the availability and adequacy of professional help. In some cases quantitative data are needed only for the evaluation of treatment outcome, while in others the data are necessary to document cause-and-effect relationships associated with the problem behavior. The most common methods of obtaining quantitative data on the targeted problem are self-report, self-monitoring, observation, and physiological measurements.

4.1. Self-Report

A differentiation can be made between the type of verbal data obtained during the early stages of the initial interview and the structured, quantitative verbal data obtained later. Self-report data as defined here take the second form; quantitative analysis of qualitative dimensions have proven valuable in behavioral assessment as a means of obtaining verifiable data. The differences can be best illustrated by comparing the statements "I experienced 3 asthma attacks last week" and "I have asthma problems." The first statement lends itself to functional and evaluative analysis; the second statement is useful only during an initial interview when the first identification of a target behavior is made. The quantitative self-report data may be obtained through either conversation or written questionnaires.

Beyond a certain age the child may be the source of self-report data, and in combination with the initial interview this information is often the only source for the initial determination of the target behavior and the evaluation of subsequent progress and eventual outcome. Not surprisingly, it is common within the behavioral tradition to downplay both the utility and the validity of the self-report as a method (Ayllon & Azrin, 1968; Azrin, Holz, & Goldiamond, 1961; Begelman & Hersen, 1971; Gordon, 1975; Simkins, 1971). The majority of data collected is self-report; however, most behaviorists will state the desirability of more observational forms of data since the validity of self-report data, particularly from patients or family, has been challenged by many. This particular difficulty in behavioral assessment is actually less serious in the field of inpatient behavioral pediatrics because children, especially very young children, are not typically expected to provide valid verbal information. In addition, as some form of referral typically initiates the evaluation, a presumably objective observer of the child's behavior is already actively involved in the treatment process.

For those children whose age and cognitive abilities are sufficient, however, the collection of self-report data remains a viable source of information. Many recent behavioral assessors have spoken in support of the self-report (Lick & Katkin, 1976). Although early studies have interpreted the low correlations between self-report measures and behavioral and physiological measures of fear as evidence of its poor validity or utility (Lang, 1969; Rutner, 1973), others have used this evidence to recommend the self-report as a flexible assessment technique when used to assess the cognitive component of multifaceted assessment (Lick & Katkin, 1976).

While noting that self-report information may be controlled by a different set of contingencies than those governing motoric responses (Hersen & Barlow, 1976), a growing volume of literature suggests that self-report measures may be no less valid or unreliable than other forms of measurement (Cautela & Upper, 1976; Russo et al., 1980). Clearly, patient's self-reports are behaviors in and of themselves (Thomas, 1974), and when these verbal behaviors, such as complaints of pain, are themselves the main focus of interest, "the question of their validity as indicators of other phenomena is not central" (Cautela & Upper, 1976, p. 79).

4.2. Self-Monitoring

An attempt to make self-report data more reliable and externally valid may be made through the use of self-monitoring. The difference between the two forms of data lies primarily in the temporal relationship between the targeted behavior and the recording of that behavior. Rather than relying on verbal report, self-monitoring involves the collection of written records by the patient obtained over time. Information concerning the duration, frequency, or magnitude of the problem behavior, its antecedent stimuli, and its consequences may be obtained in this manner. Numerous methods of monitoring data have been devised including such techniques as (1) continuous recording, in which the number of times a behavior occurs is counted; (2) time samples, interval recording, and duration measures which are based on units of time rather than discrete behaviors; and (3) the measurement of behavior products, effects, and causes. Ease of data collection and the probability of offering representative information should determine the choice of method (Gambrill, 1977).

Although self-monitoring is likely to produce more externally valid and specific data than self-report, the simple act of recording one's behavior has been noted to alter the behavior itself (Lipinski & Nelson, 1974). Generally the effect is in a positive direction and is to the benefit of the patient; many have suggested that self-monitoring may be valuable as a major therapeutic intervention (Emmelkamp, 1974; Hepner & Cauthen, 1975; Leitenberg, Agras, Allen, Butz, & Edwards, 1975; Rutner, 1973). Some, however, have noted that the effects of self-monitoring tend to dissipate over time (Kazdin, 1974). A feedback theory (Kanfer, 1970) suggested to account for the reactivity of the self-monitoring method proposed that more than assessment occurs during the process; self-evaluation and self-regulation in addition to self-observation are believed to be simultaneous and unseparable in effect. In addition, numerous individual differences appear to be present in the tendency to produce accurate self-monitoring (Bellack & Schwartz, 1976; Logan, 1973). Self-monitoring is typically the first step in a self-control program; it is also one of the most unreliable components because many patients do not regularly provide records of the desired form (Bellack & Schwartz, 1976). This may arise from the tedious and difficult nature of the task, the potential embarrassing aspects if the recording process is public, and the potential aversiveness of forcing the patient to be aware of undesirable behavior or breach of contract. The accuracy of self-monitoring appears to increase if the recorded behavior is of low frequency, overt, and observable (Epstein, 1976). In the inpatient setting, independent observations can often be made that provide a reliability check of sorts.

4.3. Behavioral Observations

Observation of behavior has been the hallmark of behavioral therapy since its inception. In many ways the hospital environment is ideal for this form of assessment, for the potential control over variables that may be exercised by the behavior therapist is extensive. The major problems associated with this form of assessment include the necessity of numerous personnel and the relatively demanding expenditure of time. Unfortunately, the availability of both time and personnel is likely to be limited within the hospital environment.

When direct observation of the child is feasible, the methods of choice are best determined by whether (1) the identification of the problem behavior, (2) the determination of the supporting contingencies of the target behavior, or (3) the evaluation of the outcome of treatment is the purpose of the assessment. If identification of the problem behavior or treatment evaluation is the purpose, then one of many methods of observation such as frequency counts, interval sampling (Repp, Roberts, Stack, Repp, & Berkler, 1976), or "one-shot recording" (Gambrill, 1977) may be utilized. If, however, the goal of observation is the determination of the maintaining conditions of a behavior, a much more complicated observational procedure is required (Achenbach, 1982). In this case, reliable data on sequences of the child's behavior and situational events, particularly the behavior of other individuals, is necessary. Progress has been made in the development of sequential-event recording techniques (Roberts & Forehand, 1978), but at the present time the techniques are too difficult to implement and analyze to be practical in most cases. Regardless of the observational method eventually chosen, variables of potential use include the duration of the behavior, the interresponse time, the latency from stimulus to response, and the intensity of the response. A careful description of the target behavior that enables distinct units of behavior to be counted and that allows a consensus to be reached regarding the topography of the behavior will serve to increase the ability of the observer to produce meaningful information (Doke, 1976).

Several sources of contamination can effect the validity and accuracy of data obtained from observation. Prior knowledge of expected results of an intervention program can influence the interpretation (Kass & O'Leary, 1970; O'Leary, Kent, & Kanowitz, 1975). "Instrument decay" (Cambell & Stanley, 1966) or observer drift may also serve to bias the data. In this case, observers may do the following:

(1) Forget some fine points of the initial response definitions or measurements details, (2) make changes on their own in definitions or measurement operations when the child begins exhibiting a slightly different form of the target behavior, (3) miss episodes of behavior due to distractibility or "boredom," (4) fabricate data, or (5) adopt "shortcut" methods of data collection. (Doke, 1976, p. 532)

Unannounced and covert reliability checks, expected by the observers, can help prevent this form of bias.

4.4. Physiological Measurement

Many physiological responses are modifiable by psychologically based interventions and thus may serve as the target response during both assessment and treatment evaluations. The assessment of physiological responses may be of interest whenever a physiological process is suspected of being involved in the acquisition or maintenance of the disorder even when the targeted behavior is self-report or motoric such as in the report of pain or the production of pain behaviors (Epstein, 1976). Physiological assessment frequently utilizes the response systems of cardiovascular (i.e., blood pressure, heart rate), respiratory, electrodermal, and muscular measures. As with most other assessment methods, assessment during the course of treatment and evaluation of treatment outcome should include physiological measurement if the selection of the appropriate target response is made through physiological means.

For most psychophysical disorders the choice of response system to be assessed (i.e., cardiovascular, muscular response) is best determined by the nature of the disorder (hypertension or spasticity). When the form of illness does not easily determine the appropriate physiological system to target, that response system which is the most reactive in response to stress is typically the most productive choice (Epstein, 1976). On a more general level, those individuals whose physiological response shows variability and who can verbally discriminate variations in their physiological response have been found to be the most successful in treatment directed toward changing their physiological responses (Epstein, 1976; Mathews, Johnston, Shaw, & Gelder, 1974).

Although direct physiological assessment is desirable in any case wherein arousal appears to be an important contributing factor in a problem, there are a number of instances in which the physiological response itself can not be measured. These difficulties occur primarily when the laboratory measuring devices are not available. Indirect physiological measurement in the from of direct observation, outcome recording, and self-monitoring may be an option in some cases. Many physiological responses have behavioral manifestations that are easily measurable through observation such as asthma attacks, seizures (Zlutnick, Mayville, & Moffat, 1975), and vomiting (Kohlenberg, 1970). Outcome recording may be a viable alternative when the problem behavior produces a permanent effect on the environment; examples of this method include amount of medication consumed, number of school days missed, and number of trips to the hospital emergency room.

Despite the objectivity of direct physiological measurement, psychophysiological assessments have reliability difficulties that involve the technological recording of physiological signals (Schwitzgebel, 1976) and physiological limits (Epstein, 1976). For some physiological measures the reliability is quite good (Greenfield & Sternbach, 1972), but for several commonly utilized measures such as surface-recorded measures of muscle activity (Basmajian, 1976) considerable artifactual confounding may occur. Thus some caution is warranted during the interpretation of these physiological measurements.

4.5. Summary of the Assessment Process

The preceding sections have reviewed the process of behavioral assessment as it applies to the child with chronic disease. Reference has been made throughout to the alterations and extensions of typical behavioral assessment that are necessitated by the hospital environment, the specific disease process, and the presence of physical symptoms and medical treatments. Consideration of these issues simultaneously with behavioral and developmental issues is necessary for the institution of effective assessment, but unfortunately the process by which these issues are jointly considered is more a clinical skill than a science at the present time.

Similarly, the application of these assessment techniques within the context of ongoing treatment represents, as yet, an area of minimal study. The following sections represent an overview of the empirical literature and clinical practice of behavioral intervention with chronically ill children.

5. Applications

Ideally, the comprehensive assessment of the chronically ill child should be completed prior to the initiation of any treatment. In practice, however, this is often not the case. Demands for immediate medical treatment, delayed recognition of psychological contributors to patient symptoms, and the consultative nature of behavioral services in the hospital environment are some of the factors which determine the timing and urgency of behavioral interventions. In many cases, consults will be requested only after the behavior or symptom in question has grown to life-threatening proportions, or alternately after staff behavior patterns are well developed in response to the patients. Thus, although treatment intervention is always best determined by a functional analysis, emergency procedures must occasionally be undertaken on the basis of presenting symptomatology.

The first three sections will present an overview of intervention techniques available for the treatment of certain identified problem areas, and the fourth section will summarize the process undertaken during the determination of treatment intervention. As discussed earlier, current treatments can be classified under the three broad categories of operant and social learning procedures, cognitive and self-regulation procedures, and physiological self-regulation procedures (Russo & Varni, 1982). Frequently several techniques are applied simultaneously or sequentially in conjunction with pharmacological, medical, and surgical treatments. Table 1 illustrates a sample of some typical identified problem behaviors often associated with behavioral referrals across different chronic illnesses. The table is not exhaustive, nor should assignments be considered fixed.

A review of this table suggests certain commonalities among problem behaviors. First, within individual disorders, a number of problems may arise that are secondary to the chronic nature of the disease, the presentation of symptoms, and the requirements of a medical regimen. Second, across different disorders affecting different bodily systems there exist striking similarities as to the general classes of problems presented. This table provides a sampling of diseases and symptom constellations which are used here primarily for illustrative purposes. In reality, problems are not typically as discrete, and complex interactions may be seen with changes in medical regimen, chronicity, and the course of the illness.

The targeted referral problems can generally be placed into three categories: (1) therapeutic nonadherence, (2) fears and anxieties, and (3) symptom management. In preference to a review of specific disease entities or bodily systems, classification of problems will be made by their behavioral function or topography.

5.1. Nonadherence to Medical Treatment

Since the success of any treatment is highly dependent upon the cooperation of patients and their adherence to the treatment regimen,

TABLE 1
Referral Problems Often Present in Certain Chronic Disorders

Disease	Referral problem
Respiratory:	
Cystic fibrosis	Hyperventilation
	Poor nutrition
	Medication compliance
Asthma	Increased severity and frequency of attacks
	Medication compliance
Neurology:	
Epilepsy	Increased severity and frequency of attacks
	Medication compliance
Gastroenterology:	
Colitis	Exaggerated pain responses
	Medication compliance
Dermatology:	
Atopic dermatitis	Scratching, increase of erruptions
Oncology:	
Leukemia	Nausea, emesis, and decreased eating
Renal:	
End-stage renal disease	Dietary noncompliance
	Medication noncompliance
Cardiovascular:	
Hypertension	High blood pressure
	Medication compliance

treatment compliance or adherence stands as a behavioral issue of at least equal importance to the medical regimen itself (Masek & Jankel, 1982). Definitions of nonadherence vary greatly in precision and in attribution of blame; for the purposes of the present discussion, adherence will be defined as "the extent to which the life style of a patient is changed to correspond to a therapeutic regimen . . . (which typically includes alterations involving) . . . the necessity of taking medications, returning for follow-up medical care, and variations in diet or exercise" (Ruley, 1978, p. 175). The rates of estimated noncompliance to treatment in adults range from 33% to 82% depending on the nature of the medical intervention (Dunbar & Agras, 1980); estimates of pediatric non-adherence are generally reported to be lower than the adult figures (Masek & Jankel, 1982).

Although nonadherence to medical regimens has been the subject of extensive discussion, the procedures for assessing and improving adherence have not been so rigorously researched (Masek & Jankel, 1982). No single measure of adherence appears to be highly reliable; interestingly, the least effective method appears to be the clinician's judgment or rating of the patient's behavior (Dunbar & Agras, 1980). The major techniques used to assess adherence have been physiological measures in the form of biochemical assessment, self-report, self-monitoring, and the use of pill counts. Because of the poor reliability of each of these methods, some have advised the combination of two or more modes of assessment if reasonably practical during clinical assessment.

Variables such as the clinician characteristics of warmth and empathy (Baekeland & Lundwall, 1975), the manner of appointment scheduling (Nazarian, Michalier, Charney, & Coulter, 1974), the seriousness and length of illness, and the complexity of the medication regimen (Sackett & Haynes, 1976) have all been implicated in group outcome studies as affecting the likelihood of adherence. Many programs developed to increase the probability of medical adherence have include detailed instructional information that the patients and family are capable of understanding (Colcher & Bass, 1972; Linkewich, Catalano, & Flack, 1974; Sharpe & Mikeal, 1974) and feedback as to the progress of patient's treatment (Gundert-Remy, Remy, & Weber, 1976; Sherwin, Robb, & Lechter, 1973). In addition, token economies have increased and maintained adherence to complex treatment regimens (Allyon & Azrin, 1968; Lowe & Lutzker, 1979; Magrab & Papadopoulou, 1977) and response cost procedures involving a loss of money have demonstrated effectiveness in the treatment of problematic medication adherence (Epstein & Masek, 1978).

In the treatment of the individual case, however, knowledge of group outcome or correlational data is likely to have little direct relevance to assessment or treatment. The assessment of the individual child often does not include a detailed functional analysis of the maintaining conditions of nonadherence, although it may. Instead, the therapist typically proceeds on the assumption that the conditions sufficient to maintain therapeutic adherence are not present and initiates attempts to restructure the environment so that contingencies do support the appropriate behavior.

Nonadherence may take several forms. Chronic care regimens require that complex self-care, medication, or exercise routines be followed over extended periods of time. For example, such regimens as self-injection of insulin for diabetics, self-infusion of concentrate for hemophialiacs, compliance with dietary restrictions for end-stage renal disease, maintenance of medications for hypertensives, and exercise and physical therapy for cerebral palsy sufferers all entail complex series of behaviors required on a regular basis. Appropriate behavior is often observed to be cued by temporal events, disease-related symptoms, or some form of self-assessment. Unfortunately, the immediate outcome of compliant behavior is often negative and punishing, such as in the pain associated with self-injection; only the extended effects of the behavior may be rewarding. In these circumstances the negative outcome of non-adherence may bear little temporal relationship with the occurrence of the noncompliant behavior. From this perspective, clearly a number of factors make long-term adherence a tenuous phenomenon.

Treatment of the child who is noncompliant typically falls into one of two categories; stimulus control and consequence or operant control (Masek, 1982). Stimulus control may proceed in some cases by tailoring a medication to the child's routine so that normal daily activities serve as cues for appropriate treatment behavior. In other cases in which disease-related cues signal the need for early intervention (e.g., tightness or wheezing in asthma), effective treatment requires extensive training of the patient in therapeutic skills to be instituted in the event of symptom onset. Consequence control, on the other hand, may involve the manipulation of reinforcers that follow adherence to the medical regimens. Positive verbal feedback and tangible reinforcement, response cost, and punishment may all be effective operant control interventions for short-term change. Change programs should be chosen on the basis of the child's capacity to delay immediate reinforcement, on the requirements of significant others' participation in the treatment, and on the apparent aversiveness of the immediate effect of the treatment.

Regardless of the form of the treatment intervention, simply initiating a program for therapeutic adherence is rarely sufficient for continued maintenance of the appropriate behavior. As with other behaviors, generalization across settings or individuals is not assured by initial behavior changes; compliance problems observed in the hospitalized child are likely to have existed prior to admission and may continue following discharge. Posthospitalization maintenance and follow-up assessments are a particularly important component of adherence related consultation.

An example of the behavioral treatment of a medical fear will be made with the case of an 11-year-old boy suffering osteochondrodysplasia (an abnormality of skeletal formation that produces a form of dwarfism) who was admitted for corrective surgery. A referral was made to behavioral medicine for evaluation and treatment of this patient's acute anxiety which occurred during injections and the withdrawal of blood samples. On one occasion the patient had run off the ward when approached by a nurse attempting to obtain a blood sample; he was found several hours later hiding under a bed in another area of the hospital. Surgery was imminent, but his extreme anxiety gave rise to a consideration of cancelling the operation or maintaining continual sedation (which was medically contraindicated). Behavioral treatment involved an initial interview and assessment session with both the child and the parents. As a result of the initial interview, it was determined that the patient had a tolerance for other painful phenomena such as the frequent extraction of fish hooks during fishing expeditions. The patient was willing to attempt relaxation techniques and other self-management strategies such as imagery. The patient was then taught meditative relaxation with imagery; the imagery involved a fishing trip during which he would experience the imbedding and removal of a fish hook. The patient's tolerance of an injection while using this technique was probed with satisfactory results.

The nurse who was primarily involved in this case was further instructed to assist the patient in this technique; it was agreed that he would be given advance notice of an injection for preparation. Through the proficient use of relaxation and the establishment of a site of injection to match imagery, subsequent injections were completed without difficulty and surgery was performed successfully on schedule.

5.2. Medical Fears and Anxieties

The hospital environment itself may elicit fears and anxieties that are often the focus of intervention. The stress of hospitalization involves many factors such as separation from parents, the distress of unfamilar surroundings, fear about unpleasant or painful treatments, and discomfort originating from illness, injury, or surgery. Cassell (1965) suggested that large numbers of children experience transient or moderately severe behavioral disturbances upon hospitalization; as many as 92% of the hospitalized children have been reported as experiencing acute behavioral difficulties such as increased dependency, loss of toilet training, and excessive fears (Melamed, Robbins, & Graves, 1982). The number of children who suffer long-term dysfunctions, however, is likely to be much smaller.

The desire to alleviate or reduce fear and anxiety is not based solely on the intent to make the child more comfortable. Chronically elevated levels of stress and anxiety are implicated in many physiological disease processes. For some disorders, stress and anxiety appear directly involved in the production of symptoms, such as in cases of tension headache and essential hypertension (Deffenbacher & Suinn, 1982; Rimms & Sommerville, 1977). In other diseases, these variables serve to exacerbate the disease processes that are initially not caused by stress-related factors. For example, several studies have demonstrated a functional relationship between emotional precipitants and the occurrence of an asthmatic episode (Alexander, Miklich, & Hershkoff, 1972; Clarke, 1970; Hahn, 1966; Straker & Tamerin, 1974; Tal & Miklich, 1976).

Smith (1980) has suggested that factors of age, inability to communicate, emotional stability of the parents, previous traumatic hospital experience, and fear of the expected operation are variables which serve to predispose children to increased anxiety. Other patient characteristics such as the child's cognitive development and individual coping predisposition appear to relate to the level of anxiety (Knight, Atkins, Eagle, Evans, Finkelstein, Fukushima, Katz, & Weiner, 1979). Parental variables such as the relationship to the child, support available to the parents from within the family and from the larger community, and competing demands on the parents' time (Melamed et al., 1982) also indirectly affect the child's anxiety and ability to cope. Despite the usefulness of these general concerns, little pragmatic research has been completed in this area. The absence of sequential, theoretically based research makes the identification of more specific factors that predictably lead to excessive fears very difficult.

Medical fears can be general, as in fear of the total hospital environment, or they can be specific to certain medical procedures, as in excessive fear of receiving injections. The conditions maintaining the two forms of fear may be quite different; in the first case the absence of familiar caretakers and environment, as well as fear of physical well-being and potential death, may be the major contributory factors. In the second case the fear seems to take the form of a more stimulus-bound conditioned response. Most children referred for behavioral treatment fall within the second category, and the majority of behavioral techniques fit that conceptualization; more general fears, unless they lead to increased symptomatology, appear to respond well to typical nursing practices or are not perceived by the staff as requiring behavioral interventions.

The clinical assessment of fears can be made through the use of physiological measures, observation of behavior, and self-report both formally through rating scales (Johnson & Melamed, 1979) or informally through unstructured subjective questioning. A baseline of anxiety against which the evaluation of change can be made is desirable

(Melamed *et al.*, 1982). Several assessment sessions of more than one assessment mode are useful because the rate at which different systems reflect psychological preparation may be nonlinear and desynchronous (Hodgson & Rachman, 1974). The older the child, the more fear appears to generalize across situations and time from the feared stimulus; thus the timing between the baseline of assessment of fear and the expected feared event should depend upon the age of the child.

Four major behavioral techniques have been demonstrated as useful in the treatment of medical fears. Exposure either in imagination or in real life to medical events and concerns through systematic desensitization has resulted in successful treatment for the fear of injections (Taylor, Ferguson, & Wermuth, 1977) as well as for fears of intravenous procedures and hemodialysis (Katz, 1974; Nimmer & Kapp, 1974). Modeling by peers and by films have been quite well documented as effective techniques to reduce anxiety, particularly with older children (Melamed *et al.*, 1982). Some caution is warranted, however, since sensitization appears to occur in young children if the exposure is made too far in advance of the feared procedure (Melamed & Siegel, 1975). Behavioral rehearsal, which includes many aspects of modeling but encourages the participant to try new behavior in imagination, role playing, or in life, is a promising technique that has some empirical support for its effectiveness in reducing fears of injection (Chertok & Bornstein, 1979). Finally, in those cases in which children have learned extreme and undesirable behaviors in previous hospital experiences, a combination of positive reinforcement for appropriate behaviors and punishment for the inappropriate has been recommended as leading to less fear and more cooperative behavior (Melamed *et al.*, 1982).

An illustration of the use of behavioral procedures in the treatment of dietary nonadherence can be provided by the case of a 12-year-old boy with an eight-year history of hemodialysis treatment. The child was referred for an evaluation and the development of a program to increase daily caloric intake. Excessive intake of foods and fluids is a common problem in chronic dialysis patients, but in this case a medical evaluation demonstrated insufficient caloric intake to maintain weight. The negative caloric intake resulted in an increased risk to his general health as well as a weakness in his legs which, in conjunction with other factors, resulted in an inability to walk independently. Previous attempts by parents and nursing staff failed to produce any significant or durable increase in caloric intake.

Careful evaluation of this child required a systematic evaluation of behavioral contributions as well as in-depth knowledge of the medical disorder and dialysis process. The side effects of dialysis often include a change in taste perception (most pronounced immediately prior to dialysis treatment) and a decrease (or increase) in appetite. Monitoring of food consumption indicated that the patient's major caloric intake occurred immediately following dialysis.

A sequential program was then designed to (1) increase the frequency of oral intake, (2) place intake on a regular time base, (3) balance the food groups equally across time, and (4) increase intake amount. The program utilized a token economy procedure by which meals that met a minimal intake criteria were reinforced by checks on a menu sheet. These checks were subsequently exchanged for extra privileges such as computer games, time with staff, and special trips. As a first step, a "mini-meals" program, with specified times for intake, was established. The child could eat as much as he wished, although he was required to eat one tablespoon of any food he preferred on this schedule to obtain reinforcement. This program resulted in well above 90% compliance that was maintained over a 1-month period. A second stage was then implemented. The child was required to consume at least one protein source at each meal as well as one other food of his choice. The purpose of this phase was to balance intake so that he would be better able to use the nutrients. Later phases included a gradual increase in the amount of food intake.

With the use of multiple measures of compliance, improvement was seen in token sheets, parent reports, and physiological measures such as weight, creatinine, and BUN (indicators in the blood of the breakdown of food). The child continued to maintain high levels of compliance with increased intake. As the program progressed, an increase in weight gain and better nutritional status was clearly observed and documented.

5.3. Symptom Management

Other problems frequently referred for behavioral intervention in the hospital are the symptoms which interface between physiology and behavior and which are a cause or a result of symptoms expected of the disease. These symptom clusters can be conceptualized as falling into three categories: (1) behaviors which produce symptoms, (2) maladaptive behaviors which are produced by symptoms, and (3) autonomic responses which effect the expression of symptoms. The three categories may be labeled, as a group, *symptom management*.

5.3.1. Behaviors That Produce Symptoms

The first category refers to behavior that is generally conceived of as being under conscious control: the behavior can be easily altered by verbal instruction on a short-term basis. Generally these behaviors are a natural response to disease-related stimuli, although the unusual conditions of stimulus deprivation and reinforcement appear to be a factor when social variables such as attention, are contributory. These *symptom-causing behaviors* may range from such global dimensions as the seeking of unnecessary medication or the desire for more intrusive interventions to simpler and more clearly discrete behaviors such as scratching, fecal retention, or abuse of an implanted intravenous line. The underlying pattern of this group of target behaviors is the positive feedback relationship between the maladaptive behavior and the increasing seriousness of the physical disorder. An increase in the maladaptive behavior results in the intensification of the physical symptoms, which in turn results in the further display of the maladaptive behavior which produced them.

Once a functional analysis has determined that a positive feedback relationship exists, an assessment for the purposes of determining the form of treatment intervention is begun. Some means of disrupting the feedback loop is desired; techniques which prevent or make difficult the occurrence of the maladaptive behavior are frequently instituted. Restraints or physical devices preventing access to body parts for simple, discrete problem behaviors often suffice; more global behaviors such as seeking unnecessary medications or surgery may be similarly treated by placing the verbal demands on extinction. Reinforcement of alternative behaviors that are incompatible with the maladaptive behavior is also a frequent intervention used either by itself or in conjunction with response prevention techniques. Although not illustrative of all forms of maladaptive behaviors that fall within this category, atopic dermatitis provides a good illustration of these methods.

Atopic dermatitis is an inflamatory skin disorder characterized by redness, edema, oozing, crusting, scaling, and itching. The process of rubbing or scratching, which temporarily relieves itching, leads to increased or worsened symptomatology (Allen & Harris, 1966). In addition to the self-stimulatory aspects of this behavior, a functional assessment often reveals that the scratching is maintained by various environmental consequences and precursors. In some patients anxiety appears to trigger the itch–scratch–increased itch cycle; assessment for these focus on the identification of stressors by the use of techniques such as self-monitoring. Interventions typically involve prevention of scratching by the use of gauze coverings at night, decreasing stresses through relaxation training, and the displacement of primary care functions to the patient (use of creams and wraps) while providing reinforcement contingent upon appropriate self-care.

5.3.2. Maladaptive Behaviors Produced by Symptoms

Symptom-induced maladaptive behavior occurs quite frequently in chronic illness and may stem from such sources as altered physiology or pharmacological side effects. Pain, nausea, loss of appetite, dizziness, and other effects of disease or treatment can frequently lead to maladaptive behavior that may result in nutritional deficiencies, muscle atrophy, and life-threatening weight loss. The commonality of these problems lies in the inappropriate and potentially damaging effects of the behaviors that internal sensations appear to elicit. For example, pain typically results in a reduction of general activity or immobility of affected body parts; in acute cases this response is adaptive and allows for the repair of damaged tissues. However, when pain persists beyond the healing of damaged tissues, the physical inactivity that results no longer serves an adaptive function. Instead, new physical and psychological problems such as muscle atrophy and the withdrawal from normal everyday activities may result.

In these cases careful assessment must rule out with reasonable certainty the possibility of physical damage following behavior change; this determination is typically made by the attending physician. The involvement of operant maintaining conditions as social reinforcement or avoidance of unpleasant activities should be considered during the functional analysis. If maintaining conditions such as these are highly salient, a failure to target them during the intervention is likely to result in a poor treatment outcome through the absence of adequate motivation for change. If the maintaining conditions of the target behavior appear primarily physiological, however, the intervention of choice typically necessitates instituting quite powerful auxiliary reinforcers for the completion of the adaptive behavior (i.e., physical activity, eating meals). The potency of these reinforcers is very important for internal (physical) reactions to the adaptive behavior may be quite punishing (e.g., vomiting or increased pain). Occasionally the detailed, careful explanation of this process will be sufficient to motivate the mature adolescent who has no secondary-gain issues associated with his or her symptoms. More often, however, strong operant procedures such as tangible or social reinforcement and strict requirements for participation in activities are necessary.

The problems of children undergoing radiation for the treatment of cancer provide a useful example of the process. A serious side effect of the treatment is nausea and loss of appetite; very little or no intake of food frequently occurs with the result of further weakening of the body. Ingestion of food may be punishing if vomiting generally follows. Even given these conditions, other maintaining conditions can develop quickly. Nursing staff may coax and cajole the child to eat; if their encouragement is contingent upon episodes of poor food consumption, they may reinforce continued or increased difficulties. Successful treatment may result from a restructuring of the contingencies by providing attention following the consumption of food.

5.3.3. Autonomic Responses That Affect the Expression of Symptoms

The third category of symptom management involves physiological antecedents and consequences of disease symptomatology. The interactions between stress and the exacerbation of the disease process have been discussed in the sector on medical fears and anxieties; in that context, the target problem was the reduction of fears without regard for other associated complications. In the present section, however, the treatment of anxiety or stress is discussed as a means to reduce or eliminate the expression of a chronic disease. Symptoms included in this category include vasospasm (spasmodic contraction of the muscle surrounding small arteries), bronchiospasm (spasmodic narrowing of certain air passages), pain, sleep problems, gastric motility, and cardiac dysfunction.

As previously mentioned, many disease processes such as asthma and hypertension are exacerbated by stress. In many more cases, the subjective discomfort experienced by the patient is increased with higher levels of stress. Assessment of cases in which symptom-reduction is targeted typically involves a screening for possible secondary-gain or operant contingencies that may serve to maintain the complaint. Attempts are made to determine whether certain stimuli "set the stage" for increased stress through self-monitoring, self-report, and observation. Given a certain minimum level of maturity, stress management techniques such as relaxation and biofeedback are the most frequently successful intervention techniques.

Cystic fibrosis, an inherited disease of the exocrine glands, provides a good example of such a case. This disease affects the pancreas, respiratory system, and sweat glands and is characterized by chronic respiratory difficulties and infection, pancreatic insufficiency, and other systemic complications. Hospitalization typically occurs during serious respiratory distress; these episodes tend to precipitate a state of acute anxiety and panic. The anxiety in turn leads to hyperventilation and thus increases the severity of the symptoms. Training in coping skills, relaxation, and stress management are quite effective in reducing respiratory distress and preventing hyperventilation. As with all self-control strategies, relative maturity and the absence of secondary-gain and psychiatric symptoms tend to predict a more favorable outcome. Interestingly, behavioral

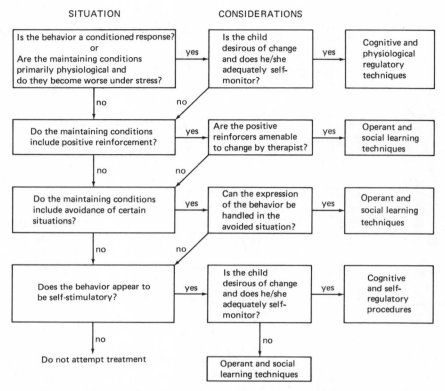

FIGURE 2. Process undertaken in the determination of treatment technique.

interventions are usually recognized by physicians as superior form of treatment for these presenting complaints since the alternative, medication, very often involves side effects more serious than the original problem.

5.4. The Determination of Intervention Technique

As can be seen by the previous discussion, many treatment interventions may be appropriate for any given problem behavior; in most cases institution of one intervention will be sufficient to alleviate the problem and will help limit confusion associated with multiple treatments. The determination of treatment method in a given case is made once the relevant variables affecting the problem behavior are identified and the most potent maintaining conditions targeted. A model of the process typically taken by a therapist is presented in Figure 2. Because more than one form of treatment is often appropriate in a given case, some means of determining the optimal technique must be made. Typically, self-control strategies are preferable to operant strategies because of the generalization of positive gains frequently found to be associated with those strategies. In addition, self-control strategies are less susceptible to sabotage from parents or medical staff since only the patient need fully understand and carry out the techniques. Another major consideration involves the degree of control the therapist will have over relevant variables. Particularly when the appropriateness of an operant technique is under consideration, both the ability to change the positive reinforcers that are serving to support the behavior and the feasibility of requiring participation in unpleasant activities when the maintaining conditions involve negative reinforcement will largely determine whether the rescheduling of events will prove an effective intervention. Most frequently, developmental issues and the ability to control variables translate into the use of cognitive, physiological, and self-control strategies with adolescents and the use of operant procedures for younger children.

In any given case, more than one treatment intervention may be possible: typically, the easiest procedure to implement is the treatment of choice, although in some cases the severity of symptomatology may require the simultaneous administration of all potentially beneficial interventions. As can be seen from the model, a certain percentage of the children referred for intervention should not be treated with behavioral methods; in these cases, either the control over variables necessary for effective treatment is absent or the problem presented by the child has not yet been found, on an empirical basis, to improve following behavioral intervention.

6. Discussion

The individual components of behavioral assessment and treatment have been discussed as they apply to the hospitalized, chronically ill child. In addition, differences in the conceptualization between the behavioral approach and the traditional approach have been mentioned as a means of better illustrating the behavioral philosophy. However, although the intent to use only valid and reliable methods is clearly reflected in the individual components of behavioral interventions, the actual process of dealing with a chronically ill child in the hospital involves a number of variables and interactions which have not yet received empirical study. The following section will discuss the gestalt of intervention process.

6.1. The Individual Process

In the attempt to discuss in some detail the components of the assessment and treatment of the chronically ill, hospitalized child, the overall process of handling such a case tends to become lost. Steps of an essential nature tend not to be mentioned if current research or theoretical research issues are not associated. A well-informed but inexperienced individual may thus have an excellent knowledge of the strengths and weaknesses of certain technical aspects of assessment and treatment but may have no idea of the pragmatic aspects. The following discussion will attempt to place these issues in perspective.

Figure 3 illustrates the typical process of dealing with the hospitalized, chronically ill child from the perspective of the behavior therapist. The actual process is likely to vary somewhat from hospital to hospital, although the basic pattern is typically the same. A *consult* generally initiates the procedure; this is a formal or informal request typically from the attending physician in charge of the overall medical treatment of a child. Within a short time of receipt (12–24 hours) of the consult, the behavioral therapist is expected to begin assessment and/or treatment. Information gathered from the medical chart and discussion of the case with nursing staff and/or the resident physician are generally the first sources of information. An interview and/or observation of the patient, often followed by an interview with the family or significant others, typically concludes the first assessment phase. Identification of the target problem is then crystalized, and hypotheses regarding the maintaining conditions are generated. Formal assessment then begins; often this phase occurs simultaneously with the initiation of a treatment if the problem is urgent. The course of treatment typically involves ongoing evaluation of progress obtained from medical chart notes, verbal feedback from physicians and nurses, and conversation with the patient and/or the family. From this feedback, decisions regarding the termination or adjustment of treatment are made.

Clearly only a fraction of the activities completed in a hospital setting are researched empirical areas that are under the presumed control of the behavior therapist; significant but difficult areas to define involve complex social interactions with hospital staff and preexisting (from the behavior therapist's point of view) medical philosophy and practices. The following section will discuss some of the difficulties or limitations present during the practice of behavioral medicine in the hospital setting.

6.2. Limitations

A few difficulties unique to the hospital setting can be identified. In a medical hospital, physical concerns are obviously seen as primary to

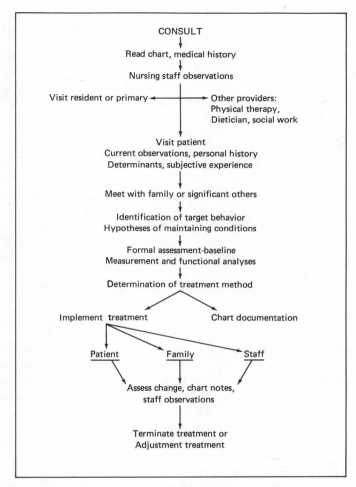

FIGURE 3. Model for the behavioral intervention of the hospitalized, chronically ill child.

behavioral concerns. The interactions between physical and behavioral factors are typically best recognized by the behavioral therapist rather than the physician, yet it is the physician who initiates a behavioral intervention by referring the child. In addition, once an intervention has begun, the behavior therapist is often place in a manager position but does not have sufficient authority to make necessary changes in the environment. Most contact with medical personnel typically occurs with the nursing staff; problems in communication, motivation, and mixed messages from allied medical personnel can often prevent an appropriate intervention from being successful. Many of these problems are minimized after repeated involvement with the same personnel.

Managerial difficulties, or problems associated with typical hospital practices, may not easily be solved from within the field of behavioral medicine. However, advances in technique and instrumentation should lead to improvements in certain areas. Assessment techniques in particular have obvious limitations; the rapidity with which assessment and treatment must progress (90 % of the consults start and finish, excluding followup, within a 2-week period) and the number and training of the personnel typically involved in the intervention require the use of valid, yet simple, assessment techniques and treatment interventions. The validity and reliability of assessment in the hospital rarely matches the optimal, and in cases such as observation for the purposes of a functional analysis, no practical yet objective method is available. Intervention techniques are more adequate in terms of simplicity and effectiveness, although the absence of research on the long-term effectiveness of treatment may conceal inadequacies from the practicing clinician.

Contraindications to behavior interventions, although not common, do exist. As previously mentioned, treatment should not proceed if previous research has not indicated that a successful outcome is likely unless all parties involved are aware of the experimental nature of the intervention. Patients who display extremely complex, atypical behavior patterns that require psychiatric hospitalization, or whose physical problems are such as to require all available time with life-supporting equipment but who are otherwise appropriate for treatment, are typically not good candidates. Most frequently, however, cases are inappropriate because of (1) unwillingness or lack of sufficient motivation to participate, (2) the unavailability of necessary contingencies, or (3) a high potential for treatment sabotage on the part of hospital staff or parents. All these conditions may predict that a successful outcome is not likely. The most serious contraindication, however, arises in those cases in which treatment may disguise important symptoms the identification of which signals the need of a medical intervention. This may occur whenever a physiological target behavior is a marker or is prognostic of a system breakdown; reducing the physiological response may mask the need for a medical intervention. Cases that could potentially fall in this category can be treated, however, if the liaison with the physician is judged to be sufficient.

6.3. Summary and Implications for Future Developments

This chapter has attempted to review some of the problems faced by chronically ill children, the process and techniques involved in the treatment of these difficulties from a behavioral perspective, and the limitations of the present methodology within the hospital setting. A number of the difficulties experienced by hospitalized children are unique to their situation; thus, although the assessment and treatment techniques are obtained from standard behavioral practices, the pragmatic aspects of carrying out interventions within the hospital setting differ from typical practices. Relatively little empirical work has been completed with this patient population. Many of the techniques have been developed for use with adults, and their application to children lacks substantial documentation; other techniques have been primarily researched and utilized with nonhospitalized children presenting with quite different types of problems.

The scarcity of studies documenting the utility of behavioral methods with chronically ill, hospitalized children is quite evident when reviewing the literature. Isolated case studies appear, but they are rarely followed by a formal investigation of several children with similar complaints. This deficiency may arise from both the sporadic nature of referrals for treatment of children with the same problems and the difficulty of quickly instituting a rigorous experimental design when faced with the urgency of the child's difficulty. The absence of empirical work may also reflect the clinical rather than research orientation typically found within the hospital setting. Such difficulties must be surmounted because extensive study is now clearly necessary for the documentation of behavioral methods in this population.

The form such research may take is as yet quite unspecified. Group methodologies necessitate the presence of some common variable for the results to be interpretable; in traditional areas and frequently in behavioral areas the psychiatric diagnosis serves this purpose. A strong feeling against classification exists among some behaviorists, although others have recognized that a taxonomy is necessary within a field if communication among researchers is to take place. Some form of taxonomy for the field of behavioral pediatrics now appears desirable. At the present time the form of chronic disease experienced by children may create the necessary structure, although obviously the adoption of a taxonomy based on medical etiology may not be the most utilitarian model for the purposes of prescriptive behavior therapy. Perhaps a three-faceted categorical system involving the specification of medical diagnosis, topography of behavior (e.g., compliance or hyperventilization), and the developmental level of the child would include the variables most prescriptive of treatment techniques. Logically, natural groupings among presenting problem, disease entity, and developmental level should exist because the maintaining conditions for the presenting problem behavior tend to be very similar in children with similar medical problems and developmental achievements. Clinical experiences supports this contention. Experimental verification of these relationships would provide a highly desirable addition to the knowledge base of the field.

Further developments, such as those suggested here, will probably take place more by default than design as the field continues to expand and increase its empirical foundations. The pattern of few scientifically verifiable successes has occurred much too frequently during the application of psychological treatment techniques; it is hoped that the field of behavioral pediatrics will not follow the footsteps of its predecessors in that regard. A continued emphasis on empiricism and on the accountability of the techniques will be necessary to insure the growth and expansion of the new field.

7. References

Achenbach, T. M. Assessment and taxonomy of children's behavior disorders. In B. B. Lahey & E. E. Kazdin (Eds.), *Advances in Clinical Child Psychology* (Vol. 5). New York: Plenum Press, 1982.

Agle, D. P. (Ed.). *Mental health services in the comprehensive care of the hemophiliac*. New York: National Hemophilia Foundation, 1977.

Agle, D. P., & Mattsson, A. Psychological complications of hemophilia. In M. W. Hilgartner (Ed.), *Hemophilia in children*. Littleton, Mass.: Publishing Sciences Group, 1976.

Alexander, A. B., Miklich, D. R., & Hershkoff, H. The immediate effects of systemic relaxation training on peak expiratory flow rates in asthmatic children. *Psychosomatic Medicine*, 1972, *34*, 388–294.

Allen, K. E., & Harris, F. R. Elimination of a child's excessive scratching by training the mother in reinforcement procedures. *Behavior Research and Therapy*, 1966, *4*, 79–84.

Ayllon, T., & Azrin, N. H. *The token economy: A motivational system for therapy and rehabilitation*. New York: Appleton-Century-Crofts, 1968.

Azrin, N. H., Holz, W., & Goldiamond, I. Response bias in questionnaire reports. *Journal of Consulting Psychology*, 1961, *25*, 324–326.

Baekeland, F., & Lundwall, L. Dropping out of treatment: A critical review. *Psychological Bulletin*, 1975, *82*, 738–783.

Baer, D. M., Wolf, M. M., & Risley, T. R. Some current dimensions of applied behavior analysis. *Journal of Applied Behavior Analysis*, 1968, *1*, 91–97.

Basmajian, J. V. Facts vs. myths about EMG biofeedback. *Biofeedback and Self Regulation*, 1976, *4*, 369–371.

Bedell, J. R., Giordani, B., Amour, J. L., Tavormina, J., & Boll, T. Life stress and the psychological and medical adjustment of chronically ill children. *Journal of Psychosomatic Research*, 1977, *21*, 237–242.

Begelman, D. A., & Hersen, M. Critique of Obler and Terwilliger's "Systematic desensitization with neurologically impaired children with phobic disorders." *Journal of Consulting and Clinical Psychology*, 1971, *37*, 10–13.

Bellack, A. S., & Schwartz, J. S. Assessment for self-control programs. In M. Hersen & A. S. Bellack (Eds.), *Behavioral assessment: A practical handbook*. New York: Pergamon Press, 1976.

Blanchard, E. B., & Hersen, M. Behavioral treatment of hysterical neurosis: Symptom substitution and symptom return reconsidered. *Psychiatry*, 1976, *39*, 118–129.

Campbell, D. T., & Stanley, J. C. *Experimental and quasi-experimental designs for research.* Chicago: Rand McNally, 1966.

Cassell, S. Effects of brief puppet therapy upon the emotional responses of children undergoing cardiac catheterization. *Journal of Consulting Psychology,* 1965, *29,* 1–8.

Cataldo, M. F., Russo, D. C., Bird, B. L., & Varni, J. W. Assessment and management of chronic disorders. In J. M. Ferguson & C. B. Taylor (Eds.), *Comprehensive handbook of behavioral medicine: Vol. 3. Extended applications and issues.* New York: Spectrum, 1980.

Cautela, J. R. & Upper, D. The behavioral inventory battery: The use of self-report measures in behavioral analysis and therapy. In M. Hersen & A. S. Bellack (Eds.), *Behavioral assessment: A practical handbook.* New York: Pergamon Press, 1976.

Chertok, S. L., & Bornstein, P. Covert modeling treatment of children's dental fears. *Child Behavior Therapy,* 1979, *1,* 249–255.

Clarke, D. S. Effects of emotion and cough on airways obstruction in asthma. *Medical Journal of Australia,* 1970, *1,* 535.

Colcher, I. S.,& Bass, J. W. Penicillin treatment of streptococcal pharyngitis: A comparison of schedules and the role of specific counseling. *Journal of the American Medical Association,* 1972, *222,* 657–659.

Creek, T. L., & Christian, W. F. *Chronically ill and handicapped children.* Champaign, Ill.: Research Press, 1976.

Deffenbacher, J. L., & Suinn, R. M. The chronically anxious patient. In D. M. Doleys, R. L. Meridith, & A. R. Ciminero (Eds.), *Behavioral medicine: Assessment and treatment strategies.* New York: Plenum Press, 1982.

Doke, L. A. Assessment of children's behavioral deficits. In M. Hersen & A. S. Bellack (Eds.), *Behavioral assessment: A practical handbook.* New York: Pergamon Press, 1976.

Dunbar, J. M., & Agras, W. S. Compliance with medical instructions. In J. M. Ferguson & C. B. Taylor (Eds.), *The comprehensive handbook of behavioral medicine: Volume 3. Extended applications and issues.* New York: SP Medical & Scientific Books, 1980.

Emmelkamp, P. M. G. Self-observation versus flooding in the treatment of agoraphobia. *Behavior Research and Therapy,* 1974, *12,* 229–237.

Epstein, L. H. Psychophysiological measurement in assessment. In M. Hersen & A. S. Bellack (Eds.), *Behavioral assessment: A practical handbook.* New York: Pergamon Press, 1976.

Epstein, L. H., & Masek, B. J. Behavioral control of medicine compliance. *Journal of Applied Behavior Analysis,* 1978, *11,* 1–9.

Fordyce, W. E. *Behavioral methods for chronic pain and illness.* St. Louis: Mosby, 1976.

Gambrill, E. D. *Behavior modification: Handbook of assessment, intervention, and evaluation.* San Francisco: Jossey-Bass, 1977.

Goldfried, M. R., & Davison, G. C. *Clinical behavior therapy.* New York: Holt, Rinehart & Winston, 1976, pp. 18–54.

Goldfried, M., & Pameranz, D. M. Role of assessment in behavior modification. *Psychological Reports,* 1968, *23,* 75–87.

Goldstein, A. P. Relationship-enhancement methods. In F. H. Kanfer & A. P. Goldstein (Eds.), *Helping people change.* New York: Pergamon Press, 1975.

Gordon, S. B. Multiple assessment of behavior modification with families. *Journal of Consulting and Clinical Psychology,* 1975, *43,* 917–919.

Greenfield, M. S., & Sternbach, R. A. (Eds.). *Handbook of psychophysiology.* New York: Holt, Rinehart & Winston, 1972.

Gundert-Remy, U., Remy, C., & Weber, E. Serum digoxin levels in patients of a general practice in Germany. *European Journal of Clinical Pharmacy,* 1976, *10,* 97–100.

Hahn, W. W. Autonomic responses of asthmatic children. *Psychosomatic Medicine.* 1966, *28,* 323–332.

Harris, S. I., & Ferrari, M. Developmental factors in child behavior therapy. *Behavior Therapy*, 1983, *14*, 54–72.

Hepner, A., & Cauthen, N. R. Effect of subject control and graduated exposure on snake phobias. *Journal of Consulting and Clinical Psychology*, 1975, *43*, 297–304.

Hersen, M., & Barlow, D. H. *Single case experimental designs: Strategies for studying behavior change*. New York: Pergamon Press, 1976.

Hersen, M., Turner, S. M., Edelstein, B. A., & Pinkston, S. G. Effects of phenothiazines and social skills training in a withdrawn schizophrenic. *Journal of Clinical Psychology*, 1975, *31*, 588–594.

Hodgson, R., & Rachman, S. Desynchrony in measures of fear. *Behavior Research and Therapy*, 1974, *12*, 319–326.

Holdsworth, L., & Whitmore, K. A study of children with epilepsy attending ordinary schools. *Developmental Medicine in Child Neurology*, 1974, *16*, 746–758.

Iwata, B. A., Wong, S. E., Riordan, M. M., Dorsey, M. F., & Lau, M. M. Assessment and training of clinical interviewing skills: Analogue analysis and field replication. *Journal of Applied Behavior Analysis*, 1982, *15*, 191–203.

Johnson, S. B., & Melamed, B. G. The assessment and treatment of children's fears. In B. Lahey & A. Kazdin (Eds.), *Advances in clinical child psychology* (Vol. 2). New York: Plenum Press, 1979.

Kanfer, F. H. Verbal conditioning: A review of its current status. In T. R. Dixon & D. L. Horton (Eds.), *Verbal behavior and general behavior theory*. Englewood Cliffs, N.J.: Prentice-Hall, 1968.

Kanfer, F. H. Self-monitoring methodological limitations and clinical applications. *Journal of Consulting and Clinical Psychology*, 1970, *35*, 148–152.

Kanfer, F. H., & Karoly, P. Self-control: A behavioristic excursion into the lion's den. *Behavior Therapy*, 1972, *3*, 398–416.

Kanfer, F. H., & Saslow, G. Behavioral diagnosis. In C. M. Franks (Ed.), *Behavior therapy: Appraisal and status*. New York: McGraw-Hill, 1969.

Karoly, P. Self-management problems in children. In E. Mash & L. Terdal (Eds.), *Behavioral assessment of childhood disorders*. New York: Guilford Press, 1981.

Kass, R. E., & O'Leary, K. D. *The effects of observer bias in field-experimental settings*. Paper presented at a Symposium on Behavior Analysis in Education, University of Kansas, Lawrence, Kansas, April 1970.

Katz, R. C. Single session recovery from a hemodialysis phobia: A case study. *Journal of Behavior Therapy and Experimental Psychiatry*, 1974, *5*, 205–206.

Kazdin, A. E. The failure of some patients to respond to token programs. *Journal of Behavior Therapy and Experimental Psychiatry*, 1973, *4*, 7–14.

Kazdin, A. E. Self-monitoring and behavior change. In M. J. Mahoney & C. E. Thoreson (Eds.), *Self-control: Power to the person*. Monterey, Calif.: Brooks/Cole, 1974.

Kellerman, J., Zeltzer, L., Ellenberg, L., Dash, J., & Rigler, D. Psychological effects of illness in adolescence: I. Anxiety, self-esteem and perception of control, *Journal of Pediatrics*, 1980, *97*, 126–131.

Kove, H., & Matthews, C. G. Psychometric and adaptive abilities in epilepsy with a different etiology. *Epilepsia*, 1966, *7*, 330–338.

Knight, R., Atkins, A., Eagle, C., Evans, N., Finkelstein, J. W., Fukushima, D., Katz, J., & Weiner, H. Psychological stress, ego defenses, and cortisol production in children hospitalized for elective surgery. *Psychosomatic Medicine*, 1979, *41*, 40–49.

Kohlenberg, R. J. The punishment of persistent vomiting: A case study. *Journal of Applied Behavior Analysis*, 1970, *3*, 241–245.

Lang, P. J. The mechanics of desensitization and the laboratory study of human fear. In C. M. Franks (Ed.), *Behavior therapy: Appraisal and status*. New York: McGraw-Hill, 1969.

Lazarus, A. A. Multimodal behavior therapy: Treating the "Basic Id." *Journal of Nervous and Mental Disease*, 1973, *156*, 404–411.

Leitenberg, H., Agras, W. S., Allen, R., Butz, R., & Edwards, J. Feedback and therapist praise during treatment of phobia. *Journal of Consulting and Clinical Psychology*, 1975, *43*, 396–404.

Lick, J. R., & Katkin, E. S. Assessment of anxiety and fear. In M. Hersen & A. S. Bellack (Eds.), *Behavioral assessment: A practical handbook*. New York: Pergamon Press, 1976.

Linehan, M. Issues in behavioral interviewing. In J. D. Cone & R. P. Hawkins (Eds.), *Behavioral assessment: New directions in clinical psychology*. New York: Brunner/Mazel, 1977.

Linkewich, J. A., Catalano, R. B., & Flack, H. L. The effect of packaging and instruction in outpatient compliance with medication regimens. *Drug Intelligence in Clinical Pharmacy*, 1974, *8*, 10–15.

Lipinski, D., & Nelson, R. The reactivity and unreliability of self-recording. *Journal of Consulting and Clinical Psychology*, 1974, *42*, 118–123.

Logan, F. Self-control as habit, drive, and incentive. *Journal of Abnormal Psychology*, 1973, *81*, 127–136.

Lowe, K., & Lutzker, J. R. Increasing compliance to a medical regimen with a juvenile diabetic. *Behavior Therapy*, 1979, *10*, 57–64.

Magrab, P. R., & Papadopoulou, Z. L. The effect of token economy on dietary compliance for children on hemodialysis. *Journal of Applied Behavior Analysis*, 1977, *10*, 573–578.

Marsden, G. Content analysis studies of psychotherapy: 1954 through 1968. In A. E. Bergin & S. L. Garfield (Eds.), *Handbook of psychotherapy and behavior change: An empirical analysis*. New York: Wiley, 1971.

Masek, B. J. Compliance and medicine. In D. M. Doleys, R. L. Meridith, & A. R. Ciminero (Eds.), *Behavioral medicine: Assessment and treatment strategies*. New York: Plenum Press, 1982.

Masek, B. J., & Jankel, M. R. Therapeutic adherence. In D. C. Russo & J. W. Varni (Eds.), *Behavioral pediatrics: Research and practice*. New York: Plenum Press, 1982.

Mash, E. J., & Terdal, L. G. Behavioral assessment of childhood disturbance. In E. Mash & L. Terdal (Eds.), *Behavioral assessment of childhood disorders*. New York: Guilford Press, 1981.

Mathews, A. M., Johnston, D. W., Shaw, P. M., & Gelder, M. G. Process variables and the prediction of outcome in behavior therapy. *British Journal of Psychiatry*, 1974, *125*, 256–264.

Mattsson, A. Long-term physical illness in childhood: A challenge to psychosocial adaption. In R. H. Moos (Ed.), *Coping with physical illness*, New York: Plenum Medical Books, 1977.

Melamed, B. G., Robbins, R. L., & Graves, S. Preparation for surgery and medical procedures. In D. C. Russo & J. W. Varni (Eds.), *Behavioral pediatrics: Research and practice*. New York: Plenum Press, 1982.

Melamed, B. G., & Siegel, L. J. Reduction of anxiety in children facing hospitalization and surgery by use of filmed modeling. *Journal of Consulting and Clinical Psychology*, 1975, *43*, 511–521.

Merskey, H. On the development of pain. *Headache*, 1970, *10*, 116–123.

Mischel, W. Toward a cognitive social learning reconceptualization of personality. *Psychological Review*, 1973, *80*, 252–283.

Molnar, G. A., & Taft, L. T. Cerebral palsy. In J. Wortis (Ed.), *Mental retardation and developmental disabilities: An annual review*. New York: Brunner/Mazel, 1975.

Morganstern, K. P. Behavioral interviewing: The initial stages of assessment. In M. Hersen

& A. S. Bellack (Eds.), *Behavioral assessment: A practical handbook*. New York: Pergamon Press, 1976.

Nazarian, L. F., Michalier, J., Charney, E., & Coulter, M. P. Effect of a mailed appointment reminder on appointment keeping. *Pediatrics*, 1974, *53*, 349–352.

Nimmer, W. H., & Kapp, R. A. A multiple impact program for the treatment of an injection phobia. *Journal of Behavior Therapy and Experimental Psychology*, 1974, *5*, 257–258.

O'Leary, K. D., Kent, R. N., & Kanowitz, J. Shaping data collection congruent with experimental hypotheses. *Journal of Applied Behavior Analysis*, 1975, *8*, 43–51.

Oster, J. Recurrent abdominal pain, headache and limb pains in children and adolescents. *Pediatrics*, 1972, *50*, 429–436.

Pelcovits, M. A., Silver, B. V., & Russo, D. C. Somatic disorders in children. In M. Hersen (Ed.), *The practice of outpatient behavior therapy*. New York: Grune & Stratton, in press.

Peterson, D. R. *The clinical study of social behavior*. New York: Appleton-Century-Crofts, 1968.

Repp, A. C., Roberts, D. M., Slack, D. J., Repp, C. F., & Berkler, M. S. A comparison of frequency, interval, and time-sampling methods of data collection. *Journal of Applied Behavior Analysis*, 1976, *9*, 501–508.

Rimms, D. C., & Sommerville, J. W. *Abnormal psychology*. New York: Academic Press, 1977.

Roberts, M. W., & Forehand, R. The assessment of maladaptive parent–child interaction by direct observation: An analysis of methods. *Journal of Abnormal Child Psychology*, 1978, *6*, 257–270.

Rose, S. W., Penry, J. K., Makush, R. E., Radloff, L. A., & Putnam, P. L. Prevalence of epilepsy in children. *Epilepsia*, 1973, *14*, 133–152.

Ruley, E. J. Compliance in young hypertensive patients. *Pediatric Clinics of North America*, 1978, *25*, 175–182.

Russo, E. C., Bird, B. L., & Masek, B. J. Assessment issues in behavioral medicine. *Behavioral Assessment*, 1980, *2*, 1–18.

Russo, D. C., & Varni, J. W. Behavioral pediatrics. In D. C. Russo & J. W. Varni (Eds.), *Behavioral pediatrics: Research and practice*. New York: Plenum Press, 1982.

Rutner, I. V. The effects of feedback and instructions on phobic behavior. *Behavior Therapy*, 1973, *4*, 338–348.

Sackett, D. L., & Haynes, R. B. (Eds.), *Compliance with therapeutic regimens*. Baltimore: Johns Hopkins University Press, 1976.

Samilson, R. I. *Orthopaedic aspects of cerebral palsy*. Philadelphia: Lippincott, 1975.

Schwitzgebel, R. L. Behavior technology. In H. Leitenberg (Ed.), *Handbook of behavior modification and behavior therapy*. Englewood Cliffs, N.J.: Prentice-Hall, 1976.

Sharpe, T. R., & Mikeal, R. L. Patient compliance with antibiotic regimens. *American Journal of Hospital Pharmacy*, 1974, *31*, 479–484.

Sherwin, A. L., Robb, J. P., & Lechter, M. Improved control of epilepsy by monitoring plasma ethosuximide. *Archives of Neurology*, 1973, *28*, 178–181.

Simkins, L. The reliability of self-recorded behaviors. *Behavior Therapy*, 1971, *2*, 83–87.

Smith, R. *Anesthesia for infants and children* (4th ed.). St. Louis: Mosby, 1980.

Storrow, H. A. *Introduction to scientific psychiatry*. New York: Appleton-Century-Crofts, 1967.

Straker, N., & Tamerin, J. Aggression and childhood asthma: A study in a natural setting. *Journal of Psychosomatic Research*, 1974, *18*, 131–135.

Stuart, R. B. *Trick or treatment: How and when psychotherapy fails*. Champaign, Ill.: Research Press, 1970.

Sullivan, H. S. *The psychiatric interview*. New York: Norton, 1954.

Tal, A., & Miklich, D. R. Emotionally induced decreases in pulmonary flow rates in asthmatic children. *Psychosomatic Medicine*, 1976, *38*, 190–200.

Tavormina, J. B., Kastner, L. S., Slater, P. M., & Watt, S. L. Chronically ill children: A psychologically and emotionally deviant population? *Journal of Abnormal Child Psychology*, 1976, *4*, 99–110.

Taylor, C. B., Ferguson, J. M., & Wermuth, B. M. Simple techniques to treat medical phobias. *Postgraduate Medical Journal*, 1977, *53*, 28–32.

Thomas, E. J. (Ed.). *Behavior modification procedure: A source book*. Chicago: Aldine, 1974.

Truax, C. B., & Carkhuff, R. R. *Toward effective counseling and psychotherapy: Training and practice*. Chicago: Aldine, 1967.

Varni, J. W. Behavioral treatment of disease-related chronic insomnia in a hemophiliac. *Journal of Behavior Therapy and Experimental Psychiatry*, 1980, *11*, 143–145.

Varni, J. W., Bessman, C. A., Russo, D. C., & Cataldo, M. F. Behavioral management of chronic pain in children. *Archives of Physical Medicine and Rehabilitation*, 1980, *61*, 375–379.

Wolpe, J. *The practice of behavior therapy*. New York: Pergamon Press, 1969.

Wright, T., & Nicholson, J. Physiotherapy for the spastic child: An evaluation. *Developmental Medicine in Child Neurology*, 1973, *15*, 146–163.

Yule, W. The potential of behavioral treatment in preventing later childhood difficulties. *Behavioral Analysis and Modification*, 1977, *2*, 19–31.

Zeltzer, L., Kellerman, J., Ellenberg, L., Dash, J., & Rigler, D. Psychological effects of illness in adolescences: II. Impact of illness in adolescents: Crucial issues and coping styles. *Journal of Pediatrics*, 1980, *97*, 132–138.

Zlutnick, S., Mayville, W. J., & Moffat, S. Modification of seizure disorders: The interruption of behavioral chains. *Journal of Applied Behavior Analysis*, 1975, *8*, 1–12.

9 *Prevention of Childhood Dysfunction*

ANNETTE U. RICKEL AND LOUISE A. LAMPI

The mental health professional typically assists children in crisis situations, after an identified problem has arisen. The increasingly short supply of mental health workers leaves many of the service demands of children and their families unmet, however, and this method is no longer sufficient. An alternative model for service delivery is one of prevention. This strategy attempts to build mental health rather than repair dysfunctions. Just as the medical profession has shown that prevention plays a significant role in bringing epidemic diseases, such as diphtheria and smallpox, under control by early vaccination, so, too, can mental health problems be ameliorated by early intervention programs.

This chapter, in addressing the prevention of childhood dysfunction, will focus primarily on the early childhood years, since in young children maladaptive patterns are less firmly established and when identified may be more amenable to positive and long-lasting change. Primary and secondary preventive intervention programs specifically designed for at-risk groups will be presented in three major areas: (a) infants at risk for developmental problems due to reproductive and/or caretaking casualties, (b) children at risk for school maladjustment as a result of learning and/or behavioral problems, and (c) children at risk for schizophrenia. It is beyond the scope of this chapter to make an exhaustive review of the research pertinent to all high-risk groups of children; three exemplary groups have been selected, and a brief summary of the current status of research and theory in these broad categories of risk will be provided, as well as recent directions in preventive interventions.

1. Infants at Risk

Despite the great advances made in the past 50 years or so which have served to reduce some of the risks associated with early growth

ANNETTE U. RICKEL AND LOUISE A. LAMPI • Department of Psychology, Wayne State University, Detroit, Michigan 48202.

and development, children are still exposed to a myriad of hazards. Developmental problems will continue to occur until the knowledge on which to base effective prevention programs is acquired (Sameroff & Chandler, 1975). The identification of infancy risk factors and their nature and causes is the first step in ameliorating these developmental difficulties which incur tremendous human and fiscal costs.

Infants are considered to be at risk for developmental problems due to reproductive and/or caretaking casualties (Field, 1982). The "continuum of reproductive casualty" was first described by Pasamanick and Knobloch (1961) as a range of pre- and perinatal risk factors, including children born with congenital disorders such as cerebral palsy or intellectual deficits and those born prematurely or small for their gestational age. The caretaking casualty continuum, which is not necessarily independent of the first, includes developmental problems experienced by infants postnatally that result from being subjected to parents who are under various emotional or socioeconomic stresses. Examples of infants at risk because of both types of casualties are premature infants or low socioeconomic status teenage mothers and abused infants who are also born with some physical defect.

1.1. The Continuum of Reproductive Casualty

Three perinatal risk factors have been particularly well researched: oxygen deprivation, premature birth, and social conditions.

1.1.1. Oxygen Deprivation

During the birth process and immediately thereafter, the risk of brain damage often increases because of a blocking of oxygen supply to the brain. Oxygen deprivation, or anoxia, can damage or destroy brain cells very rapidly. Perinatal anoxia sometimes leads to deficits in later functioning; however, the long-term developmental effects depend upon the location, extent, and timing of the damage (Achenbach, 1982). Furthermore, neonatal apnea not only is a cause of damage but may also be a symptom of preexisting damage (Tanner, 1970).

Longitudinal studies have revealed some developmental patterns among anoxic children. In their well-known St. Louis study, Graham and her associates examined several hundred infants during the neonatal period (Graham, Matarazzo, & Caldwell, 1956) and followed them up at 3 years (Graham, Ernhart, Thurston, & Craft, 1962) and at 7 years (Corah, Anthony, Painter, Stern, & Thurston, 1965). Within the first few days after birth, the anoxic infants were found to be deficient on measures of maturation level, visual responsiveness, irritability, muscle tension, and pain threshold (Graham, Pennoyer, Caldwell, Greenman, & Hartman, 1957). Children who had sustained anoxia either postnatally or both prenatally and postnatally scored significantly lower on measures of cognitive functioning, but the IQ deficit among those sustaining only prenatal anoxia was not statistically significant (Graham *et al.*, 1962). This may have been due to the fact that prenatal anoxia was *inferred* from pregnancy complications. Neurological examinations showed significant signs of neural damage at age 3. At 7 years, significant IQ differences between the anoxic groups and their controls disappeared (Corah *et al.*, 1965). However, evidence for a perceptual-motor deficit in anoxics was found. Behaviorally, a deficit in social competence was found among the 7-year-old anoxic children as revealed by their performance on the Vineland Social Maturity Scale. They were particularly behind in age-appropriate social skills, and self-help behavior. The 7-year-old anoxics were also rated as significantly more impulsive and distractible than control children.

The St. Louis findings are consistent with others reported by Tizard (1978) and by Sameroff and Chandler (1975) on the effects of anoxia. Broman's (1979) national study of 36,000 children indicated that children who had other signs of neurological damage in addition to perinatal anoxia showed elevated rates of mental retardation. However, only small deficits were revealed in anoxic children lacking other signs.

1.1.2. Prematurity

Prematurity is the outcome of many pregnancy complications and represents the most common birth abnormality (Birch & Gussow, 1970). Evidence suggests that there is not necessarily a one-to-one relationship between prematurity by itself and the negative developmental outcomes associated with it. Parmelee and Haber (1973) contend that the adverse residual effects of prematurity may be due to the prematurity alone or to associated factors, for example, low birth weight, a lengthy period of incubation, concomitant perinatal trauma, or low socioeconomic conditions to which the child is exposed while growing up. These investigators argue for the possibility that an infant who experiences no trauma other than prematurity itself and who is reared in a warm, stimulating environment may fare just as well as a full-term infant brought up under the same conditions. Goldberg (1979) has suggested that some of the developmental difficulties of the premature infant may be related to factors which have the potential to interfere with the early establishment of effective, mutually responsive interactions. For example, the preterm infant lacks integrated physiologic and motoric functioning which may limit mother–infant responsiveness (Als, Tronick, & Lester, 1977; Als, Lester, & Brazelton, 1979). Siqueland (1973) found that interventions with premature infants in the first weeks after birth changed them in such a way as to evoke more responsive interaction from their mothers. Similarly, negative effects which are secondary to the preterm infant's biological immaturity may result when the child is placed in an intensive care nursery, preventing the opportunity for the infant and caregiver to develop an effective familiarity with one another (Goldberg, 1979).

Clearly, prematurity affects much more than the biology of the infant (Als & Brazelton, 1980; Field, 1977; Frodi, Lamb, Leavitt, Donovan, Neff, & Sherry, 1978; Klaus & Kennell, 1976; Shosenberg, 1980). For example, some mothers may bring about their premature labor by not obtaining adequate prenatal care. Further, premature delivery has been described as a crisis which demands tremendous emotional adjustment by the parents (Benfield, Leib, & Reuter, 1976; Cramer, 1976; Littman & Wooldridge, 1976). Some women become so depressed and anxious following the birth of their baby that their ability to care for the child is compromised. Evidence suggests that the future biological, social, and psychological functioning of preterm infants rests to a large degree on factors unrelated to the specific biological impairment of the infant.

The biological impairment measurable at birth is actually a very inefficient predictor of the future general functioning of these infants, whereas the attitudes and child-care practices of their caregivers are significantly correlated with later adjustment and development (Cohen & Beckwith, 1979; Fitzhardinge, 1976; Littman, 1979; Sigman & Parmelee, 1979). Although the incidence of developmental disorders is greater in preterm infants (Caputo & Mandell, 1970; Davies & Stewart, 1975; Hunt, 1981), prematurity alone does not necessarily lead to developmental delay (Douglas & Gear, 1976). Also, later performance of the smallest infants is not always the poorest, and healthy prematures often have very good developmental outcomes (Caputo & Mandell, 1970; Sigman, 1982; Sostek, Quinn, & Davitt, 1979). A variety of home- and nursery-based interventions have had beneficial effects on the development of preterm infants (Cornell & Gottfried, 1976; Powell, 1974; Scarr-Salapatek & Williams, 1973). It appears that risk status cannot be based solely on the presence of obstetric and perinatal medical complications but requires continuing developmental assessments of the child (Littman, 1979; Sigman & Parmelee, 1979).

1.1.3. Socioeconomic Conditions

A review of the literature on the impact of disadvantaged environments on development led Birch and Gussow (1970) to conclude that both low social status and ethnic background related to high risk in infancy. Infant mortality rates are highest within populations which are both poor and black. Whereas the proportion of infants having some complication is 5% among white upper class groups, this figure increases to 15% among low socioeconomic status whites and to 51% among all nonwhites (U.S. Bureau of the Census, 1982). Birch and Gussow (1970) state:

> The poor woman having a baby may be at risk because of her age, her nutritional status, her probable poor growth, her excessive exposure to infection in the community which she inhabits, her poor housing, and her inadequate medical supervision, as well as because of complex interactions between these and other potentially adverse influences. (p. 175)

Thus, the biological outcomes of pregnancy among individuals living in disadvantaged environments are less than optimal. These investigators also point out that according to much of the research information available, disadvantaged children experience less favorable developmental outcomes as well.

In their classic Hawaiian study, Werner and his associates (Werner, Bierman, & French, 1971) implemented one of the largest-scale longitudinal examinations of the effects of perinatal complications. From newborn assessment of their sample to a retesting at 20 months, it became evident that perinatal complications were related to subsequent physical and psychological development only when combined with consistently poor environmental conditions. Further, when good prenatal care was available, the initial socioeconomic differences in the distribution of perinatal complications disappeared.

Reassessment of the children at 10 years of age (Werner & Smith, 1977) indicated that consistency of intellectual functioning from 20 months to 10 years was significantly greater for children with IQs of less than 80. The parents of a majority of these children had little education and were of low socioeconomic status. Other studies have similarly shown that the predictive validity of socioeconomic status is greater for the low end of the IQ scale (e.g., Willerman, Broman, & Fiedler, 1970). In the Werner Hawaiian study, the correlation between parent and child IQs increased over the first 8 years of life, suggesting that risk factors operating during the prenatal period wane during childhood as the influence of family and social factors increase. The authors concluded that 10 times more children suffered physical, intellectual, or behavioral problems related to the effects of a disadvantaged early environment than the impact of perinatal difficulties.

From this discussion, it is apparent that socioeconomic factors have a place on both the reproductive and caretaking casualty continua. While the incidence of perinatal complications varies with socioeconomic status, the residual effects of these same complications also depend upon the socioeconomic conditions of the caretaking environment.

1.2. The Continuum of Caretaking Casualty

The continuum of caretaking casualty includes postnatal risk factors created by early parenting practices. Parents must create a protective and nurturing context for growth and development once their child is born. When parental behavior does not meet a minimal requirement for the child's normal, healthy development, the child is placed at risk for a variety of caretaking casualties. Disorders in the parent–child relationship can take many forms, but child abuse and neglect have been the focus of most research and documentation (Sameroff & Chandler, 1975).

1.2.1. Child Abuse and Neglect

Physical battering is the most blatant evidence of a parent–child relationship gone awry. Although parental neglect may be more difficult to identify, its results may be just as devastating. The "failure to thrive syndrome" has been described by Sameroff and Chandler (1975) as "gross parental inattention to the needs of their children, abandonment, starvation, and unusual isolation of the child from the community" (p. 225). There is no clear-cut line between child neglect and abuse; in fact, they often coexist (Gil, 1970).

1.2.1.1. Characteristics of Maltreated Children. Studies evaluating the long-term consequences of maltreatment have found serious residual effects. For example, Morse, Sahler, and Friedman (1970) sampled 55 cases of abuse to follow over a 3-year period. More than 70% of the children were below the normal range in either emotional, social, intellectual, or motor development at 3-year follow-up. Over 40% were found to have symptoms of motor hyperactivity or mental retardation *prior* to the incident of abuse. Thus, investigators have suggested that children themselves may precipitate their maltreatment, though the evidence is conflicting and studies frequently do not consider neglect separately from abuse (Dion, 1974; Friedrich & Boriskin, 1976; Vietze, Falsey, O'Connor, Sander, Sherrod, & Altemeir, 1980).

Among the congenital conditions of the child which are thought to contribute to abuse are low birth weight, prematurity, congenital defects, and birth complications (Drotar, Malone, Negray, & Dennstedt, 1981; Hunter, Kilstrom, Kraybill, & Loda, 1978; Rosenn, Loeb, & Jura, 1980). Other studies report no differences in these conditions between abused and nonabused groups of children (Crittenden & Snell, 1983;

Maden & Wrench, 1977; Starr, 1982). Studies which do find differences in congenital conditions often have not matched the control group to the abuse group by socioeconomic status (e.g., Baldwin & Oliver, 1975; Smith & Hanson, 1974), or have compared siblings (e.g., Lynch, 1976). Crittenden (1983) suggests the possibility that for parents who clearly have the capacity to abuse or neglect their children (i.e., a history of abuse), congenital conditions which make the infant less satisfying or acceptable may increase the risk that she or he will be the specific target of abuse or neglect.

Behaviorally, abused and neglected children have been reported to be more difficult, whiny, noncompliant, avoidant, unappealing, and clingy and to have finicky eating habits (George & Main, 1979; Ounsted, Oppenheimer, & Linsay, 1975; Robert & Maddux, 1982). Parents often describe their children as "different" prior to the onset of abuse (Morse et al., 1970). Abused children also have been found to show developmental delay (Baldwin & Oliver, 1975; Crittenden & Snell, 1983; Sandgrund, Gaines, & Green, 1974; Smith & Hanson, 1974). Gil's (1970) extensive survey indicated that nearly a third of the abused children studied nationwide displayed aberrant social behavior during the year prior to the abusive incident which led to their inclusion in the study. An additional 25% exhibited abnormal physical or intellectual functioning. Also, nearly 25% of the children were described by parents as displaying persistently atypical behavior. Parents reported that provoking behavior by the children often precipitated their abusive actions.

Crittenden (1981), in contrast, found that the difficult and passive interaction patterns of abused and neglected infants may represent a result of maltreatment rather than a cause. After being videotaped interacting with their mothers, maltreated infants were taped interacting with a second familiar adult. When the mother and second adult had the same pattern of interaction, the infant would produce the same pattern of behavior in both situations. However, when the adult patterns differed, infant patterns would also vary.

Some researchers have studied the relationship between infants' patterns of attachment and maltreatment. Ainsworth has posited that emotional unavailability, particularly physical rejection, tends to be associated with a pattern of anxious-avoidant attachment (Ainsworth, Blehar, Waters, & Wall, 1978). Physical abuse may constitute a type of rejection. On the basis of her work, it might also be expected that pronounced inconsistency in caregiver responsiveness would often lead to an anxious-resistant pattern of infant attachment because the child is unable to derive comfort from the caregiver (Egeland & Sroufe, 1981). These patterns of attachment should be expected to be prevalent in neglected and abused infants. Egeland and Sroufe report that although most maltreated infants in their sample were anxiously attached at 12 months of age, when reassessed at 18 months, six of the eight abused and neglected children were securely attached. Crittenden (1981) found that serious maltreatment consistently resulted in anxious attachment, whereas marginal maltreatment produced mixed results and adequate caregiving led to secure attachment.

1.2.1.2. Abusive Parents. The characteristics of abusive parents have been the focus of many investigations in this area of study. Research on the personality traits of battering parents tend to indicate that they are of lower intelligence and maturity; more aggressive, impulsive, self-centered, and self-critical than nonabusing parents (Spinetta & Rigler, 1972). Egeland, Breitenbucher, and Rosenberg (1980) also found that their group of maltreating parents displayed higher levels of anxiety and defensiveness and were lower in nurturance than controls. Personal background information on abusive parents often indicates that they were abused or neglected children and as a result have less understanding and awareness of the difficulties and demands of parenthood. Further, they lack knowledge of appropriate child-rearing practices and the skills to implement them (Egeland *et al.*, 1980; Spinetta & Rigler, 1972).

Recently there has been increasing interest in the roles of cultural and social forces and socioenvironmental stresses in the etiology of child abuse and neglect (Garbarino, 1976; Giovannoni, 1971). Several investigators have attempted to identify more specific environmental stresses within families characterized by neglect or abuse. For example, Justice and Duncan (1976) examined stress-inducing events specific to a family's history rather than the stressful conditions associated with low socioeconomic status in general. In this study, stress was defined as a life change requiring adaptive action. Abusing parents, as compared to nonabusing controls, were found to experience far greater levels of stress. The authors concluded that the life crises of abusing parents rather than the stress of general socioeconomic conditions predisposed them toward maltreatment of their children.

Egeland and Brunnquell (1979) administered the Life Event Scale, which was developed for use with lower income populations (Egeland & Deinard, 1975), as well as several other measures, to a group of mothers at risk for abuse and neglect. The families were observed and tested at regular intervals, starting in the first trimester of pregnancy through the first 2 years of the child's life. From this sample, a subsample of mothers who mistreated the infants was identified and compared with a second subsample who gave their infants adequate care. Although a number of group differences were found, there was no significant difference in the number of stressful events experienced. However, on closer inspection, it became apparent that even though there were no differences in total number of life events experienced, there was a difference in the severity of stressful life events in terms of degree of disruption and readjustment required.

Finally, Egeland *et al.* (1980) report that a modified version of the Life Events Inventory developed by Cochrane and Robertson (1973) differentiated between groups of mistreating and nonabusing mothers when administered 1 year after the child's birth. Thus, it appears that the tension created by specific stress-inducing life events may contribute to the likelihood of violent behavior in the home.

1.3. Preventive Intervention with High-Risk Infants

As stated earlier, an understanding of the obstacles to normal, healthy development makes possible the amelioration of negative effects. A sampling of recent attempts at preventive interventions will serve to illustrate how knowledge of the risk factors in infancy can be put to practical use.

1.3.1. Parent Programs for Premature Infants

Minde, Shosenberg, and Marton (1982) point out that although there are many hypotheses about how factors associated with infant prematurity relate to later parenting disorders, most researchers would agree that the premature birth of a child is a very stressful experience for any parent. In order to assist parents of premature infants in dealing with this stress, the Minde group initiated a hospital-based intervention which utilized peer-oriented self-help groups. Fifty-seven low birthweight infants and their mothers were assigned to intervention treatment or control groups. Although premature, these infants were of normal weight for their gestational age, and they suffered no physical malformations or serious medical complications. Parents met once a week, in groups of four to five families for approximately 7–12 weeks following the birth of their child. Along with a group coordinator, who was an experienced neonatal nurse, parents met with a "veteran mother" who also had had a small baby in the nursery within the previous year.

The objective of the group meetings was to provide parents with an opportunity to discuss feelings of fear, guilt, and depression associated with giving birth to such a small infant. This discussion among peers experiencing the same difficulties promoted a sense of mutual trust and support. Parents were then shown films and slides describing the medical and developmental needs of premature infants. Assistance was provided in meeting practical requirements such as obtaining unemployment benefits, finding babysitters, or seeking improved accommodations. Finally, parents were familiarized with local community services for family support, and such issues as the problems of working mothers and the father's role in child care were discussed.

Following the intervention, families who participated in the groups visited their infants in the hospital significantly more often than did the control parents (Minde, Shosenberg, Marton, Thompson, Ripley, & Burns, 1980). They also touched and talked to their infants more frequently during their visits and rated themselves as more confident in caring for them at the time of discharge. Three months after discharge, group mothers continued to display more involvement with their infants during feedings and were more concerned about their general development.

A follow-up study one year later (Minde, Shosenberg, & Thompson, 1983) again revealed differences between intervention mothers and controls. A significantly greater percentage of the mothers in the experimental group displayed age-corrected perceptions and expectations of their infants' development given the length of gestation. Experimental mothers allowed their infants greater freedom (e.g., floor space in which to play), gave a higher degree of social stimulation (e.g., vocalized and played with their infants) and shared their feelings with them more easily. Their children, in turn, displayed increased social and independent behaviors, such as general playing, food-sharing, and self-feeding. These investigators found that the experimental mothers also differed from controls in a number of behaviors related to self-image. They exhibited a higher degree of personal autonomy, a positive attitude toward their work, and improved relationships with other people. The authors suggest that the mothers' changed self-concept may have been responsible for the enriched interactions with their infants.

An intervention program for teenage black mothers of lower socioeconomic status and their preterm infants was designed by Widmayer and Field (1980). A previous study (Field, 1980) had indicated that these young mothers treated their infants like dolls that could not see or hear but could only eat, cry, and wet. This study attempted to demonstrate the skills of the newborn so that the teenage mother might, in turn, become more verbally responsive to her infant.

Thirty preterm infants who were free of medical complications requiring intensive care were randomly selected from normal nurseries. These infants were assigned to a control group, a Brazelton demonstration group, or a Mother's Assessment of the Behavior of her Infant (MABI) group. The MABI group mothers were asked to complete the mother's version of the Brazelton assessment at birth and at 1-week intervals during the first month. The Brazelton group received a demonstration of the instrument and completed the MABI at birth and weekly during the first month. The investigators speculated that the Brazelton demonstration would provide modeling of the ways in which mothers might elicit optimal interactive behaviors from their infants which would then be practiced and reinforced by their own administration of the MABI. Control mothers were asked to complete an assessment of developmental milestones and childrearing attitudes at birth and on a weekly basis.

A follow-up at 1 month indicated that the Brazelton demonstration group infants received more optimal interactive process scores than did controls and displayed a significant improvement on the Brazelton interaction scores over their neonatal scores. Brazelton and MABI mothers received better ratings on the feeding interaction scales than did control mothers, and both mothers and infants performed better on the face-to-face interaction rating scale than did the control dyads. In addition, Brazelton and MABI mothers vocalized more to their infants, and their infants averted their gaze less often than did the control children.

At 4-month follow-up, both mother and infant face-to-face interaction ratings favored the MABI and Brazelton dyads. These infants also averted their gaze less often than did infants in the control group, and their mothers engaged in more verbal interchange.

Finally, at 12 months, the Brazelton infants were somewhat heavier and taller than the control group. Additionally, the Brazelton infants received significantly higher scores on the Bayley Mental Scale, and their Bayley Motor Scores also approached significance as compared to those of the control group.

Since this study clearly indicated that teenage, black, low socioeconomic status mothers can benefit from intervention, the Field group designed and evaluated a more extensive home-based parent training program for these mothers and their preterm infants (Field, Widmayer, Stringer, & Ignatoff, 1980). Home visits were made by two-person intervention teams which included a trained interventionist and a teenage, black female work-study student. Half-hour visits were made biweekly and were aimed at educating the mothers in childrearing techniques and developmental milestones, teaching them exercises for enhancing infant sensorimotor and cognitive development; and improving mother–infant interactions in order to foster communication skills and harmonious relations.

At 4 months, it was demonstrated that the intervention group produced better results than controls on measures of infant length, weight, Denver Developmental Scores, and face-to-face interaction ratings. Their mothers also displayed an improved performance during interaction, exhibited realistic developmental expectations, and had less punitive childrearing attitudes. Further, intervention mothers rated their infants as less difficult on infant temperament than did control mothers. Intervention mothers on the 8-month assessment rated their infants higher on temperament, and their infants produced Bayley mental and motor scores that were superior to their controls. At 12 months, intervention infants were heavier and longer than controls, they re-ceived higher Bayley mental scores, and their mothers again rated their temperaments as being less difficult.

1.3.2. Infants at Risk for Academic Failure

As part of the Carolina Abecedarian Project, Ramey, MacPhee, and Yeates (1982) developed an intervention program based on a general systems model. This program represented a dual-focus attack on the conditions affecting the growth of children at risk for developmental retardation, which is defined by these authors as "any significant im-pairment in ecologically valid assessments of cognitive or adaptive func-tioning which is known to be preventable" (p. 344).

At a secondary level, intervention was provided for both experi-mental and control group families. Social services for the family, medical attention, and nutritional supplements for the children were available to both groups to ensure the socioeconomic and physical survival of the children and their families. At the primary level of intervention, only the experimental children received direct educational programming through day-care.

The Carolina Abecedarian Project attempted to intervene with in-fants and children presumed to be at high risk for academic failure. Families were referred to the project through local hospitals, clinics, and government social service departments. Once referred, mothers were invited for an interview and psychological assessment, which usually took place during the last trimester of pregnancy. Most of the families included for study were mother-headed and of low income. The moth-ers had an average education of 10th grade and a mean IQ of 85. Over 95% of the children studied were black.

The development of the day-care program was based upon the belief that "relative inferiority in the areas of language development and motivation to learn are particularly detrimental to normal development" (Ramey & Gallagher, 1975, p. 45). Activities were designed to facilitate language development and concept attainment and to foster adaptive social behavior. An attempt was made to create an environment which was predictable and supportive and which promoted self-help behavior. Trained teachers and assistants provided the educational program for the children, who began attending the center as early as 6 weeks of age. Attendance was required by 3 months.

Ramey and Campbell (1979) report that infants attending the day-care program were rated higher in social confidence than controls at 6, 12, and 18 months. At 18 months, these children scored higher in goal-directed behavior and exhibited less fear at all ages. Performance on the McCarthy Scales indicated that day-care enhanced the children's ability to attend to, understand, and execute abstract and complex tasks. Evidence also indicated that the day-care intervention improved the children's performance on psycholinguistic tasks (Gordon & Feagans, 1977; Gordon & Bernard, 1981). The Bayley scale, Stanford-Binet, and WPPSI scores suggested that the day-care was instrumental in preventing the intellectual decline observed in control children (Ramey & Campbell, 1981). Finally, the high-risk children attending the day-care center were found to be as interested in peers and as friendly and cooperative as their advantaged middle-class age mates. They were also more willing to approach and interact with a strange adult than were their home-reared, middle-class peers.

1.3.3. Psychosocial Interventions

The Pittsburgh First-Born Project, reported by Broussard (1982), focuses on the prevention of psychosocial disorders. Broussard utilized the Neonatal Perception Inventories (NPI), which compare the mother's perception of her own newborn baby to her concept of the average infant, as a measure of the adaptive potential of the mother–infant unit during the 1st month of life. The child was considered at high risk if the mother did not rate him or her as better than average, since the absence of a positive maternal perception of the neonate is associated with a very high rate of subsequent psychosocial disorder (Broussard, 1982).

A population of high-risk infants was identified for participation in the program or for inclusion in a high-risk control group. These infants were physically healthy and were the first-born child in the family. Intervention contacts consisted of an initial interview with one or both parents, participation in mother–infant group meetings, and home-based intervention sessions. The groups were composed of seven or eight mother–infant pairs who met biweekly from the time their infants were 2–4 months of age until they were 3½ years old. Broussard and a co-leader conducted these meetings, and home visits were made by child development specialists. During the course of the intervention, Broussard and her co-workers actively studied the mother–infant interaction and intervened with each dyad according to their developmental needs. This influenced both the nature and the timing of the interventions administered. Response to evolving parent and infant needs was guided by the Broussard group's understanding of basic child development principles and knowledge of the process of parenting. The developmental progress of the infants was continuously monitored, and to assess the impact of the intervention, the infants were evaluated at 1 and 2½ years of age. A naive observer–rater scored children on items reflecting (a) the separation–individuation process, (b) confidence, (c) implementation of contacts with the nonhuman environment, (d) aggression, (e) affective balance, (f) investment in the use of language for communication, (g) coping, and (h) play. The results of these evaluations indicated that the intervention groups and low-risk control groups exhibited superior functioning across the board as compared to high-risk, no-intervention controls.

1.3.4. Interventions for Abusive and Neglecting Mothers

An intervention program for abusive and neglecting mothers was designed and evaluated by Crittenden and Snell (1983). Black and white mother–infant dyads of low socioeconomic status known to be characterized by abusive, neglecting, problem-ridden (marginally maltreating), and adequate relations were included for study.

Patterns of mother–infant interaction were initially assessed through the use of minute-long videotaped play sessions. Naive raters classified maternal interactional behavior as abusing, neglecting, inept, or sensitive. Infant patterns of interaction were categorized as passive, difficult, or cooperative. In addition, the infants received assessment for developmental delay.

Twenty-four intervention dyads attended weekly parent group meetings aimed at improving mother–infant interaction. At these meetings, each parent was videotaped for one minute while she played with her infant. The parents then viewed all of the tapes in a group session and discussed and played out ways of improving their interaction. After 4 months, a second developmental assessment was administered at the infant's home. The one-minute videotape made for that week's parent group meeting served as the postintervention interaction measure.

As expected on the basis of earlier research (Crittenden, 1981), Crittenden and Snell found that maternal pattern of interaction was related to type of maltreatment. The data also confirmed that infant behavior was classified as difficult when the mother's interaction pattern was abusive. When the mother was neglecting, the infant interaction pattern was passive, and when the maternal pattern was inept or sensitive, the infant interaction was cooperative. Infants of problematic and adequate mothers were found to have the highest Developmental Quotients

(DQs), abused infants had the next highest DQs, and neglected infants had the lowest DQs.

The goal of intervention was to increase the mothers' sensitivity and appropriate responsiveness to infant cues. It was predicted that with increasing maternal sensitivity, the infants would become more cooperative and would exhibit gains in DQ. After the intervention period, the mothers were divided into two groups based on the coded videotapes indicating their patterns of interaction prior to and following the 4 months of parent meetings. One group displayed an increase in sensitivity from abusing or neglecting patterns to inept or sensitive, or from inept to sensitive. The second group included mothers whose patterns of interaction remained unchanged after the intervention and thus did not increase in their sensitivity to infant cues.

Infant patterns of interaction were also compared on the same pre- and postintervention videotapes. The infants exhibited the predicted increase in cooperation in 10 of the 16 cases in which the mother had shown an increase in sensitivity. None of the eight infants with mothers who remained unchanged displayed the increase in cooperation. Similarly, increases in infant DQ following intervention were related to maternal sensitivity. Whereas children of nonimproved mothers showed only a mean 8 point gain in DQ scores, children of mothers displaying increased sensitivity had a mean DQ gain of 24 points.

The authors concluded that maltreatment does not result from infant behavior reflecting some inherent temperamental trait. Rather, aberrant interactions appear to be set in motion by the mother and are then maintained by the infant's behavior. Abused and neglected infants have the capacity for normal behavior when their mother's behavior changes in a positive direction.

Intervention programs have been proven beneficial in ameliorating a wide variety of risk factors associated with infancy. These intervention programs include hospital-, home-, and day-care center-based efforts employing a diversity of techniques. The success of such a wide range of intervention efforts may be related to the fact that most of the variables contributing to risk in infancy are directly or indirectly created by parental attitudes and child-rearing practices. The common thread among many successful programs is that they not only provide some direct form of stimulation to the child but also promote parent change through (a) supportive peer discussion of difficulties shared in caring for their high-risk infant, (b) methods to increase the self-image of parents and their sense of competence in child-rearing, (c) parent education of physical and psychological child development, (d) teaching parents specific techniques for interacting with their infant in order to foster social-emotional and cognitive development, and (e) making parents aware of supportive social services and encouraging their utilization. Although some infant risk factors are unavoidable and inalterable, improved parental attitudes and child-care practices create a context for growth and development in which the child may still thrive normally.

2. Children at Risk for Learning and Behavioral Problems

2.1. Intervention in the Schools

In the United States, the school is a powerful socializing agent for virtually all children, second only to the family in its influence. Unfortunately, a significant proportion of children find that daily life in the classroom is a very stressful experience. Although the school would appear to be an ideal setting for organized intervention efforts, mental health services within the traditional school system have been unable to make efficient use of this important opportunity to reach children (Cowen, Trost, Izzo, Lorion, Dorr, & Isaacson, 1975).

Among teachers, there is inconsistency in definitions of school maladaptation and in methods of dealing with the specific difficulties observed. Since the primary goal of teachers is to educate the child, their identification of school maladjustment may occur only if and when their patience with the child's learning difficulties is exhausted, or if the child's disruptive behavior exceeds their personal level of tolerance. On the other hand, a behaviorally maladjusted child whose academic performance is satisfactory and who does not disrupt the classroom routine (e.g., the shy, withdrawn child) is frequently overlooked by teachers because she or he is not in conflict with the teacher's goals. Furthermore, if the teacher does single out a child as requiring mental health services, this child may not be referred for the guidance she or he needs if the teacher perceives this as an admission of inability to handle the problem. Even if this is not the case, decisions regarding the severity of the child's adjustment problem and the appropriate recourse to be taken are made by teachers on the basis of their idiosyncratic definitions of maladaptation and their equally diverse perceptions of the measures necessary to alleviate the difficulty (Rickel, 1982).

The traditional school system often deals with maladaptation in such a way that initiates unfortunate consequences for the child. The child may be isolated or labeled as a misfit, serving only to undermine further his or her educational and interpersonal development. At the same time, as previously mentioned, other children with more subtle difficulties often go unnoticed. Although many of these children are passed to each advancing grade, they are crippled by subtle deficiencies which prevent the realization of their full potential. With time, these unaddressed school maladaptation problems frequently evolve into more serious psychological and/or academic difficulties (Cowen, Gesten, & Weissberg, 1980). Adding insult to injury, mental health services within most public school systems have very limited personnel and resources at their disposal. The supply of mental health professionals affordable by the schools invariably falls short of the demand for these individuals, reflecting what is probably a conservative estimate of the proportion of children requiring some form of guidance.

One hopes that in the future primary prevention programs will create new classroom environments which promote mental health initially, rather than treating behavioral and educational difficulties once they develop. Clearly, the traditional system has failed in its attempts to do so, and yet the skills and resources for the total revamping of the system required by primary prevention is lacking (Rickel, Lampi, & Smith, 1984). Therefore, what is currently needed and feasible is an efficient as well as effective means of screening, diagnosis, and remediation of early school maladaptation which can be incorporated into the structure of the school system as it now exists.

A landmark school-based secondary prevention program, Cowen's Primary Mental Health Project (PMHP), was initiated over 25 years ago in Rochester, New York, and has served as a model for program dissemination since that time (Cowen, Davidson, & Gesten, 1980). In its approach to mental health service delivery, the PMHP uses early mass-screening of primary-grade children to identify behavioral and academic difficulties. Children exhibiting school acting-out, withdrawal, and/or learning problems are given remedial activities implemented by carefully selected, specially trained paraprofessional aides (usually housewives). Screening data, which includes intellectual and personality measures, interviews with mothers, and teacher behavior ratings for targeted children are collected by PMHP professionals. These data are pooled and reviewed in an initial assignment conference attended by the professionals, teachers and aides. At this time, children are assigned to aides, working objectives are outlined, and the aide begins seeing the child on a regular basis. At mid-year progress conferences, the same personnel evaluate changes in the children and modify goals if necessary and, finally, at the end of the year, conferences are held to decide whether each child should continue in the program or be terminated. During the course of the year, the mental health professional serves as a consultant to teachers and other school personnel and provides additional on-the-job training and supervision of the aides. For the most part, aide contacts with referred children are individual; however, some children may be seen in groups. This expanded helping team strives to bring early effective remediation to as many identified maladjusting primary graders as possible in order to avert later, more serious difficulties.

An extremely important aspect of the PMHP which has proved effective is the use of nonprofessional aides. Mental health professionals have been reluctant to utilize this valuable source of assistance, yet studies have testified to the potency of such work (Sobey, 1970). With funds for mental health services so often limited in the schools, the use of trained nonprofessional aides contributes appreciably to the parsimony of the intervention program.

Cowen, Lorion, Dorr, Clarfield, and Wilson (1975) found that at the end of the school year, referred PMHP children showed more improvement than demographically comparable control children from schools with traditional mental health services. Evaluation was based on teachers' and aides' pre- and postassessments of the children's academic and interpersonal behavior at school. Direct teacher comparisons of PMHP children and controls yielded positive data. Further, within-project treatment group change, as judged by both teachers and aides, showed significant child improvement on all criteria following the intervention.

The PMHP continues to be evaluated in order to provide current data regarding program effectiveness. A recent report (Cowen, Gesten, & Wilson, 1979) assessing 215 primary-grade children seen in the PMHP revealed significant improvement on educational and behavioral criterion measures as compared to matched retrospective controls. This innovative program model is being disseminated nationally and has been established in approximately 87 districts. Programs have been implemented in large metropolitan areas as well as rural settings, attesting to the diversity of the PMHP's adaptation potential (Cowen, Spinell, Wright, & Weisberg, 1982).

2.2. Preschool Programs

2.2.1. Head Start

Another milestone in the history of school-based secondary prevention, the multifaceted Project Head Start, was designed for economically disadvantaged children, and intervention takes place at the preschool rather than the primary grade level. Head Start, a multidimensional program, includes a variety of educational, health care, and social services for children and families. With the inception of this program in the mid-1960s, controversy over the long-term effectiveness of early intervention programs for the disadvantaged also began (Zigler, 1978). The rationale for the Head Start program required that it produce gains in children's intellectual development that would persist with time. A basic assumption underlying its creation was that if high-risk, disadvantaged children were given preschool training in learning readiness skills, this would increase their chances for success in the formal educational system. It was believed that the intervention would ultimately disrupt the poverty cycle through the increased educational and occupational opportunities that would be available to thousands of disadvantaged children as they approached adulthood (Weinberg, 1979).

Early evaluations of Head Start's intervention effectiveness produced negative results (e.g., Wolff & Stein, 1966; Westinghouse Learning Corporation, 1969). The Head Start program was initially deemed a failure because immediate gains on cognitive and personality measures were not maintained after the first two or three years of elementary school (Zigler, 1976). However, as Weinberg (1979) has discussed, these early evaluations were inadequate, since Head Start and other preschool intervention programs were not initially designed as longitudinal studies, nor were they set up for later between-program comparisons. Thus, accurate assessment of the program's impact was very difficult and evaluative research was fraught with methodological flaws (Campbell & Erlebacher, 1970; Smith & Bissell, 1970).

Various reanalyses of the early evaluative data (e.g., Barnow, 1973; Magidson, 1977; Rindskopf, 1976) which correct for some of the errors in methodology reveal more positive outcomes of the Head Start program. The most recent follow-up studies provide evidence that gains produced by the Head Start or other preschool experiences are evident well into the high school years (Darlington, Royce, Snipper, Murray, & Lazar, 1980).

With the wisdom of hindsight, it is clear that the controversy surrounding the effectiveness of Head Start and other early programs, as well as the need to reanalyze data, could have been avoided had evaluation strategies been built into the design of these programs initially. This is essential to the unequivocal demonstration of long-term intervention benefits and, in turn, to the establishment of early intervention programs in schools as a routine procedure.

2.2.2. The Preschool Mental Health Project

The 1975–76 academic year marked the inception of the Wayne State University Preschool Mental Health Project conducted in the Detroit Public Schools (Rickel, 1977; Rickel & Smith, 1979). The program was designed to prevent maladjustment in low-income, high-risk children and to promote positive cognitive and social-emotional growth through early screening, diagnosis, and remediation. The program builds, in part, on the pioneering work of Emory Cowen in the Public School system in Rochester, New York (Cowen, Trost, Izzo, Lorion, Dorr, & Issacson, 1975).

The Preschool Mental Health Project uses an approach similar to that of Cowen, Trost, Izzo, Lorion, Dorr, & Issacson (1975) to expand the delivery of preventive mental health services. However, the Preschool Project departs from the model provided by the Cowen program to make innovations in three areas: (a) the age at which screening and intervention is attempted; (b) the manner in which the multiplication of the mental health professionals' impact is achieved; and (c) the research design. For illustrative purposes, we will describe a single year's activity of the project, as well as a 2-year follow-up designed to determine the lasting effects of the program. The project is currently in its eighth year of operation.

It is a basic tenet of the Preschool Project philosophy that interventions which take place early in the child's development are more likely to be successful (Rickel & Fields, 1983). In younger children, maladaptive patterns are less firmly established and when identified may be more amenable to positive and long-lasting change. For these reasons, the project focuses on preschool-age children.

In the Preschool Project, the mental health professional's efforts are concentrated on diagnosis, training, and supervision. Using diagnostic tests, children with behavioral and/or learning difficulties are first identified with the help of teachers. Then specific prescriptive interventions are developed, tailored to each child's identified problem(s). In the context of the classroom setting, the interventions are implemented through the use of Wayne State University senior-level psychology students. These students are trained and are under the supervision of professionals.

A key aspect of the project is the use of a carefully planned, well controlled research design. Important features of the design are the use of a control group and of blind assessments. The use of a blind assessment procedure insured that the treatment effects were not an artifact of the assessor's knowledge of the type of treatment the child received.

The Preschool Mental Health Project involved two major facets. The first of these took place within the classroom context and consisted of a program of prescribed interventions for high-risk children. The other main facet of the program was a parent-training program designed to improve the home environment of the children by improving the parent's child-rearing techniques. Each of these facets is explained in greater detail in the following two sections.

2.2.2.1. *The Child Program.*   The child program consisted of the following four phases: (a) the initial observation of children's classroom behavior, (b) the identification of high-risk children and the assignment to treatment conditions, (c) training of student aides and the implementation of prescriptive interventions, and (d) program evaluation.

The first 5 weeks of the school year were established as a period in which the children were to become acclimated to the preschool setting and in which the teachers would familiarize themselves with each child. In this period, the children were engaged in traditional preschool activities. The teachers interacted with all children individually and observed each child's interactions with other children. In this phase of the program, there were 240 preschool children. All children were enrolled in Title I Preschool Programs in three schools in Region 7 of the Detroit Public School system.

Following the period of initial observation, screening and diagnosis took place to identify those children who were experiencing difficulty adjusting to the preschool setting. The instruments employed involved a developmental history obtained from the child's parents and standardized achievement and social-emotional scales.

On the basis of the assessments gathered, 64 children were identified as being at high risk. Specifically, children were considered at high risk if they were in the highest third of the maladjustment range on either the achievement or behavioral adjustment inventories, or both, or if they had physical problems (e.g., speech abnormalities), which were deemed severe enough to interfere with the child's adjustment to school. Once identified, these 64 high-risk children were randomly assigned to either a prescriptive remediation program or a placebo control group. The random assignment was done irrespective of the school in which the child was enrolled or their problem type; as such, there were experimental and control children in each of the classrooms. The experimental group consisted of 13 aggressive and 19 shy-withdrawn children, and the control group was composed of 10 aggressive and 22 shy-withdrawn children. All 64 children had learning problems of some type. In addition, the teachers were kept blind to the group assignment of each child, as well as to the subsequent nature of the experimental and control group experiences.

2.2.2.2. Training and Intervention. Wayne State University senior-level psychology students functioned as intervention aides in the classroom program, receiving academic credit for their participation. The students were required to have an overall grade point average of 3.0 (B) or better and were screened for participation on the basis of an interview with one of the project staff. All aides received general training which consisted of didactic presentations, reading assignments on normative preschool behavior, and the discussion of appropriate techniques for handling various child management situations.

Half of the aides were selected by means of random assignment to work with experimental children; the remaining half were assigned to work with control children. Each of these groups then received additional training unique to their group. In the context of this training, no indication was given to either group regarding the experimental or control nature of their training.

Those aides who were to work with experimental children received supplemental training in prescriptive intervention techniques. This training familiarized the aides with the behavioral symptoms of the following specific problem types: the shy-withdrawn child, the hostile or aggressive child, and the child experiencing learning difficulties. A thorough understanding of the prescriptive techniques is best achieved through a reading of the program training manual (Rickel, 1979).

The aides who were assigned to work with control children received supplemental training based on a control training manual. The manual and the training consisted of instructions for conducting a variety of traditional preschool activities such as playing with blocks, coloring, and singing songs.

The intervention phase of the program was begun in the third month of the school year (November). The project staff developed a program of prescriptions and activities for each experimental and control child. These programs were written in a standard form, reviewed with each aide, and referenced specific activities in the aide's training manual. As the program progressed, the project staff made on-site visits once every month to observe each child and the child's aide. Separate meetings for experimental and control aides were conducted by the staff every 4 weeks. In these meetings, the progress of each child was reviewed and the prescriptive program was updated by the project staff as needed.

The intervention phase of the program lasted 8 months (November–June). In this period, each child was scheduled to be seen four times a week by the aide for 15–20 min each session. Because of illness and weather, this was not always achieved. However, each child was worked with at least twice a week for approximately 20 min each session.

2.2.2.3. *Evaluation of the Classroom Program.* The effect of the program was evaluated at two different times. The first evaluation took place at the completion of the program. A second evaluation designed to assess the lasting quality of the program's impact was done 2 years after the completion of the program.

The first evaluation of the program, conducted at the end of the intervention year, showed a definite advantage for treatment children relative to control children. Comparisons were made of the children's scores on the achievement and behavioral adjustment scales. As previously indicated, teachers who administered these instruments were blind to the treatment status of the children. A factorial Multivariate Analysis of Variance and follow-up univariates were performed on postprogram scores. The two factors used in these analyses were treatment (treatment vs. control) and problem type (shy vs. acting-out/aggressive). The analysis revealed the treatment effect to be highly significant favoring the experimental children and to be equally effective for both problem types (Rickel, Smith, & Sharp, 1979).

In general, postprogram analyses suggest that the Preschool Mental Health Project was effective in addressing the problems of high-risk children, facilitating a much more satisfactory adjustment to the classroom environment than was observed in children who were not in the prescriptive intervention program. In order to determine whether these effects were temporary or of a more lasting quality, these same children were reevaluated 2 years after the completion of the program. The 2-year follow-up was done by 70 children who were then in the first grade. Of those, 42 were originally diagnosed as high risk and were involved in the intervention program either as experimental children or as control children. A group of 28 subjects, initially identified as low-risk children, were also included in this study to serve as a normal standard of comparison for the high risk groups. The 2-year follow-up multivariate analysis compared data from three time periods: pre-, post-, and follow-up, utilizing the criterion measures (Rickel & Lampi, 1981).

Overall, the results of these analyses revealed significantly more maladjustment for high-risk controls than for the low-risk, normal controls at each time period. Conversely, contrasts between the high-risk treatment groups and the normal controls revealed nonsignificant differences after treatment and at follow-up. Also, the shy treatment children experienced greater benefits from the intervention at follow-up than did the aggressive treatment children.

The results of the 2-year follow-up establish the extended effectiveness of the Preschool Mental Health Project's program of prescriptive interventions. Two years after the intervention program, the high-risk treatment children more closely approximate the low-risk normal controls than do the high-risk control group children.

2.2.2.4. The Parent Training Program. Another major objective of the Preschool Mental Health Project was to extend the influence of the project into the home by means of a parent-training program. This extension was as much a research endeavor as it was a program of service delivery. As such, the goals of the Parent Training Program were twofold: First, the program sought to develop additional insight into the relationship between the parenting styles to which the child is exposed and the child's adjustment; and second, the program was an effort to gain a greater understanding of how to conduct an effective training program in parenting techniques (Rickel, Williams, & Loigman, 1982).

In order to develop greater understanding of the relationship between parenting style and the child's adjustment, an initial assessment of parenting styles was made in the context of the parenting program. The assessment of parenting technique employed a modified version of the Block (1965) Child Rearing Practices Report (CRPR) developed by Rickel and Biasatti (1982). The original Block Child Rearing Practices Report consisted of 91 statements of self-reported child-rearing practices administered in a Q-sort format (Block, 1965). The modified version of the Block CRPR consists of 40 of the original 91 items presented in the form of a questionnaire utilizing a 6-point Likert Scale. In its modified form, the Block CRPR yields scores on two subscales, Nurturance and Restrictiveness. These two subscales have an alpha coefficient of .82 for the restrictiveness scale and .82 for the nurturance scale (Rickel & Biasatti, 1982).

The training program consisted of five consecutive weekly sessions and a follow-up session of approximately 2½ hours each (Berman & Rickel, 1979). These sessions were held at the local school during regular school hours. At each session, topics were introduced by the group leaders, which included how to handle the expression of a child's anger, children's fights, and appropriate discipline techniques. Parents were generally instructed in what is typical and atypical behavior for a preschool child. Techniques for dealing with inappropriate child behaviors were explained. Handout sheets outlining the most important points discussed in each session were also distributed to each parent for future reference. Parents were given a notebook for keeping the handouts and additional notes they might have taken in the sessions or at home.

The majority of time in each session was used for having the parents practice the concepts which were presented through the use of role playing and modeling. Since for most parents these were new experiences, every effort was made to help parents feel comfortable in discussing their thoughts and feelings.

Each session ended with a behavioral homework assignment. The assignment encouraged the parent to use some aspects of the new techniques at home. In addition, parents were encouraged to discuss these concepts with their spouse or the person with whom they lived. At the beginning of each session, parents were asked to share the experiences they had in using the techniques at home.

In general, the sessions were received very favorably by the parents who participated in the program, who indicated that they felt better about themselves as parents. Parents also reported feeling more confident about their ability to handle specific problem situations.

The effectiveness of the training program was evaluated with a control group format involving both center-city and suburban parents. The placebo control group programs consisted of the same number and length of sessions as those in the treatment programs and were nondirective discussions of the participants' parenting experience. Prior to the program, center-city parents as a whole were more restrictive (i.e., expected conformity to demands) than were suburban parents as measured on the modified Block CRPR. There was no preprogram difference between center-city parents and suburban parents on the nurturance dimension. From pre- to postprogram, experimentally trained parents decreased significantly on self-reports of restrictiveness. Further, a significantly greater change was noted for center-city experimental parents trained in conjunction with the Preschool Project than for the suburban parents given the experimental training (Jones, Rickel, & Smith, 1980; Rickel, Dudley, & Berman, 1980).

The main limitation of the results obtained is that the criterion measure is a self-report of parenting behavior. As such, the parent-training program continues to be evaluated. Currently, direct observations of parent–child interactions are being obtained pre- and posttraining, using videotape procedures in order to assess behavioral change more effectively (Rickel & Dudley, 1983). It will be of interest to determine in future research whether the training program is having a positive effect on the behavior of children.

2.2.3. A Relational-Behavioral Program

Another educational intervention program for economically disadvantaged preschoolers was developed over a 6-year period by Jason and his associates (Jason, DeAmicis, & Carter, 1978) on the basis of constant evaluation. Their final program format combined the previously demonstrated effective elements of relational and behavioral approaches and aimed to enhance children's social, behavioral, and academic skills. Home and health center intervention sessions with the children focused on the enrichment of their environment, teaching prosocial behavior and language skills, and allowing warm relationships with helping agents to develop. Parents were also involved in the program through observation and subsequent participation in the teaching activities with their children during home sessions and through attendance at weekly parent group meetings.

Jason's intervention efforts have produced positive change in a variety of areas, including improved academic and motor skills (Jason, 1977; Jason, Gesten, & Yock, 1976), increased social adjustment and interest in the environment (Jason, Clarfield, & Cowen, 1973), and more positive maternal child-rearing attitudes (Jason *et al.*, 1973). Jason (1977) attributes the sustained gains in school-related skills found at a 3-month follow-up to the extensive involvement of parents in the program, which provides them with the ability and desire to continue working with their children after termination of the project.

2.2.4. Survival Training

Risley (1972) also proposes that the positive effects of early intervention are more likely to be maintained if circumstances subsequent to termination encourage the continued practice and elaboration of program lessons. Therefore, in Risley's intervention model, disadvantaged preschool children are taught specific skills, attitudes, and concepts which are likely to be maintained when they enter the formal school system. This "survival training" approach emphasizes the remediation of language skills, because these are highly correlated with public school success. The program was developed on the basis of continuous monitoring of the children to determine the impact of various survival training techniques on their behavior. Risley discusses a number of these behavioral procedures and their rates of effectiveness (Risley, Reynolds, & Hart, 1970). For example, Risley demonstrates that the child's rate of spontaneous speech can be increased dramatically through a described schedule of social and material reinforcements which are administered by the preschool classroom teacher. The training techniques also remediate other aspects of the language deficits often observed in disadvantaged preschool children such as speaking at appropriate times, social skills, and various imitation skills.

2.2.5. Social Skills Training

Intervention programs involving social skills training often assume that the competencies they develop will be maintained through their generalization to situations outside of the intervention context. Spivack and Shure (1974), for example, designed a program to promote interpersonal problem-solving skills in young children. Classroom activities help children to develop a cognitive problem-solving style for real-life situations and to generate strategies for solving everyday kinds of interpersonal conflicts. Children learn to cope more effectively through the promotion of the language and cognitive skills necessary to deal with real-life social conflicts, and they overtly manifest this improvement through increased behavioral adjustment. Regardless of their adjustment status, all children participate together in the classroom exercises. This provides remediation for maladapting preschoolers, as well as opportunities to interact with adjusted peer models who may be more adept interpersonal problem-solvers. The program serves a primary preventive purpose for relatively well-adjusted children, with classroom activities further building and reinforcing healthy behavior and thus reducing the risk of future difficulties (Rickel & Burgio, 1982).

Evaluative data reported by the Spivack and Shure group indicated an increase in the preschool children's ability to generate alternative strategies to deal with interpersonal conflicts and to predict their consequences. Further, these improved cognitive skills were reflected in teacher ratings indicating increased behavioral adjustment (Spivack, Platt, & Shure, 1976). However, other investigators utilizing strategies similar to those of Spivack and Shure have not been so consistently successful with training efforts in social problem-solving skills (Conger & Keane, 1981; Urbain & Kendall, 1980).

Competencies produced through social problem-solving training do not necessarily generalize to classroom performance (Krasnor & Rubin, 1981; Weissberg, Gesten, Rapkin, Cowen, Davidson, Flores de Apodaca, & McKim, 1981). For example, Berler, Gross, and Drabman (1982) implemented social skills training which improved the responses of learning disabled, socially deficient children to role-play situations. However, these enhanced skills did not transfer to the classroom environment and they did not affect peer ratings of acceptance. Additionally, Rickel, Eshelman, and Loigman (1983) point out that few researchers have examined the endurance of problem-solving abilities successfully trained through intervention (e.g., Gresham & Nagle, 1980; Houtz & Feldhusen, 1976; Stone, Hinds, & Schmidt, 1975). Those follow-up studies that have been performed indicate that positive results observed immediately after intervention are sustained for less than 4 months thereafter (McClure, Chinsky, & Larcen, 1978; Rickel et al., 1983).

The diverse school-based intervention programs reviewed have met with varying degrees of success. The importance of evaluation planning becomes apparent in order that the longitudinal impact of early childhood intervention can be assessed. Further, the competence that intervention should facilitate must involve a healthy interaction with the social environment, as well as academic success. Those intervention efforts that focus only on learning deficits may be ignoring crucial social-emotional needs that may be creating the learning difficulties and vice versa. Thus, the significance of dealing with the total child is paramount in promoting the greatest change.

2.2.6. Building Parenting Skills

Although primary and secondary preventive intervention efforts with young children have been proposed to foster social and academic success, early intervention can succeed best when parents are involved in the educational process, since the child's most influential experiences take place in the context of parent–child relationships (Bronfenbrenner, 1979; Mesibov & Johnson, 1982; Valentine & Stark, 1979). Preventive parent education programs have been developed in conjunction with child intervention efforts aimed at reducing dysfunctional parenting behavior and creating psychologically healthy environments that will build mental health and competence in children. The direct purpose of parent training is to change parental role performance, that is, how parents understand, nurture, guide, manage, communicate with, and discipline their children. The parent education groups reviewed will range from basic information-giving to therapeutic techniques.

A model of parent education that focuses on information-giving of normal developmental issues was implemented by Schroeder (1979). The leaders provide parents with age-specific information and support in a series of group sessions, and if more individualized assistance is needed, a call-in and come-in service is available. Jackson and Terdal (1978) also developed a program which has as its goal the imparting of information to parents that will give them understanding of child development principles. This parent education model utilizes videotapes and films to help individuals relate the training to actual life situations. The Early Intervention Program (EIP) for Preschoolers and Parents emphasizes parent training and skill development through the application of behavioral-social learning principles. The EIP is organized into service modules that focus on specific needs of the child and/or the parent, such as individual tutoring and child management (Reisinger & Lavigne, 1980). These strategies teach parents more effective ways of stimulating children's intellectual development and dealing with child management issues, and they combine the benefits of parent education books with an individualized and/or supportive method.

Working with parents to modify children's behavior by helping them to modify their own represents a more therapeutic approach for dealing with the problems of children and their parents. It provides greater access to the natural environment of children, which most often is composed primarily of family. The parents can, therefore, become not merely recipients of therapy but also active behavior cotherapists (Berkowitz & Graziano, 1972). Traditionally, experts have attempted to influence the child directly and to change his or her behavior. However, according to Glogower and Sloop (1976), behavior change may be brought about more effectively by controlling the child's environment through the manipulation of behavioral contingencies. Parents, who are the primary socializing agents of the child (Baumrind, 1978), are in a better position to bring about change than are professionals who see the child for only a few hours each week.

Mash, Lazere, Terdal, and Garner (1973) conducted a study using a group of mothers to modify their children's problem behaviors. Their focus was on the modification of maladaptive mother–child interactions. They found that the altered response repertoires of the mothers resulted in behavior change on the part of their children and pointed out that their results supported the usefulness of working with the child-care agents as vehicles for modifying children's behavior. Other studies have demonstrated positive results using parents as change agents and indicated that they are very effective in eliciting positive changes in their children, who exhibited a wide range of behavior problems (Johnson & Katz, 1973; O'Dell, 1974; Reisinger, Frangia, & Ora, 1976; Tavormina, 1974). These problems included antisocial and immature behavior, speech dysfunction, school phobias, and oppositional behavior. The authors, however, pointed out that the success of therapeutic intervention by parents depends on the ability of a backup professional to produce reliable changes in the behavior of parents toward their children.

O'Leary, Turkewitz, and Toffel (1973) also involved parents in the treatment of their children and produced important therapeutic changes. Their focus was on consulting with parents concerning how they could change their children's behavior through systematic shaping of inappropriate behavior, timing of punishment, modeling appropriate behavior, and the establishment of incentive systems. Patterson (1974, 1980) and his associates (Taplin & Reid, 1977), in one of the most extensive parent-mediated child treatment programs for aggressive boys, obtained significant reduction in targeted deviant behavior by parents through the use of behavior modification procedures.

The intervention programs reviewed show that the social-emotional and cognitive development of the child can be enhanced through a well-planned, systematically conducted parent program to prevent and modify the development of inappropriate child-rearing attitudes and behaviors. Factors that have been shown to be beneficial include (a) increasing the parents' knowledge of the stages of child development, (b) modifying inappropriate parental attitudes and behavior associated with child-rearing, (c) improving parenting skills in using behavioral child management techniques, and (d) enhancing the skills of parents in providing a cognitively enriched environment for the child.

3. Children at Risk for Schizophrenia: Vulnerabilities

Within the past 15 years, evidence has rapidly accumulated indicating the genetic heritability of various psychopathologies. Disorders found to have a genetic component include early infantile autism (Folstein & Rutter, 1977), stuttering (Kidd, Kidd, & Records, 1978), hyperactivity (Ross & Ross, 1976), antisocial personality (Mednick & Christiansen, 1977), various neuroses, depressive illnesses, and schizophrenia (Fieve, Rosenthal, & Brill, 1975; Tsuang, 1978). Among these, schizophrenia has been the focus of the largest body of research, and, as Garmezy (1976) points out, the empirical support for genetic involvement in schizophrenia is greater than that for any other etiological model of the disorder.

3.1. Genetic Heritability of Schizophrenia

Studies by Fischer (1973), Gottesman and Shields (1972), Heston (1966), Kety, Rosenthal, Wender, and Schulsinger (1968), and others clearly indicate a genetic contribution to schizophrenia. With one schizophrenic biological parent, a child has a 12 to 14% chance of ultimately becoming schizophrenic, and the figures jump to 35 to 45% for children with two schizophrenic parents (Cancro, 1979). Although exact percentages vary with the sample and the diagnostic criteria used, reviewers of the schizophrenia literature (e.g., Cancro, 1979; Gottesman, 1978; Kety, 1978; Matthysse & Kidd, 1976; Rosenthal, 1970) tend to agree that the 1% base-rate incidence of the disorder rises to at least a 10% risk for first-degree relatives of schizophrenics. Further, as relation to the schizophrenic individual increases or decreases in terms of the proportion of shared genes, the probability of becoming schizophrenic varies similarly. Thus, whereas the risk for a first cousin of a schizophrenic individual is roughly 2% to 3%, the risk for a monozygotic twin soars to 50%. In addition, schizophrenia is not the only risk to which offspring of schizophrenic parents are vulnerable. Higgins (1976) estimates that 75% of these high-risk children develop some form of psychiatric disturbance.

3.2. The Transactional Model

Despite this impressive evidence for a strong genetic component in schizophrenia, investigators have recognized that genes do not exist in a vacuum. Rather, genes require an environment in which to express themselves, and the quality of that environment affects the observed outcome of any constitutional predisposition. Therefore, a transactional viewpoint of schizophrenia has been promoted by a number of researchers (e.g., Asarnow & Asarnow, 1980; Garmezy, 1976; Sameroff, Seifer, & Zax, 1982). Garmezy (1976) discusses diathesis, or the predisposition to a disorder, and the potentiating power of specific stressors as a means of explaining the great diversity of outcomes and the wide range of adaptation exhibited by children presumed to be at risk for schizophrenia. Bioconstitutional factors present at birth can take more adaptive or maladaptive forms depending upon the family environment into which the child is thrust. Asarnow and Asarnow (1980) believe that schizophrenia represents a "systems disorder." Their research suggests that the underlying vulnerabilities to schizophrenia are quite subtle and manifestiations of these vulnerabilities vary with developmental phases. Both maturational changes and environmental transactions can serve to augment the relatively subtle early individual differences, producing increasingly divergent developmental trajectories. Thus Sameroff *et al.* (1982) believes that transactional analysis of schizophrenia requires the identification of the constitutional characteristics of the child, the functional attributes of the environment, and the development of these elements within a unified system. If maldevelopment does arise from the reciprocal effects of such transactions, intervention can take place at various points in the ontogenesis of the child at risk and can focus upon various aspects of both the child and the environment at each phase of development (Asarnow & Asarnow, 1980; Sameroff, 1974).

3.3. The "High-Risk" Method

Asarnow and Asarnow (1980) believe that our knowledge of schizophrenia is presently sufficient to justify first steps in the direction of primary prevention, that is, preventively oriented intervention research. Most investigations to date have focused upon the initial task of identifying the primary etiological deficits of children who are relatively likely, at some point in time, to be diagnosed as schizophrenic. The high-risk method utilized in much of this research was developed in reaction to the following difficulties: (a) the experimental manipulative method is obviously unethical for use in the study of human psychopathology, (b) attempts to trace the antecedents to disorder through retrospective reports of early experiences are often inaccurate or systematically distorted by knowledge of the current state of affairs (Robins, 1966; Yarrow, Campbell, & Burton, 1970), and (c) follow-back studies of objective records of schizophrenic adults (e.g., school records) provide varying information which is often difficult to compare across individuals (Watt, Stolorow, Lubensky, & McClelland, 1970).

High-risk research attempts to predict schizophrenia in groups of children in which prevalence rates are elevated. According to Garmezy (1976),

> a child is at risk for mental disorder if actuarial data exist to suggest that other children who share in common with the target child certain specific attributes are known to have a higher probability for developing psychopathology in

On the basis of evidence cited earlier, clearly, parent schizophrenia is a good selection criterion for risk to schizophrenia and has indeed often been used as such. The best high-risk design involves the longitudinal study of children identified as being at risk for schizophrenia. The goal of such research is to identify patterns of performance on premorbid measures which distinguish high-risk individuals who later become schizophrenic from those who do not, as well as from low-risk controls. Mednick and Schulsinger (1968), for example, compared a sample of children born to schizophrenic parents in Denmark with a matched group of controls in order to determine a constitutional marker for later schizophrenia. Their subjects were initially given measures of psychophysiology and cognitive performance during adolescence, and then follow-up data using the same measures were obtained through adulthood. The starting point for the investigation was set at adolescence because it was assumed that the entire risk period for schizophrenia would be completed during the lifetime of these researchers.

This type of high-risk investigation provides indicators for theories of etiology and central deficits, and possibilities for intervention in schizophrenia (Mednick & Witkin-Lanoil, 1977). Premorbid measures which distinguish individuals destined to become schizophrenic can be applied to normal populations to detect children who are potential schizophrenics. Intervention can be designed to focus on those deviant processes identified by the discriminating measures. For example, Goldstein (1975) discusses a family communication disturbance observed in adolescents who are at high risk for schizophrenia. As a mode of intervention, one might consider social skills training for these individuals. Differential success of various types of intervention procedures may help to verify or reject hypotheses concerning factors contributing to the development of schizophrenic behavior.

3.4. Vulnerabilities of High-Risk Children

What information has high-risk research yielded thus far concerning the specific vulnerabilities of children at risk for schizophrenia? Areas of investigation include (a) biological risk factors, (b) attentional and information-processing dysfunction, (c) family patterns, and (d) behavioral competence.

3.4.1. Biological Risk Factors

Biological risk factors include the incidence of pregnancy and birth complications, neurological maturational dysfunction, and physiological responsivity. Reports of birth and pregnancy complications among schizophrenic parents are mixed, though in general the data appear to be negative. McNeil and Kaij (1978) find that most studies indicate no differences between schizophrenics and controls in birth weight, sex of infant, the number of the pregnancy, birth or neonatal complications, or the total combined number of these obstetric complications. However, the rate of fetal and neonatal death is higher among schizophrenic mothers, but this is also true for women with other mental illnesses. Neither onset nor severity of the mother's illness is related to neonatal status among schizophrenics.

With regard to the neurological status of high-risk children, Fish and her associates (Fish, 1963, 1980; Fish & Hagin, 1973) found that neurointegrative deficit or pandevelopmental retardation (PDR) occurred more frequently in the offspring of schizophrenics than in a group of controls and was related to the incidence of schizophrenia and mental disorders during childhood and early adulthood. On the basis of neurological examinations of Swedish newborns, McNeil and Kaij (1980) concluded that infants born to mentally ill women had, as a group, poorer neurological status. However, this effect was not specific to schizophrenic diagnosis.

Examining newborn physiology in high-risk children, Schachter, Kerr, Lachin, and Faer (1975) found no significant heart rate differences between newborns of schizophrenics and controls. In their Copenhagen study, Mednick and Schulsinger (1968) report that another physiological indicator, rate of recovery of skin conductance, is an important possible premorbid indicator of later pathology in children of schizophrenics.

3.4.2. Attentional and Information-Processing Dysfunction

Studies indicate that subtle differences in attentional processes may be present in some children born to schizophrenic mothers. Asarnow, Steffy, MacCrimmon, and Cleghorn (1978) found deficits in foster-reared children with no biological family history of mental illness on measures of span of apprehension, concept attainment, competing voices, and the Spokes test. Asarnow and Asarnow (1980) also found that on the span of apprehension task, children at high-risk for schizophrenia produced the same pattern of results that discriminates adult schizophrenics from their normal controls. In related studies, Cornblatt and Erlenmeyer-Kimling (1980) and Nuechterlein (1980) utilized tasks that made information-processing demands similar to the span of apprehension measures. Subgroups of children at risk for schizophrenia were identified and differentiated from controls. Erlenmeyer-Kimling and Cornblatt (1978) report that high-risk children made more errors of omission than children of normal parents on the continuous performance test, which is a measure of sustained attention. Nuechterlein, Phipps-Yonas, Driscoll, and Garmezy (1982) found that children with schizophrenic mothers had poor sequential discrimination of relevant and irrelevant stimuli in a set of five sustained attention tasks. All of these attention and information-processing tasks require a series of rapid decisions about complex information which contain intrinsic distractors and may tap a precursor quality which leaves the child vulnerable to stress and in turn to psychopathology.

Less definitive results have been found by Neale and Weintraub (1975). Many of their attention and information-processing variables discriminated between children of psychiatric and normal groups, but not between children of schizophrenics versus unipolar and bipolar depressive patients. Finally, in a Boston project, (Gamer, Gallant, Grunebaum, & Cohler, 1977; Grunebaum, Weiss, Gallant, & Cohler, 1974) attentional processes were studied in 3-year-old children of mothers who had been hospitalized for psychosis after the child's birth. Two-thirds of these mothers were schizophrenic. Attentional performance measures did not differentiate between the high-risk children and control children whose mothers were without mental illness.

3.4.3. Family Patterns

Researchers have reported on family types which characterize the home environments of children at risk for schizophrenia. For example, Anthony (1972) describes three patterns observed in families with a psychotic parent. One pattern type exhibits the "growth and differentiation" typical of healthy, effective family units, despite a parent's psychosis. A second type is prone to "breakdown and rally." Momentary breakdown occurs under the stress of the parent's psychosis. Also, according to Anthony, there may be: family constriction so that children become phobic or counterphobic in reaction to new situations; confusion and anxiety which can lead to poor communication; paralogical thinking; and even an incipient thought disorder in the children. Following this breakdown, manifestations of family strength may again appear, and the family rallies and reintegrates. The third group is characterized by "rout and disintegration." These families are typified by dissociated behavior, fragmented relationships, and a drifting apart of family members. Anthony further explains that children cease to achieve in school and are characterized by teachers as "living in a world of their own." Anthony's observations on his original sample are notable, since he included black and white middle- and lower-income families which represented intact as well as broken homes.

Watt (1979) describes two distinct types of families in high-risk samples: (a) "Hard-core" families are disorganized and often include a severely disturbed or absent parent. These families are known by most of the local social service agencies (however, social services have little effect in alleviating family disruption, and offspring are likely to become the next generation of "hard-core" clients). (b) "Elusive" families are somewhat ineffective as a system and, in contrast to hard-core families, are often alienated from service institutions in the community. These individuals frequently are suspicious and inclined to reject offers to service for themselves or children. Watt found a greater frequency of both types of families at lower socioeconomic levels. This is not surprising, given the amount of data relating schizophrenia to the lower social classes (Kohn, 1973).

Research indicates a greater frequency of parental death, internal family conflicts, and organic handicaps that could interfere with psychological growth in families at risk (Watt, 1974). Also, higher levels of communication deviance are found in families with a schizophrenic member. It is unclear, however, whether this deviant behavior is a causal factor or the result of the pathology brought by the schizophrenic individual to the family (Goldstein & Rodnick, 1975). Rodnick, Goldstein, Doane, and Lewis (1982) discuss an estimate of risk for schizophrenia which is provided by a parental measure of communication deviance (CD) derived from their TAT protocols. This measure, developed by Jones (1977), reflects difficulties in sharing foci of attention, the inability to minimize the distractions of intrusions of personally significant but contextually irrelevant associations, and the communication of misperceptions or distortions of central aspects of the stimulus. Parental communication deviance related significantly to the outcome of their adolescent offspring 5 years later, with high CD scores associated with offspring schizophrenia. Finally, Doane, West, Goldstein, Rodnick, and Jones (1981) found that parental affective style relates to outcome diagnosis of offspring 5 years later. The negative parental styles (i.e., use of personal criticism, guilt induction, and excessive intrusiveness) were manifest significantly more often among parents of schizophrenics.

Some investigators interested in family processes have focused on pre- and postnatal experiences and the quality of mother–infant interactions. McNeil and Kaij (1980) found that mentally ill mothers as compared to controls report less external support from their families during pregnancy, and more external stresses, unwanted pregnancies, and fear of delivery. However, direct observations of mother–infant interaction in an Ainsworth-type strange situation procedure showed no group differences at one year or differences specific to maternal schizophrenia.

Schachter, Elmer, Ragins, Wimberly, and Lachin (1977) studied mother–infant interactions at 14 months during a laboratory feeding session. The schizophrenic mothers' behavior was more contingent upon the behavior of their infants than was that of control mothers. Also, infants of schizophrenic women were more reactive to their mothers' behavior than were the controls. It appears that schizophrenic mothers are anxious as caretakers and more dependent on their infants' demands for controlling their own behavior. In their Rochester Longitudinal Study, Sameroff et al., (1982) report that indices of maternal behavior during home observations suggest less involvement with their 4-month-old children by schizophrenics than by control mothers.

3.4.4. Behavioral Competence

Studies of behavioral competence in high-risk children have ranged from examination of infant temperament to observation of school behavior. McNeil and Kaij (1980) found no differences on individual scales of an infant temperament questionnaire, although children of mentally ill women in general (but not schizophrenics in particular) produced higher proportions of difficult and slow-to-warm-up profiles. Semantic analysis of the children's language revealed that children of mentally ill women are more likely to use "object-oriented" or "socially-expressive" language, whereas control children used "action-describing" language.

In a study of behavioral competence, Hanson, Gottesman, and Heston (1976) were able to isolate a subgroup of poor performers that included some children from a schizophrenic sample but no control children. Three behavioral criteria were used to define the groups: (a) motor skills at 4 years, (b) variability in psychometric test scores at 8 months, 4 years, and 7 years, and (c) behavior ratings at 4 years and at 7 years. These criteria were the best, among a pool of measures, in discriminating between children of schizophrenics and children of control mothers.

Sameroff et al. (1982) claim that studies of school-age children have been unable to isolate a set of variables that separate children of schizophrenics from children of parents with other mental illnesses. Fisher, Kokes, Harder, and Jones (1980) found that child competence ratings made by teachers and peers failed to distinguish groups. Instead, severity of illness and symptom dimensions related significantly to competence ratings. Similarly, El-Guebaly, Offord, Sullivan, and Lynch (1978), using teacher checklists of child behaviors, found no differences between teacher ratings among children of schizophrenics, depressives, and alcoholics.

Using teacher and peer ratings of competence, Rolf (1972) discovered some differences for children of schizophrenic and depressed parents as compared to controls, but not comparisons were made between these two illness groups. Worland, Lander, and Hesselbrock (1979) found little difference between children of schizophrenics and those of depressives on an extensive clinical test battery, although on a number of measures both groups differed from controls. Finally, Weintraub, Neale, and Liebert (1975), using teacher ratings of child competence, also failed to differentiate among diagnostic groups, though children of ill parents were less competent than no-illness controls.

3.5. Intervention Modes

Intervention prior to the onset of symptoms in children at high risk for schizophrenia has been attempted by several investigators. In order to explore the development of cognitive competencies and the enhancement of their resistance to stress, Anthony (1972) engaged children of schizophrenic mothers in a variety of games and activities aimed at promoting an awareness of the fact that they need not take part in their mother's delusional system. Tests of suggestibility and the perception of illusion were utilized to show the child that appearances can be deceiving and that various kinds of evidence or confirmation are required before one can accept the visual experiences or belief systems of another as reflecting reality. Anthony also sought to create a better understanding of psychotic behavior in the children and utilized support systems, such as the well spouse as a therapeutic ally. Since this program was clinically oriented, its effectiveness was not assessed relative to no-treatment controls or alternative treatments.

As noted previously, Fish (1980) has found that pandevelopmental retardation (PDR) in infancy predicts vulnerability to later schizophrenia. On the basis of this finding, Fish identified infants of schizophrenic mothers who exhibited specific neurointegrative disorders using standard measures of physical growth and infant development tests. Eight of 12 infants with schizophrenic mothers were identified as having PDR. All of these children, as well as 12 control subjects, were studied longitudinally from birth to 20–27 years of age. Fish discovered that the incidence of PDR was related to maternal schizophrenia and to blind evaluations of severe to moderate psychopathology in children at 10 years of age. At 20–22 years of age, six of the high-risk infants with PDR were diagnosed as having severe schizophrenia spectrum disorders. However, these diagnoses were based upon MMPIs and evaluations made by the experimenter, who was not blind to the individual's experimental status.

The range of interventions to which the high-risk children were exposed after age 2 varied depending upon the child's family and home circumstances and accessibility to the Fish group. At one extreme, Fish describes a case study of a child who was adopted by an affluent, white, suburban family who had optimal treatment resources at their disposal. In this case, the Fish group played a peripheral and intermittant role as consultants. The most active role of the Fish group was in the case of a high-risk child who was moved back and forth between a psychotic mother and a number of agencies. In this case, the Fish group served as child advocate, agency consultant, crisis interventionist, and primary therapist for nearly 2½ years.

Since the PDR infants eventually became schizophrenic, Fish (1980) admits that it is not known to what extent the interventions changed the psychiatric outcomes, if at all. The Fish group researchers do not believe that they were able to produce substantial change in the personality characteristics or to avert chronic impairment, although the adaptation of some individuals may have been enhanced through the intervention. They do feel that they may have helped to lessen symptoms and per-haps even short-circuit a full-fledged breakdown during the course of the lives of subjects who now appear schizotypal. The Fish group plans a blind, independent evaluation to determine which subjects are schizo-phrenic or schizotypal and to what degree negative and therapeutic experiences have affected their outcomes.

Watt, Shay, Grubb, and Riddle (1982) believe that early identifica-tion and intervention with emotionally vulnerable children can be ac-complished efficiently through public schools. On the basis of follow-back studies of school and hospital records of adult psychiatric patients (Watt, Fryer, Lewine, & Prentky, 1979), as well as prospective analyses of children at high risk for schizophrenia (Erlenmeyer-Kimling, Marcus, Cornblatt, Friedman, Rainer, & Rutschmann, 1980), these researchers concluded that a significant proportion of adult schizophrenics can be identified by traditional methods of evaluation at school as being emo-tionally vulnerable children, although their specific disposition to schizophrenic disorder will probably not be detected or labeled as such. Deviance in the social-emotional realm is likely to be observed some years prior to the clear-cut thought disorder of a full-blown psychosis. Although screening for emotionally vulnerable children to identify those who are at risk for schizophrenia will result in many "false positives," these researchers believe that the false positives may also benefit from intervention aimed at preventing schizophrenic disorder.

With these considerations in mind, a pilot intervention project was implemented by Watt and his colleagues in Springfield, Massachusetts. Its purpose was to determine whether group counseling with maladjusted junior high school students would produce positive changes in the children's attitudes, behavior, or academic performance (Shay, 1974). Students included in the project were emotionally withdrawn, negativistic toward teachers and peers, disruptive in the classroom, threatened with suspension or disciplinary action, or living in a family environment that was likely to create psychological problems. The treatment groups met for counseling one hour per week for seven months. Sessions focused on the enhancement of self-image and the improvement of relations with peers, parents, and other authority figures. Other intervention activities included gym and outdoor sports, art projects, and trips to community facilities.

The group counseling was found to be effective primarily in terms of changing the attitudes of the maladjusted children toward themselves and their role at school. Watt et al. (1982) interpret their findings to suggest that improvement in self-concept promoted better rapport with classroom teachers which consequently allowed them to profit more from instruction and improve their academic performance. These researchers believe that group counseling has potential for improving conduct and academic achievement which follow attitudinal change.

Rolf, Fischer, and Hasazi (1982) have developed a multimodal intervention project for preschool children at the University of Vermont. This program offered therapeutic and competence-building activities to disturbed children and their families. The multirisk target group included preschool children who fell into one or more of the following categories: (a) children with psychologically disturbed, psychiatrically hospitalized, and/or incarcerated parents; (b) disturbed children with significant environmental and/or genetic components to their disorder; (c) children with distinct developmental lags or physical or neurological handicaps; and (d) children suffering severe cultural or economic deprivation.

For each child, individualized intervention goals were defined, based upon an assessment of the child's cognitive and social development and the characteristics of his or her family system. Six basic intervention modes were utilized; day-care curricula, consultation, referral, direct child contact, parent and family contact, and advocacy and follow-through. More specifically, in addition to regular day-care activities, the intervention included individualized treatment programs comprised of play therapy, small group social modeling by peer "therapists," behavior modification activities, consultation with day-care teachers, nonsocial developmental skill training, parent training and consultations, speech and language therapies (if needed), and the development of age-appropriate coping and social interaction skills.

Rolf et al. (1982) report that following the intervention the treated target children showed significant improvement on measures of developmental competence, including the Stanford-Binet IQ, the Vineland Social Quotient, and the Portage Developmental Scale. In addition, they exhibit enhanced performance on the Visual recognition, Verbal Communication, Motor Skills, and Externalizing factor scores of the Vermont Behavior Checklist.

Mednick, Venables, Schulsinger, and Cudeck (1982) have reported on a primary prevention effort taking place on the island of Mauritius. In their previous research, the Mednick group examined 207 Danish children who were at risk for schizophrenia (i.e., the children had schizophrenic mothers). This group was followed for 5 years, during which time 20 of these individuals suffered some form of psychiatric breakdown. It was found that an autonomic nervous system variable, fast rate of skin conductance recovery, was the best discriminator of the disturbed subjects from their high- and low-risk controls (Mednick & Schulsinger, 1973). Later, when diagnostic labels had been given to each subject (Schulsinger, 1976), ANS variables were also shown to predict schizophrenia, especially in males (Mednick, Schulsinger, Teasdale, Schulsinger, Venables & Rock, 1978).

The next step for the Mednick group was to examine a normal population in order to identify those individuals who were potential schizophrenics and then to consider the possibilities for intervention. In the Mauritius project (Mednick et al., 1982), 1,800 preschool children were given a psychophysiological assessment, their play behavior was observed and coded, and their cognitive development tested. Also, family interviews were conducted, medical examinations were performed, and perinatal information was recorded.

Two hundred high-risk children were identified on the basis of the psychophysiological data. Half of these high-risk children attended the project nursery school, and half remained in the community as controls. The project also included matched, low-risk controls who participated in the preschool activities.

At the nursery school, the children were provided with a bus ride to and from school, nutritious hot lunches, training in coping with frustration, group social participation, reinforcement of prosocial behavior, and contact with warm, enthusiastic teachers. After 3 years of the nursery school experience, the high-risk children displayed an increase in positive social interactions and spent less time in isolated, inactive activities.

An 11-year follow-up is planned. The Mednick group has collected information on the entire sample's progress in primary school through teacher questionnaires. Parents' ratings of the children's behavior, parental attitudes, and an assessment of the home environment will be obtained for this follow-up examination. Psychophysiological measures and visual processing measures will also be administered, which predict or relate to schizophrenic disturbance.

Giving the existing knowledge about vulnerable children, one must decide on a general mode of intervention to deal most effectively with those specific variables presumed to be predisposing factors in the development of schizophrenia. Moreover, intervention should be introduced as early as possible to maximize its positive effects and reduce the destructive influence of these precursor conditions on healthy, normal development (Hobbs, 1979).

As Fish (1980) has shown, the neonatal period holds great potential for the early detection of risk for pathology, as well as for intervention. During this period, the mental health professional may have systematic access to both child and parents through pediatric facilities. Further, Mednick (1975) established that neonatal status has predictive value for adolescent behavior.

Even more promising is the possibility of intervention in nursery schools and at the primary grade level (e.g., Anthony, 1972; Mednick et al., 1982; Rolf et al., 1982). Increasing numbers of children are attending nursery schools as mothers enter the work force and, of course, primary education is universal. In both preschools and elementary schools, teachers are an invaluable resource as potential raters of child behavior. With children spending at least 4 or 5 hr a day in either setting, there is ample opportunity to observe and intervene. The preferable approach within this context may be to build competence in vulnerable children as a way of providing them with extra reinforcements against psychopathology.

Beyond the early elementary years, intervention is likely to take the form of treatment as opposed to prevention (as in Watt et al., 1982). Since prevention of schizophrenia is the ultimate goal of researchers in this area, diagnosis and intervention should take place prior to the time when schizophrenic behavior typically becomes manifest, that is, well before adolescence. This allows time for the process of intervention should the child be identified as at high risk for schizophrenia.

4. Summary

A recurrent theme appearing throughout the previous discussion is the importance of incorporating parental involvement in the design of prevention efforts. The most effective intervention, in terms of both immediate and long-range positive change, has been associated with a continuing, active involvement of parents in the treatment process. Their participation not only benefits the child directly and improves the parent–child relationship but also improves the parent's own self-concept, sense of autonomy and feeling of competence. The latter change may, in fact, be responsible for the first two. Much of the literature supports the notion that intervention should focus on the parents of high-risk children, because enhancement of child performance follows naturally from positive changes effected in the caretaker (Rickel, Gerrard, & Iscoe, 1984).

During infancy, it has been shown that parental attitudes toward perinatal risk factors (e.g., prematurity) have more impact on the child's subsequent course of development than the presence of these biological stressors themselves. Alleviating the anxiety associated with giving birth to a premature infant may be the most direct and effective means of reducing the child's risk potential. Mothers must also be educated in the capabilities of their preterm or full-term infants to increase maternal sensitivity to the child's cues and to encourage realistic expectations for the child at various stages of development. Education promotes an understanding of the appropriate kinds of stimulation to give the infant at any point in time to optimize cognitive and social-emotional development. In addition, this may reduce the risk of abuse or neglect, since aberrant adult interaction patterns appear to produce behaviors in the infant which serve to maintain them. Finally, fostering positive maternal perceptions whether other risk factors are present, is essential to the healthy psychosocial development of the child.

In the case of schizophrenic individuals, genetic susceptibility to psychopathology cannot be altered. However, once again the research evidence suggests that parents may be the preferable targets of intervention to reduce the risk of schizophrenia in their children. Remediation of parental communication deviance is a promising possibility for optimizing the developmental course of children with psychotic parents. Intervention at the level of the family may also help to alter more general negative family patterns associated with the development of schizophrenic behavior in the offspring. In this approach, utilization of the well spouse as therapeutic ally may prove to be the most effective instrument of change within the family system. Future intervention attempts should focus on teaching parents to implement activities designed to remediate some of the specific deficits of children at risk for schizophrenia, such as those associated with attention and information-processing dysfunction. This may enhance the child's cognitive development as well as reinforce the parent–child relationship.

Children at risk for learning difficulties are also well served by prevention efforts which promote appropriate parenting attitudes and skills and which train parents to engage in remedial activities with their children. The development of specific techniques for motivating parents to continue using their new teaching skills with their children after termination of the formal intervention project should be one of the primary goals of researchers in this area. Low socioeconomic status mothers, for example, can effectively implement intervention exercises with their children to improve cognitive and language skills (e.g., Jason, 1977). When these teaching activities become a permanent part of the parent–child relationship, immediate gains found after intervention programs are sustained over longer periods of time.

Finally, intervention with parents of high-risk children may take the form of social services, and especially of supportive counseling. This may help to alleviate some of the stress and chaos experienced by parents who have very limited economic resources or who suffer mental illness, which can compromise their ability to provide consistent yet stimulating care for their children. Likewise, supportive services for families grappling with the turmoil created by specific life events may ease tension in the home which can lead to such problems as child abuse, and in the case of divorcing parents preventive counseling prior to a separation may reduce the risk of adverse effects in the children (Rickel & Langner, 1983).

Until very recently, parent participation in intervention programs generally involved only mothers of high-risk children. Although fathers contribute relatively little to child care, as compared to mothers, research indicates that fathers do have an impact on the social-emotional and cognitive-motivational development of their children (Belsky, 1981; Clarke-Stewart, 1978; Lamb, 1981). Clearly, efforts to intervene with paternal behavior could enhance child functioning. In fact, the available research evidence on intervention programs for fathers and their newborn infants indicates that this is so (Parke, 1979). Questions of the effectiveness of intervention involving fathers of children at risk for a variety of difficulties should be further pursued.

To conclude this discussion, we should stress that mental health professionals as well as other groups concerned with families and children must constantly voice the need for government policy and funding to support prevention-oriented research and intervention programs. Lawmakers often overlook the needs of children, who are not a very powerful or profitable constituency to cultivate, since they do not vote, protest, or pay taxes. Recent cuts in the social service budget also threaten programs for families of high-risk children. Today there is a greater incidence of single-parent households, child abuse, teen-age pregnancies, and child and adolescent suicides than ever before; yet lawmakers divert available funds to adult-oriented projects. Recently, Representative George Miller of California fought a long, hard battle to establish the Select Committee on Children, Youth, and Families (Miller, 1983).

Currently its chairman, Miller hopes to draw attention to these problems which have been ignored by the more established and rigid power structures in Congress. His efforts are most laudable and should serve as a model for others who are sincerely concerned with the destiny of our children and our nation.

5. References

Achenbach, T. M. *Developmental psychopathology* (2nd ed.). New York: Wiley, 1982.

Ainsworth, M. D. S., Blehar, M., Waters, E., & Wall, S. *Patterns of attachment: Observations in the strange situation at home.* Hillsdale, N.J.: Erlbaum, 1978.

Als, H., Brazelton, T. B. A new model of assessing behavioral organization in preterm and fullterm infants. *Journal of the American Academy of Child Psychiatry,* 1980, *20,* 239–263.

Als, H., Tronick, E., Lester, B. The Brazelton Neonatal Behavioral Assessment Scale (BNBAS). *Journal of Abnormal Child Psychology,* 1977, *5,* 214–231.

Als, H., Lester, B. M., & Brazelton, T. B. Dynamics of the behavioral organization of the premature infant: A theoretical perspective. In T. M. Field, A. M. Sostek, S. Goldberg, & H. H. Shuman (Eds.), *Infants born at risk.* New York: Spectrum, 1979.

Anthony, E. J. Primary prevention with school children. In H. A. Barten & L. Bellak (Eds.), *Progress in community mental health* (Vol. 2). New York: Grune & Stratton, 1972.

Asarnow, R., & Asarnow, J. R. *Attention–information processing dysfunction and vulnerability to schizophrenia: Implications for preventive intervention.* Paper presented at the Rodnick Conference on Preventive Intervention in Schizophrenia, Los Angeles, May 1980.

Asarnow, R. F., Steffy, R. A., MacCrimmon, D. J., & Cleghorn, J. M. The McMaster Waterloo project: An attentional and clinical assessment of foster children at risk for schizophrenia. In L. C. Wynne, R. L. Cromwell, & S. Matthysse (Eds.), *The nature of schizophrenia: New approaches to research and treatment.* New York: Wiley, 1978.

Baldwin, J. A., & Oliver, J. E. Epidemiology and family characteristics of severely abused children. *British Journal of Preventive Social Medicine,* 1975, *29,* 205–221.

Barnow, B. S. *The effects of Head Start and socio-economic status on cognitive development of disadvantaged children.* Doctoral dissertation, University of Wisconsin, 1973.

Baumrind, D. Parental disciplinary patterns and social competence in children. *Youth & Society,* 1978, *9,* 239–276.

Belsky, J. Early human experience: A family perspective. *Developmental Psychology,* 1981, *17,* 3–23.

Benfield, D. G., Leib, S. A., & Reuter, J. Grief response of parents after referral of the critically ill newborn to a regional center. *The New England Journal of Medicine,* 1976, *294,* 975–978.

Berkowitz, B., & Graziano, A. Training parents as behavior therapists: A review. *Behavior Research and Therapy,* 1972, *10,* 297–317.

Berler, E. S., Gross, A. M., & Drabman, R. S. Social skills training with children: Proceed with caution. *Journal of Applied Behavior Analysis,* 1982, *15,* 41–53.

Berman, S. F., & Rickel, A. U. Assertive training for low income black parents. *Clinical Social Work Journal,* 1979, *7,* 123–132.

Birch, H., & Gussow, G. D. *Disadvantaged children.* New York: Grune & Stratton, 1970.

Block, J. H. *The childrearing practices report.* Berkeley: University of California Institute of Human Development, 1965.

Broman, S. H. Perinatal anoxia and cognitive development in early childhood. In T. M. Field (Ed.), *Infants born at risk: Behavior and development.* Larchmont, N.Y.: SP Medical & Scientific Books, 1979.

Bronfenbrenner, U. *The ecology of human development*. Cambridge: Harvard University Press, 1979.

Broussard, E. R. Primary prevention of psychosocial disorders: Assessment of outcome. In L. A. Bond & J. M. Joffe (Eds.), *Facilitating infant and early childhood development*. Hanover, N.H.: University Press of New England, 1982.

Campbell, D. T., & Erlebacher, A. How regression artifacts in quasi-experimental evaluations can mistakenly make compensatory education look harmful. In J. Hellmuth (Ed.), *Compensatory education: A national debate: Vol. 3. The disadvantaged child*. New York: Brunner, Mazel, 1970, 185–210.

Cancro, R. The clinical relevance of genetic studies in schizophrenia. *Psychiatric Annals*, 1979, *9*, 52–57.

Caputo, D. V., & Mandell, W. Consequences of low birth weight. *Developmental Psychology*, 1970, *3*, 363–383.

Clarke-Stewart, K. A. And daddy makes three: The father's impact on mother and young child. *Child Development*, 1978, *49*, 466–478.

Cochrane, R., & Robertson, A. The life events inventory: A measure of the relative severity of psychosocial stressors. *Journal of Psychosomatic Research*, 1973, *17*, 135–139.

Cohen, S. E., & Beckwith, L. Preterm infant interaction with the caregiver in the first year of life and competence at age two. *Child Development*, 1979, *50*, 767–776.

Conger, J. C., & Keane, S. P. Social skills intervention in the treatment of isolated or withdrawn children. *Psychological Bulletin*, 1981, *90*(3), 478–495.

Corah, N. L., Anthony, E. J., Painter, P., Stern, J. A., & Thurston, D. L. Effects of perinatal anoxia after seven years. *Psychological Monographs*, 1965, *79*, 3 (Whole No. 596).

Cornblatt, B., & Erlenmeyer-Kimling, L. Early attentional predictors of adolescent behavioral disturbances in children at risk for schizophrenia. In N. Watt, J. Anthony, L. Wynne, J. Rolf (Eds.), *Children at risk for schizophrenia*. New York: Cambridge University Press, 1980.

Cornell, E. H., Gottfried, A. W. Intervention with premature human infants. *Child Development*, 1976, *47*, 32–39.

Cowen, E. L., Lorion, R. P., Dorr, D., Clarfield, S. P., & Wilson, A. B. Evaluation of a preventively oriented school based mental health program. *Psychology in the Schools*, 1975, *12*, 161–166.

Cowen, E. L., Trost, M. A., Izzo, L. D., Lorion, R. P., Dorr, D., & Issacson, R. V. *New ways in school mental health: Early detection and prevention of school maladaptation*. New York: Human Sciences Press, 1975.

Cowen, E. L., Gesten, E. L., & Wilson, A. The primary mental health project (PMHP): Evaluation of current program effectiveness. *American Journal of Community Psychology*, 1979, *7*, 293–303.

Cowen, E. L., Davidson, E., & Gesten, E. L. Program dissemination and the modification of delivery practices in school mental health. *Professional Psychology*, 1980, *11*, 36–47.

Cowen, E. L., Gesten, E. L., & Weissberg, R. P. An interrelated network of preventively oriented school based mental health approaches. In R. H. Price & P. Politzer (Eds.), *Evaluation and action in the community context*. New York: Academic Press, 1980.

Cowen, E. L., Spinell, A., Wright, J., & Weissberg, R. P. *Continuing dissemination of a school-based mental health program*. Unpublished manuscript, University of Rochester, 1982.

Cramer, B. A. A mother's reactions to the birth of a premature infant. In M. W. Klaus & J. H. Kennell (Eds.), *Maternal–infant bonding*. St. Louis: Mosby, 1976.

Crittenden, P. M. Abusing, neglecting, problematic, and adequate dyads: Differentiating by patterns of interaction. *Merrill-Palmer Quarterly*, 1981, *27*, 201–218.

Crittenden, P. M. *Maltreated infants: Vulnerability and resilience*. Paper presented at the biennial meeting of the Society for Research in Child Development, Detroit, Mich., April 21–24, 1983.

Crittenden, P. M., & Snell, M. E. Intervention to improve mother–infant interaction. *Infant Mental Health Journal*, 1983, *4*, 23–31.

Darlington, R. B., Royce, J. M., Snipper, A. S., Murray, H. W., & Lazar, I. Pre-school programs and later school competence of children from low-income families. *Science*, April 11, 1980, *208* (4440), 202–204.

Davies, P. A., Stewart, A. L. Low-birth-weight infants: Neurological sequelae and later intelligence. *British Medical Bulletin*, 1975, *31*, 85–91.

Dion, K. K. Children's physical attractiveness and sex as determinants of adult punitiveness. *Developmental Psychology*, 1974, *10*, 772–778.

Doane, J. A., West, K. L., Goldstein, M. J., Rodnick, E. H., & Jones, J. E. Parental communication deviance and affective style as predictors of subsequent schizophrenia spectrum disorders in vulnerable adolescents. *Archives of General Psychiatry*, 1981, *38*, 679–685.

Douglas, J. W. B., & Gear, R. Children of low birthweight in the 1946 cohort: Behavior and educational achievement in adolescence. *Archives of Diseases in Childhood*, 1976, *51*, 820–826.

Drotar, D., Malone, C. A., Negray, J., & Dennstedt, M. Psychosocial assessment and care for infants hospitalized for nonorganic failure to thrive. *Journal of Clinical Child Psychology*, 1981, *10*, 63–66.

Egeland, B., & Brunnquell, D. An at-risk approach to the study of child abuse: Some preliminary findings. *Journal of the American Academy of Child Psychiatry*, 1979, *18*, 219–235.

Egeland, B., & Deinard, A. *Life event scale*. Unpublished test, University of Minnesota, 1975.

Egeland, B., & Sroufe, L. A. Attachment and maltreatment. *Child Development*, 1981, *52*, 44–52.

Egeland, B., Breitenbucher, M., & Rosenberg, D. Prospective study of the significance of life stress in the etiology of child abuse. *Journal of Consulting and Clinical Psychology*, 1980, *48*(2), 195–205.

El-Guebaly, N., Offord, D. R., Sullivan, K. T., & Lynch, G. W. Psychosocial adjustment of the offspring of psychiatric patients. *Canadian Psychiatric Association Journal*, 1978, *23*, 281–289.

Erlenmeyer-Kimling, L., & Cornblatt, B. Attentional measures in a study of children at high-risk for schizophrenia. In L. C. Wynne, R. L. Cromwell, & S. Matthysse (Eds.), *The nature of schizophrenia*. New York: Wiley, 1978.

Erlenmeyer-Kimling, L., Marcus, Y., Cornblatt, B., Friedman, D., Rainer, J. D., & Rutschmann, J. *The New York high-risk project*. Paper presented at the Plenary Conference of the Risk Research Consortium, San Juan, Puerto Rico, March 11–13, 1980.

Field, T. M. Effects of early separation, interactive deficits, and experimental manipulations on infant–mother face-to-face interaction. *Child Development*, 1977, *48*, 763–771.

Field, T. Interactions of preterm and term infants with their lower and middle class teenage and adult mothers. In T. Field, S. Goldberg, D. Stern, & A. Sostek (Eds.), *Hish-risk infants and children: Adult and peer interactions*. New York: Academic Press, 1980.

Field, T. M. Infants born at risk: Early compensatory experiences. In L. A. Bond & J. M. Joffe (Eds.), *Facilitating infant and early childhood development*. Hanover, N.H.: University Press of New England, 1982.

Field, T., Widmayer, S., Stringer, S., & Ignatoff, E. Teenage, lower class black mothers and their preterm infants: An intervention and developmental follow-up. *Child Development*, 1980, *51*, 426–436.

Fieve, R. R., Rosenthal, D., & Brill, H. *Genetic research in psychiatry: Proceedings of the Sixty-Third Annual Meeting of the American Psychopathological Association*. Baltimore: Johns Hopkins University Press, 1975.

Fish, B. The maturation of arousal and attention in the first months of life: A study of variations in ego development. *Journal of the American Academy of Child Psychiatry*, 1963, *2*, 253–270.

Fish, B. *Offspring of schizophrenics from birth to adulthood*. Paper presented at the Risk Research Consortium Plenary Conference, San Juan, Puerto Rico, March, 1980.

Fish, B., & Hagin, R. Visual motor disorders in infants at risk for schizophrenia. *Archives of General Psychiatry*, 1973, *28*, 900–904.

Fischer, M. Genetic and environmental factors in schizophrenia. *Acta Psychiatrica Scandinavia*, 1973, Suppl. 238, 1–158.

Fisher, L., Kokes, R. F., Harder, D. W., & Jones, J. E. Child competence and psychiatric risk. VI. Summary and integration of findings. *Journal of Nervous and Mental Disease*, 1980, *168*, 353–355.

Fitzhardinge, P. Follow-up studies on the low birth weight infant. *Clinics in Perinatology*, 1976, *3*, 503–516.

Folstein, S., & Rutter, M. Genetic influences and infantile autism. *Nature*, 1977, *265*, 726–728.

Friedrich, W. N., & Boriskin, J. A. The role of the child in abuse: A review of the literature. *American Journal of Orthopsychiatry*, 1976, *46*, 580–59.

Frodi, A., Lamb, M., Leavitt, L., Donovan, W., Neff, C., & Sherry, D. Fathers' and mothers' responses to the faces and cries of normal and premature infants. *Developmental Psychology*, 1978, *14*, 490–498.

Gamer, E., Gallant, D., Grunebaum, H., & Cohler, B. J. Children of psychotic mothers. *Archives of General Psychiatry*, 1977, *34*, 592–597.

Garbarino, J. A preliminary study of some ecological correlates of child abuse: The impact of socioeconomic stress on mothers. *Child Development*, 1976, *47*, 178–185.

Garmezy, N. *Vulnerable and invulnerable children: Theory, research and intervention*. Presented at the American Psychological Association Master Lecture Series, 1976.

George, C., & Main, M. Social interactions of young abused children: Approach, avoidance, and aggression. *Child Development*, 1979, *50*, 306–318.

Gil D. *Violence against children*. Cambridge: Harvard University Press, 1970.

Giovannoni, J. M. Parental mistreatment: Perpetrators and victims. *Journal of Marriage and the Family*, 1971, *33*, 649–657.

Glogower, F., & Sloop, E. W. Two strategies of group training of parents as effective behavioral modifiers. *Behavior Therapy*, 1976, *7*, 177–184.

Goldberg, S. Premature birth: Consequences for the parent–infant relationship. *American Scientist*, 1979, *67*, 214–220.

Goldstein, M. J. *Psychotherapeutic intervention with families of adolescents at risk for schizophrenia*. Copenhagen: World Health Organization, 1975.

Goldstein, M. J., & Rodnick, E. H. The family's contribution to the etiology of schizophrenia: Current status. *Schizophrenia Bulletin*, 1975, *14*, 48–63.

Gordon, A. M., & Bernard, J. A. *Effects of day-care intervention on the language performance of high-risk children*. Paper presented at the Biennial Meeting of the Society for Research in Child Development, Boston, April 1981.

Gordon, A. M., & Feagans, L. *Assessing the effects of systematic daycare on the language development of high-risk children*. Paper presented at the Biennial Meeting of the Society for Research in Child Development, New Orleans, March 1977.

Gottesman, I. I. Schizophrenia and genetics: Where are we? Are you sure? In L. C. Wynne, R. L. Cromwell, & S. Matthysse (Eds), *The nature of schizophrenia: New approaches to research and treatment*. New York: Wiley, 1978.

Gottesman, I. I., & Shields, J. *Schizophrenia and genetics*. New York: Academic Press, 1972.

Graham, F. K., Matarazzo, R. G., & Caldwell, B. M. Behavioral differences between normal and traumatized newborns: II. Standardization, reliability, and validity. *Psychological Monographs*, 1956, *70*, 21 (Whole No. 428).

Graham, F. K., Pennoyer, M. M., Caldwell, B. M., Greenman, M., & Hartman, A. F. Relationship between clinical status and behavior test performance in a newborn group with histories suggesting anoxia. *Journal of Pediatrics*, 1957, *50*, 177–189.

Graham, F. K., Ernhart, C. B., Thurston, D. L., & Craft, M. Development three years after perinatal anoxia and other potentially damaging newborn experiences. *Psychological Monographs*, 1962, *76*, 3(Whole No. 522).

Gresham, F. M., & Nagle, R. J. Social skills training with children: Responsiveness to modeling and coaching as a function of peer orientation. *Journal of Consulting and Clinical Psychology*, 1980, *48*(6), 718–729.

Grunebaum, H., Weiss, J. L., Gallant, D., & Cohler, B. J. Attention in young children of psychotic mothers. *American Journal of Psychiatry*, 1974, *131* (8), 887–891.

Hanson, D. R., Gottesman, I. I., & Heston, L. L. Some possible childhood indicators of adult schizophrenia inferred from children of schizophrenics. *British Journal of Psychiatry*, 1976, *129*, 142–154.

Heston, L. L. Psychiatric disorders in foster home reared children of schizophrenic mothers. *British Journal of Psychiatry*, 1966, *112*, 819–825.

Higgins, J. Effects of child rearing by schizophrenic mothers: A follow-up. *Journal of Psychiatric Research*, 1976, *13*, 1–9.

Hobbs, N. *Helping disturbed children: Psychological and ecological strategies. II: Project Re-ED, Twenty years later*. Nashville: Vanderbilt Institute for Public Policy Studies, 1979.

Houtz, J., & Feldhusen, J. The modification of fourth-graders' problem-solving abilities. *Journal of Psychology*, 1976, *93*, 229–237.

Hunt, J. V. Predicting intellectual disorders in childhood for preterm infants with birthweight below 1501 grams. In S. Friedman & M. Sigman (Eds.), *Preterm birth and psychological development*. New York: Academic Press, 1981.

Hunter, R. S., Kilstrom, N., Kraybill, E. N., & Loda, F. Antecedents of child neglect and abuse in premature infants: A prospective study in a newborn intensive care unit. *Pediatrics*, 1978, *61*, 629–635.

Jackson, R. H., & Terdal, L. Parent education within a pediatric practice. *Journal of Pediatric Psychology*, 1978, *3*, 2–5.

Jason, L. A. A behavioral approach in enhancing disadvantaged children's academic abilities. *American Journal of Community Psychology*, 1977, *5*, 413–421.

Jason, L. A., Clarfield, S., & Cowen, E. L. Preventive interventions with young disadvantaged children. *American Journal of Community Psychology*, 1973, *1*, 50–61.

Jason, L. A., Gesten, E., & Yock, T. Relational and behavioral interventions with economically disadvantaged toddlers. *American Journal of Orthopsychiatry*, 1976, *46*, 270–278.

Jason, L. A., De Amicis, L., & Carter, B. Preventive intervention programs for disadvantaged children. *Community Mental Health Journal*, 1978, *14*, 272–278.

Johnson, C. A., & Katz, R. C. Using parents as change agents for their children: A review. *Journal of Child Psychology and Psychiatry*, 1973, *14*, 181–200.

Jones, D. C., Rickel, A. U., & Smith, R. L. Maternal child rearing practices and social problem solving strategies among preschoolers. *Developmental Psychology*, 1980, *16*, 241–242.

Jones, J. E. Patterns of transactional style deviance in the TATs of parents of schizo-
·phrenics. *Family Process*, 1977, *16*, 327–337.
Justice, B., & Duncan, D. F. Life crises as a precursor to child abuse. *Public Health Reports*, 1976, *91*, 110–115.
Kety, S. S. Biochemical approaches: Introduction. In L. C. Wynne, R. L. Cromwell, & S. Matthysse (Eds.), *The nature of schizophrenia: New approaches to research and treatment*. New York: Wiley, 1978.
Kety, S. S., Rosenthal, D., Wender, P. H., & Schulsinger, F. The types and prevalence of mental illness in the biological and adoptive families of adopted schizophrenics. In D. Rosenthal & S. S. Kety (Eds.), *The transmission of schizophrenia*. Oxford: Pergamon Press, 1968.
Kidd, K. K., Kidd, J. R., & Records, M. A. The possible causes of the sex ratio in stuttering and its implications. *Journal of Fluency Disorders*, 1978, *3*, 13–23.
Klaus, M. H., & Kennell, J. H. *Maternal-infant bonding*. St. Louis: Mosby, 1976.
Kohn, M. L. Social class and schizophrenia: A critical review and a reformulation. *Schizophrenia Bulletin*, 1973, *7*, 60–79.
Krasnor, L. R., & Rubin, K. H. The assessment of social problem-solving skills in young children. In T. Merluzzi, C. Glass, & M. Genest (Eds.), *Cognitive assessment*. New York: Guilford Press, 1981.
Lamb, M. E. (Ed.), *The role of the father in child development*. New York: Wiley, 1981.
Littman, B. The relationship of medical events to infant development. In T. M. Field, A. M. Sostek, S. Goldberg, & H. H. Shuman (Eds.), *Infants born at risk*. New York: Spectrum, 1979.
Littman, B., & Wooldridge, P. Caring for families of high-risk infants. *The Western Journal of Medicine*, 1976, *124*, 429–322.
Lynch, M. Risk factors in the child: A study of abused children and their siblings. In H. Martin (Ed.), *The abused child*. Cambridge, Mass.: Ballinger, 1976.
Maden, M. F., & Wrench, D. F. Significant findings in child abuse research. *Victimology: International Journal*, 1977, *2*, 196–224.
Magidson, J. *Toward a causal model approach for adjusting for pre-existing differences in the non-equivalent control group situation: A general alternative to ANCOVA*. Cambridge, Mass.: Abt Associates, 1977.
Mash, E., Lazere, R., Terdal, L., & Garner, A. Modification of mother–child interaction: A modeling approach for groups. *Child Study Journal*, 1973, *3*, 131–143.
Matthysse, S. W., & Kidd, K. K. Estimating the genetic contribution to schizophrenia. *American Journal of Psychiatry*, 1976, *133*, 185–191.
McClure, L. F., Chinsky, J. M., & Larcen, S. W. Enhancing social problem solving performance in an elementary school setting. *Journal of Educational Psychology*, 1978, *4*, 504–513.
McNeil, T. F., & Kaij, L. Obstetric factors in the development of schizophrenia: Complications in the births of preschizophrenics and in reproduction by schizophrenic parents. In L. C. Wynne, R. L. Cromwell, & S. Matthysse (Eds.), *The nature of schizophrenia: New approaches to research and treatment*. New York: Wiley, 1978.
McNeil, T. F., & Kaij, L. *Offspring of women with nonorganic psychoses: Progress report, February, 1980*. Paper presented at the Risk Research Consortium Plenary Conference, San Juan, 1980.
Mednick, B. *Neonatal neurological symptomatology predictive of the minimal brain damage syndrome in preadolescence*. New York: Columbia University Press, 1975.
Mednick, S. A., & Christiansen, K. O. (Eds.). *Biosocial bases of criminal behavior*. New York: Gardner Press, 1977.
Mednick, S. A., & Schulsinger, F. Some premorbid characteristics related to breakdown in

children with schizophrenic mothers. In D. Rosenthal & S. S. Kety (Eds.), *The transmission of schizophrenia.* Oxford: Pergamon Press, 1968.

Mednick, S. A., & Schulsinger, F. Studies of children at high-risk for schizophrenia. In S. R. Dean (Ed.), *Schizophrenia: The first ten Dean award lectures.* New York: MSS Information, 1973.

Mednick, S. A., & Witkin-Lanoil, G. H. Intervention in children at high risk for schizophrenia. In G. W. Albee & J. M. Joffe (Eds.), *Primary prevention of psychopathology.* Hanover, N.H.: University Press of New England, 1977.

Mednick, S. A., Schulsinger, F., Teasdale, T. W., Schulsinger, H., Venables, P. H., & Rock, D. R. Schizophrenia in high-risk children: Sex differences in predisposing factors. In G. Serban (Ed.), *Cognitive defects in the development of mental illness.* New York: Brunner/Mazel, 1978.

Mednick, S. A., Venables, P. H., Schulsinger, F., & Cudeck, R. The Mauritius project: An experiment in primary prevention. In M. J. Goldstein (Ed.), *Preventive intervention in schizophrenia: Are we ready?* U.S. Public Health Service Publication No. (ADM) 82–1111, 1982.

Mesibov, G. B., & Johnson, M. R. Intervention techniques in pediatric psychology. In J. M. Tuma (Ed.), *Handbook for the practice of pediatric psychology.* New York: Wiley, 1982.

Miller, G. Children and the congress. *American Psychologist,* 1983, *38,* 70–76.

Minde, K., Shosenberg, N., Marton, P., Thompson, J., Ripley, J., & Burns, S. Self-help groups in a premature nursery—A controlled evaluation. *Journal of Pediatrics,* 1980, *96,* 933–940.

Minde, K. K., Shosenberg, N. E., & Marton, P. L. The effects of self-help groups in a premature nursery on maternal autonomy and caretaking style 1 year later. In L. A. Bond & J. M. Joffe (Eds.), *Facilitating infant and early childhood development.* Hanover, N.H.: University Press of New England, 1982.

Minde, K., Shosenberg, N., & Thompson, P. Self-help groups in a premature nursery— Infant behavior and parental competence 1 year later. In E. Galenson & J. Call (Eds.), *Frontiers of infant psychiatry.* New York: Basic Books, 1983.

Morse, C., Sahler, O., & Friedman, S. A. A three-year follow-up study of abused and neglected children. *American Journal of Diseases of Children,* 1970, *120,* 439–446.

Neale, J. M., & Weintraub, S. Children vulnerable to psychopathology: The Stony Brook high-risk project. *Journal of Abnormal Child Psychology,* 1975, *3,* 95–113.

Nuechterlein, K. Sustained attention among children vulnerable to adult schizophrenia and among hyperactive children. In N. Watt, J. Anthony, L. Wynne, & J. Rolf (Eds.), *Children at risk for schizophrenia.* New York: Cambridge University Press, 1980.

Nuechterlein, K. H., Phipps-Yonas, S., Driscoll, R. M., & Garmezy, N. The role of different components in attention in children vulnerable to schizophrenia. In M. J. Goldstein (Ed.), *Preventive intervention in schizophrenia: Are we ready?* U.S. Public Health Service Publication No. (ADM) 82-1111, 1982.

O'Dell, S. Training parents in behavior modification: A review. *Psychological Bulletin,* 1974, *81,* 418–433.

O'Leary, K. D., Turkewitz, H., & Toffel, S. Parent and therapist evaluation of behavior therapy in a child psychological clinic. *Journal of Consulting and Clinical Psychology,* 1973, *41,* 279–283.

Ounsted, C., Oppenheimer, R., & Linsay, J. The psychopathology and psychotherapy of the families: Aspects of bonding failure. In A. Franklin (Ed.), *Concerning child abuse.* Edinburgh: Churchill Livingston, 1975.

Parke, R. D. Perspectives on father–infant interaction. In J. D. Osofsky (Ed.), *Handbook of infant development.* New York: Wiley, 1979.

Parmelee, A. H., & Haber, A. Who is the "risk infant"? In H. J. Osofsky (Ed.), *Clinical obstetrics and gynecology*. New York: Harper & Row, 1973.

Pasamanick, B., & Knobloch, H. Epidemiologic studies on the complications of pregnancy and the birth process. In G. Caplan (Ed.), *Prevention of mental disorders in children*. New York: Basic Books, 1961.

Patterson, G. R. Retraining of aggressive boys by their parents: Review of recent literature and follow-up evaluation. *Canadian Psychiatric Association Journal*, 1974, *19*, 142–158.

Patterson, G. R. Mothers: The unacknowledged victims. *Monographs of the Society for Research in Child Development*, 1980, *45*, 1–64.

Powell, L. G. The effects of extra stimulation and maternal involvement on the development of low-birth-weight infants and on maternal behavior. *Child Development*, 1974, *45*, 106–113.

Ramey, C. T., & Campbell, F. A. Compensatory education for disadvantaged children. *School Review*, 1979, *82*, 171–189.

Ramey, C. T., & Campbell, F. A. Educational intervention for children at risk for mild retardation: A longitudinal analysis. In P. Mittler (Ed.), *Frontiers of knowledge in mental retardation* (Vol. 1). Baltimore: University Park Press, 1981.

Ramey, C. T., & Gallagher, J. J. The nature of cultural deprivation: Theoretical issues and suggested research strategies. *North Carolina Journal of Mental Health*, 1975, *7*, 41–47.

Ramey, C. T., MacPhee, D., & Yeates, K. O. Preventing developmental retardation: A general systems model. In L. A. Bond & J. M. Jaffe (Eds.), *Facilitating infant and early childhood development*. Hanover, N.H.: University Press of New England, 1982.

Reisinger, J. J., & Lavigne, J. V. An early intervention model for pediatric settings. *Professional Psychology*, 1980, *11*, 582–590.

Reisinger, J. J., Frangia, G., & Ora, J. Parents as change agents for their children: A review. *Journal of Community Psychology*, 1976, *4*, 103–123.

Rickel, A. U. Screening and remediation of preschool children from low income families. *Perceptual and Motor Skills*, 1977, *45*, 757–758.

Rickel, A. U. *Preschool mental health project: Training manual*. Lansing: State of Michigan Department of Mental Health, 1979.

Rickel, A. U. Perceptions of adjustment problems in preschool children by teachers and paraprofessional aides. *Journal of Community Psychology*, 1982, *10*, 29–35.

Rickel, A. U., & Biasatti, L. R. Modification of the Block Child Rearing Practices Report. *Journal of Clinical Psychology*, 1982, *38*, 129–134.

Rickel, A. U., & Burgio, J. C. Assessing social competencies in lower income preschool children. *American Journal of Community Psychology*, 1982, *10*, 635–645.

Rickel, A. U., & Dudley, G. A parent training program in a preschool mental health project. In R. Rosenbaum (Ed.), *Varieties of short term therapy groups: A handbook for mental health professionals*. New York: McGraw-Hill, 1983.

Rickel, A. U., & Fields, R. B. Storybook models and achievement behavior of preschool children. *Psychology in the Schools*, 1983, *20*, 105–113.

Rickel, A. U., & Lampi, L. A. A two-year follow-up study of a preventive mental health program for preschoolers. *Journal of Abnormal Child Psychology*, 1981, *9*, 455–464.

Rickel, A. U., & Langner, T. S. *Short and long term effects of broken homes on children*. Paper presented to the American Psychological Association Annual Convention, Anaheim, Calif., 1983.

Rickel, A. U., & Smith, R. L. Maladapting preschool children: Identification, diagnosis, and remediation. *American Journal of Community Psychology*, 1979, *7*, 197–208.

Rickel, A. U., Smith, R. L., & Sharp, K. C. Description and evaluation of a preventive mental health program for preschoolers. *Journal of Abnormal Child Psychology*, 1979, *7*, 101–112.

Rickel, A. U., Dudley, G., & Berman, S. An evaluation of parent training. *Evaluation Review*, 1980, 4, 389–403.

Rickel, A. U., Williams, D. L., & Loigman, G. L. *Personal and situational predictors of child rearing: Implications for intervention*. Paper presented to the American Psychological Association Convention, Washington, D.C., 1982.

Rickel, A. U., Eshelman, A. K., & Loigman, G. A. A follow-up evaluation of social problem-solving training: Cognitive and behavioral effects. *Journal of Abnormal Child Psychology*, 1983, 11, 15–28.

Rickel, A. U., Gerrard, M., & Iscoe, I. (Eds.). *Social and psychological problems of women: Prevention and crisis intervention*. New York: McGraw-Hill, Hemisphere, 1984.

Rickel, A. U., Lampi, L. A., & Smith, R. L. Prevention with preschoolers. In M. Roberts & L. Peterson (Eds.), *Prevention of problems in childhood*. New York: Wiley, 1984.

Rindskopf, D. *A comparison of various regression–correction methods for evaluating non-experimental research*. Doctoral dissertation, Iowa State University, 1976.

Risley, T. Spontaneous language and the preschool environment. In J. C. Stanley, (Ed.), *Preschool programs for the disadvantaged: Five experimental approaches to early childhood education*. Baltimore: Johns Hopkins University Press, 1972.

Risley, T., Reynolds, N., & Hart, B. The disadvantaged: Behavior modification with disadvantaged preschool children. In R. H. Bradfield (Ed.), *Behavior modification: The human effort*. San Rafael, Calif.: Dimensions Publishing, 1970.

Robert, M. C., & Maddux, J. E. A psychosocial conceptualization of nonorganic failure to thrive. *Journal of Clinical Child Psychology*, 1982, 11, 216–226.

Robins, L. N. *Deviant children grown up*. Baltimore: Williams & Wilkins, 1966.

Rodnick, E. H., Goldstein, M. J., Doane, J. A., & Lewis, J. M. Association between parent–child transactions and risk for schizophrenia: Implications for early intervention. In M. J. Goldstein (Ed.), *Prevention intervention in schizophrenia: Are we ready?* U.S. Public Health Service Publication No. (ADM) 82-1111, 1982.

Rolf, J. E. The social and academic competence of children vulnerable to schizophrenia and other behavior pathologies. *Journal of Abnormal Psychology*, 1972, 80(3), 225–243.

Rolf, J. E., Fischer, M., & Hasazi, J. Assessing preventive interventions for multirisk preschoolers. In M. J. Goldstein (Ed.), *Preventive intervention in schizophrenia: Are we ready?* U.S. Public Health Service Publication No. (ADM) 82-1111, 1982.

Rosenn, D. W., Loeb, L. S., & Jura, M. B. Differentiation of organic from non-organic failure to thrive syndrome in infancy. *Pediatrics*, 1980, 66, 698–704.

Rosenthal, D. *Genetic theory and abnormal behavior*. New York: McGraw-Hill, 1970.

Ross, D. M., & Ross, S. A. *Hyperactivity: Research, theory and action*. New York: Wiley-Interscience, 1976.

Sameroff, A. J. *Infant risk factors in developmental deviancy*. Paper presented to the meeting of the International Association for Child Psychiatry and Allied Professions, Philadelphia, July 1974.

Sameroff, A. J., & Chandler, M. J. Reproductive risk and the continuum of caretaking casualty. In F. D. Horowitz, M. Hetherington, S. Scarr-Salapatek, & G. Siegel (Eds.), *Review of child development research* (Vol. 4). Chicago: University of Chicago Press, 1975.

Sameroff, A. J., Seifer, R., & Zax, M. Early development of children at risk for emotional disorder. *Monograph of the Society for Research in Child Development*, 1982, 47(7, Serial No. 199).

Sandgrund, A., Gaines, R. W., & Green, A. H. Child abuse and mental retardation: A problem of cause and effect. *American Journal of Mental Deficiency*, 1974, 79, 327–330.

Scarr-Salapatek, S., & Williams, M. The effects of early stimulation on low-birth-weight infants. *Child Development*, 1973, 44, 94–101.

Schachter, J., Elmer, E., Ragins, N., Wimberly, F., & Lachin, J. M. Assessment of mother–

infant interaction: Schizophrenic and non-schizophrenic mothers. *Merrill-Palmer Quarterly*, 1977, 23(3), 193–206.

Schachter, J., Kerr, J., Lachin, J. M., & Faer, M. Newborn offspring of a schizophrenic parent: Cardiac reactivity to auditory stimuli. *Psychophysiology*, 1975, 12, 483–492.

Schroeder, C. S. Psychologist in a private pediatric practice. *Journal of Pediatric Psychology*, 1979, 4, 5–18.

Schulsinger, H. A ten-year follow-up of children of schizophrenic mothers: Clinical assessment. *Acta Psychiatrica Scandinavica*, 1976, 53, 371–386.

Shay, J. J. *Therapeutic intervention with maladjusted junior high school pupils.* Unpublished master's thesis, University of Massachusetts, 1974.

Shosenberg, N. Self-help groups for parents of premature infants. *Canadian Nurse*, 1980, July–August, 30–33.

Sigman, M. Plasticity in development: Implications for intervention. In L. A. Bond & J. M. Joffe (Eds.), *Facilitating infant and early childhood development.* Hanover, N.H.: University Press of New England, 1982.

Sigman, M., & Parmelee, A. H. Longitudinal evaluation of the preterm infants. In T. M. Field, A. M. Sostek, S. Goldberg, & H. H. Shuman (Eds.), *Infants born at risk.* New York: Spectrum, 1979.

Siqueland, E. R. Biological and experiential determinants of exploration in infancy. In L. J. Stone, J. T. Smith, & L. B. Murphy (Eds.), *The competent infant.* New York: Basic Books, 1973.

Smith, M. S., & Bissell, J. S. Report analysis: The impact of Head Start. *Harvard Educational Review*, 1970, 40(1), 51–104.

Smith, S. M., & Hanson, R. Battered children: A medical and psychological study. *British Medical Journal*, 1974, 3, 666–670.

Sobey, F. *The nonprofessional revolution in mental health.* New York: Columbia University Press, 1970.

Sostek, A. M., Quinn, P. D., & Davitt, M. K. Behavior, development, and neurologic status of premature and fullterm infants with varying medical complications. In T. M. Field, A. M. Sostek, S. Goldberg, & H. H. Shuman (Eds.), *Infants born at risk.* New York: Spectrum, 1979.

Spinetta, J. J., & Rigler, D. The child-abusing parent: A psychological review. *Psychological Bulletin*, 1972, 77, 296–304.

Spivack, G., & Shure, M. B. *Social adjustment in young children.* San Francisco: Jossey-Bass, 1974.

Spivack, G., Platt, J., & Shure, M. B. *The problem solving approach to adjustment: A guide to research and intervention.* San Francisco: Jossey-Bass, 1976.

Starr, R. H., Jr. *Child abuse prediction: Policy implications.* Cambridge, Mass.: Ballinger, 1982.

Stone, G., Hinds, W., & Schmidt, G. Teaching mental health behaviors to elementary school children. *Professional Psychology*, 1975, 6, 34–40.

Tanner, J. M. Physical growth. In P. H. Mussen (Ed.), *Carmichael's manual of child psychology* (3rd ed., Vol. 1). New York: Wiley, 1970.

Taplin, R. S., & Reid, J. B. Changes in parent consequences as a function of family intervention. *Journal of Consulting and Clinical Psychology*, 1977, 45, 973–981.

Tavormina, J. B. Basic models of parent counseling: A critical review. *Psychological Bulletin*, 1974, 81, 827–835.

Tizard, J. P. M. Pre-natal and perinatal factors. In J. W. Littlefield, J. DeGrouchy, & F. J. G. Ekling (Eds.), *Birth defects.* Proceedings of the fifth international conference, Montreal, Canada, August 21–27, 1977. Amsterdam: Excerpta Medica, 1978.

Tsuang, M. T. Genetic counseling for psychiatric patients and their families. *American Journal of Psychiatry*, 1978, 135, 1465–1475.

U.S. Bureau of the Census. *Characteristics of the population below the poverty level: 1980* (Current Population Reports, Series P-60, No. 133). Washington, D.C.: U.S. Government Printing Office, 1982.

Urbain, E. S., & Kendall, P. C. Review of social-cognitive problem-solving interventions with children. *Psychological Bulletin*, 1980, *88*(1), 109–143.

Valentine, J., & Stark, E. The social context of parent involvement in Head Start. In E. Zigler & J. Valentine (Eds.), *Project Head Start: A legacy of the war on poverty*. New York: Free Press, 1979.

Vietze, P. M., Falsey, S., O'Conner, S., Sandler, H., Sherrod, K., & Altemeier, W. A. Newborn behavioral and interactional characteristics of nonorganic failure-to-thrive infants. In T. Field (Ed.), *High-risk infants and children: Adult and peer interactions*. New York: Academic Press, 1980.

Watt, N. F. Childhood and adolescent routes to schizophrenia. In D. F. Ricks, A. Thomas, & M. Roff (Eds.), *Life history research in psychopathology* (Vol. 3). Minneapolis: University of Minnesota Press, 1974.

Watt, N. F. Patterns of childhood social development in adult schizophrenics. *Archives of General Psychiatry*, 1979, *35*, (2), 160–165.

Watt, N. F., Stolorow, R. D., Lubensky, A. W., & McClelland, D. C. School adjustment and behavior of children hospitalized for schizophrenia as adults. *American Journal of Orthopsychiatry*, 1970, *40*(4), 637–657.

Watt, N. F., Fryer, J. H., Lewine, R. R. J., & Prentsky, R. A. Toward longitudinal conceptions of psychiatric disorder. In B. A. Maher (Ed.), *Progress in experimental personality research* (Vol. 9). New York: Academic Press, 1979, pp. 199–283.

Watt, N. F., Shay, J. J., Grubb, T. W., & Riddle, M. Early identification and intervention with emotionally vulnerable children through the public schools. In M. J. Goldstein (Ed.), *Preventive intervention in schizophrenia: Are we ready?* U.S. Public Health Service Publication, No. (ADM) 82-1111, 1982.

Weinberg, R. A. Early childhood education and intervention: Establishing an American tradition. *American Psychologist*, 1979, *34*, 912–916.

Weintraub, S., Neale, J. M., & Liebert, D. E. Teacher ratings of children vulnerable to psychopathology. *American Journal of Orthopsychiatry*, 1975, *45* (5), 838–845.

Weissberg, R. P., Gesten, E. L., Rapkin, B. D., Cowen, E. L., Davidson, E., Flores de Apodaca, R., & McKim, B. J. Evaluation of a social problem-solving training program for suburban and inner-city third-grade children. *Journal of Consulting and Clinical Psychology*, 1981, *49*(2), 251–261.

Werner, E. E., & Smith R. S. *Kauai's children come of age*. Honolulu: University Press of Hawaii, 1977.

Werner, E. E., Bierman, J. M., & French, F. E. *The children of Kauai*. Honolulu: University Press of Hawaii, 1971.

Westinghouse Learning Corporation, Ohio University. *The impact of Head Start: An evaluation of the effects of Head Start on children's cognitive and affective development*. Washington, D.C.: U.S. Office of Economic Opportunity, 1969.

Widmayer, S., & Field, T. Effects of Brazelton demonstrations on early interactions of preterm infants and their mothers. *Infant Behavior and Development*, 1980, *3*, 79–89.

Willerman, L., Broman, S. H., & Fiedler, M. Infant development, preschool IQ, and social class. *Child Development*, 1970, *41*, 69–77.

Wolff, M., & Stein, A. *Factors influencing the recruitment of children into the Head Start Program, summer 1965: A case study of six centers in New York City (Study II)*. New York: Yeshiva University, 1966.

Worland, J., Lander, H., Hesselbrock, V. Psychological evaluation of clinical disturbance in children at risk for psychopathology. *Journal of Abnormal Psychology*, 1979, *88* (1), 13–26.

Yarrow, M. R., Campbell, J. D., & Burton, R. V. Recollections of childhood: A study of the retrospective method. *Monographs of the Society for Research in Child Development*, 1970, *35* (138).

Zigler, E. F. Head Start: Not a program but an evolving concept. In J. D. Andrews (Ed.), *Early childhood education: It's an art? It's a science?* Washington, D.C.: National Association for the Education of Young Children, 1976.

Zigler, E. F. America's Head Start Program: An agenda for its second decade. *Young Children*, 1978, *33*, 4–11.

Index